IRELAND'S BUTTERFLIES

Orange Tip

IRELAND'S Butterflies

A REVIEW

David Nash, Trevor Boyd
and Deirdre Hardiman

2012

THE CATERPILLAR

I find among the poems of Schiller
No mention of the caterpillar.
Nor can I find one anywhere
In Petrarch or in Baudelaire.
So here I sit in extra session
To give my personal impression
The caterpillar as it's called,
Is often hairy, seldom bald;
It looks as if it never shaves;
When as it walks, it walks in waves;
And from the cradle to the chrysalis
It's utterly speechless, songless, whistleless.

OGDEN NASH

ISBN 978 0 9530037 2 3

Published in 2012 by The Dublin Naturalists' Field Club,
35 Nutley Park, Dublin 4

© David Nash, Trevor Boyd and Deirdre Hardiman, 2012

Drawings and Photographs where not listed below are © Deirdre Hardiman.
© Peter Eeles: Pearl-bordered Fritillary (ova), Purple Hairstreak (pupa), Ringlet (larva and pupa), Monarch, Camberwell Beauty, Pale Clouded Yellow, Queen of Spain Fritillary.
© Reg Fry: Pearl-bordered Fritillary (larva and pupa), Meadow Brown (egg), Essex Skipper (larva and pupa).
© Margaret and Freddie Walsh: Clouded Yellow (egg).
© Ben Smart: Meadow Brown (larva and pupa).
© Paul Kipling: Bath White and Small Mountain Ringlet.
© Derek Ramsey: American Painted Lady.
© Gnu: electron micrographs of Peacock.

This book is typeset in 11pt on 13pt Scala and designed by
SUSAN WAINE

Contents

Preface

THERE HAS BEEN a growing interest in the study, recording and conservation of butterflies in Ireland in recent years, subsequent to the more fallow years in the 1980s and early 1990s. This interest has been aided by the growth in communications technology with the emergence of the internet, email, websites, interest groups, 'friendly' databases and the coming of age of the digital camera.

Trevor Boyd had an interest in Lepidoptera which commenced during a childhood sojourn in the United States. As Recorder for Butterfly Conservation Northern Ireland (BCNI) he assiduously fulfilled the onerous but enjoyable experience of collating and verifying all the records for Northern Ireland for *The millennium atlas of butterflies in Britain and Ireland.* As a meteorologist and gardener he was very interested in the impact of climate on our vegetation and insect populations.

In the mid-1990s, The Dublin Naturalists' Field Club (DNFC) was approached and agreed to encourage and co-ordinate recording in the Republic of Ireland for the *Millennium Atlas* although the project was already well underway in the United Kingdom. The task of co-ordination, collation and validation fell to David Nash and Mary Willis, with considerable assistance from other members of DNFC. A number of Butterfly Conservation members were persuaded to sacrifice their planned holiday periods and spend them recording in some of the less well recorded parts of Ireland.

Relations between BCNI and DNFC developed during the Millennium Atlas period and the authors were also in communication in other areas of natural history through The Belfast Naturalists' Field Club (BNFC). Work commenced afterwards on a butterfly publication. Originally conceived as an atlas, the book metamorphosed into *Ireland's Butterflies A Review*.

Deirdre Hardiman, who designed the Butterfly Ireland website, developed an interest in photographing all Ireland's butterflies at all stages of their development. She brought herself and her camera to the four corners of the island and to many of Ireland's prime butterfly sites. She has also acquired an understanding and an appreciation of the anatomy, physiology and functioning of the butterfly as an insect.

This publication is designed to be read by both the beginner and those with a more detailed knowledge of butterflies but it is not intended to be read from cover to cover in one sitting. Inevitably in places, some of the necessary scientific terminology may initially challenge the reader but the authors encourage you to persist. Readers are referred to the *Glossary of Terms*.

Siver-washed Fritillary

Towards Ireland's Butterflies A Review

THERE IS LITTLE EVIDENCE of any significant interest in the butterflies or moths of Ireland before the end of the 18th Century. Giraldus Cambrensis' rather dismissive *Topographia Hiberniae* of 1188 stimulated a somewhat delayed response by Don Philip O'Beare in the defence of Ireland's heritage in his *Zoilomastix* of c.1626, which was rediscovered in Uppsala (O'Sullivan 2009). O'Beare, having consulted Pliny's *Natural History*, includes a brief section on Lepidoptera:

> The butterflies of Ireland before which eyes little horns stretch out, are born and also die in a wonderful way. The caterpillar worm which increases in size, immobile, on the leaves of vegetables, and then covered by a hard cover and protected from spiders is called a chrysalis. From that finally, when covering breaks, out flies the butterfly, which is of such nature that it perishes by burning its wings flying around oil lamps...

The widespread collection of insects and their mounting in cabinets, a practice which now seems so abhorrent to most of us, commenced in earnest in Ireland in the late Georgian period (the early decades of the 19th Century) and extended well into the mid-20th Century. This great interest, or possibly obsession, is exemplified by the existence of collections of insects containing butterflies from this period. Public collections in Dublin were held by organisations such as the (Royal) Dublin Society, Trinity College and the Dublin Natural History Society. In 1792 the Dublin Society, with a grant from the Irish Parliament, purchased the Leske Collection which included butterfly species described by J.F. Gmelin.

Of particular note was James Tardy's "fine collection" of insects, including butterflies, which was purchased in 1842/43 by Trinity College for the sum of £162.2s.0d. Details about Tardy (1773?-1835) whose Huguenot parents came to Ireland around 1760 are scarce. He collected in eastern Ireland in the early decades of the 19th Century. His cabinet contained about 10,000 specimens and the John Curtis cabinet of 'British Insects' of a similar magnitude was also purchased by Trinity College. Curtis was the most eminent British illustrator of insects of the era. These two collections were vouched for by Alexander Henry Haliday (1806-1870) of Holywood, Co Down, arguably Ireland's most eminent entomologist of his generation. Part

Rev. Joseph Greene (1824-1906)

of Tardy's assimilated collection is still to be found in the Zoology Museum of Trinity College. Unfortunately, it does not contain details of the origin of his butterfly specimens (Good & Linnie 1990). Haliday's own manuscript list of Lepidoptera was never published but is held by the National Museum of Ireland.

REV. JOSEPH GREENE (1824-1906), who graduated from Dublin University, lived at one time at Mount Pleasant, Dublin. 'Parson' Greene compiled, in conjunction with his fellow student of divinity, Rev. A. R. Hogan, the first published Irish catalogue – *A list of Lepidoptera hitherto taken in Ireland as far as the end of the Geometrae* – of butterflies and moths which was presented by the latter at a meeting of the Dublin Natural History Society in 1854. His list of Rhopalocera (butterflies) ran to thirty eight species, eleven of which were taken from 'Mr. Haliday's list' and ten including the Black-veined White, Small Skipper [recently again reported from Ireland] and Large Skipper were attributed to Mr. Tardy. For some of the species brief information such as "generally distributed" is supplied. While the presence of specimens such as the Duke of Burgundy in Tardy's collection raises some unanswered questions, it is likely that Tardy obtained these specimens in Britain from or with his friend and fellow Irish entomologist, N.A.Vigors, and that unjustified inferences were drawn in relation to the origin of some of these specimens.

Greene spent most of life in the ministry in England. He is particularly well known for his book *The Insect Hunter's Companion* first published in 1857 before he departed from Dublin and which was reissued in many editions. His complementary pamphlet *Pupa Digging* also appeared in the same year. He had an unparalleled ability to find underground pupae, together with a propensity to exaggerate the magnitude of some of his finds. Salmon (2000) refers to his claim to have a thousand pupae of the Clouded Drab moth and it was calculated that digging daily for five hours, for six days a week (excluding Sundays), it would have taken him five months to find this number. Greene and Hogan were amongst a number of clergymen who involved themselves in the study of insects in Ireland. Others included J. Bristow, W.W. Flemying, W.F. Johnson and P. O'Kelly (S.J.).

EDWIN BIRCHALL (1819-1884) was born near Leeds and later moved to Dublin for business reasons. He was well known for his field work on butterflies in Yorkshire which included species which are no longer extant there. His field work and collecting in Ireland extended to Killarney and the Burren in Co Clare. He retired to Douglas in the Isle of Man after his field activities were severely curtailed by an injury believed to be the result of a fall from a cliff in Howth, Co Dublin. Some ten years after Greene, in 1866, he published a revised list of butterflies and moths, stating "I have been unwilling to reject any reputed indigenous species which could be retained with the last shadow of reason." Birchall retains 'doubtful' species in his list including Chalkhill Blue, Silver-studded Blue, Duke of Burgundy and both the Large and Small Skippers. He appears to confirm having personally seen the two skippers mentioned above from Wicklow and the Small Skipper also from near Cork. He reported the Heath Fritillary as at "Killarney, abundant", a finding never confirmed by others.

An interesting addition is his specific report of seeing the Small Mountain Ringlet on Croagh Patrick in Co Mayo, one of a very small number of 19th century reports of this species from the west of Ireland. Because of the existence of museum specimens of the Small Mountain Ringlet labelled from Nephin Beg in Co Mayo and Lough Gill in Co Sligo, these reported sightings have continued to arouse controversy for a century and a half. Some have argued that Birchall was too trusting of others and it is interesting to read his personal view in relation to fraudulent entomological reports, quoted in *The Aurelian Legacy* (Salmon 2000), which annunciates that no collector could be sure of the provenance of any specimen unless he had captured it himself.

Edward Newman's (1801-1876) *The natural history of British butterflies and moths* (1871) is well known for the high quality of its illustrative black and white woodcuts. In relation to Ireland, it contains very little new information as it appears to rely almost entirely on the Greene and Birchall publications, quoting, for example, Birchall's assessment of the distribution of the Peacock as "rare in Ulster". At the same time he expresses strong doubts, on geographical and climatic considerations, as to the reliability of their reports of the presence of species such as the Black-veined White in Ireland.

Rev. Francis Orpen Morris (1810-1893) was born in Cobh, Co Cork and spent his early youth in the south-west of Ireland before his family moved to England in 1824. He is well known for his publications on birds and butterflies with their very attractive colour plates. His *History of British Butterflies* was first published in 1853 and ran to many editions. While he does give mention of butterflies in Ireland, the 1895 edition adds little to our knowledge and he quotes an (erroneous) report of the Marbled White as being "plentiful near Clonmel, in Ireland". Interestingly, he refers to the ability of individual Red Admirals to successfully overwinter in Britian and Ireland.

WILLIAM FRANCIS DE VISMES KANE (1840-1918) was born in Exmouth of an Irish father and in his early twenties purchased Drumreaske House, Co Monaghan which was his main residence in Ireland. He was a founding member of the Dublin Naturalists' Field Club and its President in 1901. He extensively collected butterflies in Europe and in 1885 he published a catalogue called *European butterflies*. This was the first time that insects were illustrated by photographs using plates reproduced by the isochromatic process.

His *A catalogue of the Lepidoptera of Ireland* (*with supplement*) (1901), was in essence a consolidation of the various articles he had published in the *Entomologist* between 1893 and 1901. In it he discusses the biogeography of butterflies and moths in Ireland in the context of climate, soil and the impact of glaciation on diversity and distribution. The information in his catalogue reflects his expertise and knowledge of butterflies in a European context. His own field work in Ireland was mainly at Drumreaske and at Favour Royal in Tyrone but he did travel around Ireland by yacht. He drew on reports and specimens from some forty lepidopterists almost all of whom were resident in Ireland. The increase in knowledge of Irish butterflies since the time of Greene and Birchall is demonstrated by the attention paid to variations in the Green-veined White, Common Blue and Large Heath. He devotes more than four pages to various forms of the Marsh Fritillary including var. *hibernica* still recognised by some as an Irish sub-species. In contrast, with regard to the unconfirmed species of Birchall's catalogue, he merely briefly quotes from it without comment. He does, however, introduce some new heresy: High Brown Fritillary "A few taken in Co. Galway in 1887 (R.E.D[illon].)" and Small Pearl-bordered Fritillary at Edenderry, Co. Offaly which was misidentified by F.W. Sinclair. Kane also admits the Brown Argus to his catalogue having seen specimens allegedly 'taken' by Hon. R.E. Dillon who succeeded his father becoming the last Lord Clonbrock.

Clonbrock reported a large number of very rare insects from his estate at Ahascragh and its general locality in Co Galway. In 1894 publications he claimed 26 species of Macrolepidoptera new to Ireland, 27 species which had been reported before, but were debatable, and over 40 rarities. While these records created suspicions it was left to C.G. Barrett, author of the incomplete *Lepidoptera of the British Isles* (1893), to debunk Clonbrock's fictitious claims. He wrote to Kane in this matter. It has been alleged that Clonbrock, who was very keen on the discovery of new species on his estate, gave a reward of a guinea to his gamekeeper for each such detection. One day by chance he intercepted a package containing a 'new discovery' which had been ordered by his gamekeeper from an entomological supplier. However, his gamekeeper can only be credited with a small number of the bogus findings. Beirne's (1985) most charitable assessment is that Clonbrock had decided to perpetrate a hoax assuming that his publications would be rejected and then found himself unable to recant.

In his Supplement, Kane includes the Grizzled Skipper having received a report of two collected from the Killarney copper mines area. However, this latter record was subsequently disowned by Kane as being "in error in relation to their origin". The Supplement has a report of two sightings of the Bath White from Co Wexford in 1893 – a very rare report of this migrant. In the main text Kane states that he has never seen the Small Mountain Ringlet in Ireland. However, in the supplement he reports that he had just "been fortunate to meet a few specimens on Nephin" but had been unable to further investigate his finding. Kane virtually abandoned his work on Lepidoptera about 1902 and deposited his collection in the National Museum of Ireland.

It has been speculated that his reason for this was that he could not bring himself to expose the fraud of his friend Clonbrock which had been forcefully brought to his attention by Barrett.

LT.-COL. CHARLES DONOVAN (1863-1951) was born in Calcutta and at the age of thirteen was sent to Cork City to live with his grandparents. He trained as a doctor in Ireland and then joined the Indian Medical Service and was stationed at Mandalay. He had two entomologist sisters living in Timoleague, Co Cork and while visiting them did much of the field work for his *Catalogue of the Macrolepidoptera of Ireland* (1936) published after retirement. In it he recognised the major contribution made by Kane but at the same time he criticises him for not being sufficiently critical in his acceptance of the "delinquencies of Birchall and Dillon". Acknowledged contributors to Donovan's work included Mr. T. Greer, Rev. Canon G. Foster, Sir Charles Langham, Mr. Dudley Westropp, Mr. L.H. Bonaparte Wyse, Rev. K. Dunlop and his own sisters Miss B. Donovan and Mrs. G.E. Lucas.

THOMAS GREER (1874-1949) made a remarkable contribution to entomology over a period of more than 60 years from his Tyrone base. As a person of independent means, his two occupations of motor-cycling and study of Lepidoptera were intertwined. Greer (1922, 1923, 1925) had a particular interest in the variations and aberrations of butterfly forms. For most of this career he averaged two publications per annum and he accumulated a remarkable collection of insects numbering more than 10,000. In 1923 the Belfast Naturalists' Field Club published his paper on the *Distribution of the Lepidoptera of Northern Ireland*. Financial circumstances eventually forced him to sell his insect collection which was broken up. Ten years later Foster's *Lepidoptera of County Down* was also made available by the BNFC. Peters (1962) gives a very comprehensive and critical account of the Butterflies of Northern Ireland and contains some very interesting observations on distribution, phenology and forms. Subsequent up-dates have been published by Ian Rippey (1986, 1989).

EDWARD STUART AUGUSTUS BAYNES (1889-1972) was born in Yorkshire and spent his career in the Foreign Office. From 1946 he was attached to the British Embassy in Dublin and on retirement lived in Glenageary, Co Dublin. He then focused his entomological interests almost exclusively on Irish Lepidoptera. In addition to compiling an annual report on migrants for the *Irish Naturalists' Journal* he decided to revise Donovan's Catalogue. In this task he drew widely from published and unpublished sources, critically evaluated specimens and records and consulted experts of the day including H.C. Huggins, B.P. Beirne and C.A. Cockayne in the British Museum. Some of the others consulted included R.F. Haynes, H.G. Heal, J.V. Peters and the lighthouse keepers of Ireland notably D.J. O'Sullivan who served on Tory Island, Inistrahull and latterly on Rathlin. Baynes published his *A revised catalogue of Irish Macrolepidoptera (butterflies and moths)* in 1964. The list of Irish butterflies is reduced to 39 species including eight migrants/vagrants. The latter includes rarities such as the Monarch (first reported from Castletownshend, in 1916) and the American Painted Lady, as well as the recurring migratory Red Admiral, Painted Lady and Clouded Yellow. Eight species which were included by Donovan are banished to an appendix because there was not sufficiently reliable evidence to provisionally include them.

The National Grid System introduced by Colonel Niall MacNeill, Head of the Irish Ordnance Survey, facilitated the evolution of biological recording in Ireland from the exclusive use of the vice-county to the 10 km square recording unit. MacNeill's paper on Hemiptera using the 10 km square recording units was posthumously published in 1973. The first comprehensive distribution Atlas was produced by the Botanical Society of the British Isles in conjunction with the British Biological Records Centre at Monkswood. In Ireland a Records Centre was set up in An Foras Forbartha in 1971 with financial assistance from the Carnegie Trust. This initiative gave a great boost to biological recording and (provisional) Atlases were produced for a number of groups.

In relation to butterflies, during the 1970s the Irish Biological Records Centre set itself the task of involving members of the pubic in submitting records. The *Provisional atlas of butterflies in Ireland* (Crichton & Ní Lamhna 1975) based its distribution maps on 4500 records submitted by 160 listed recorders. The final publication was the *Distribution atlas of butterflies in Ireland* (Ní Lamhna 1980). A very major contributor to these atlases was Paul Hillis who did extensive field work, and encouraged other recorders to look for butterflies. Other important contributors were Sean Fleming, Patrick O'Mahony, the Cork Naturalist Association, Ian Rippey, Robert Nash and Ken Preston.

The first *Atlas of butterflies in Britain and Ireland* (Heath, J., Pollard, E. & Thomas, J.A. 1984) relied very heavily on the data compiled for the Irish third edition. Unfortunately, the demise of An Foras Forbartha brought an abrupt end to the functioning of the Irish Biological Records Centre and this recording initiative. Norman Hickin's (1992) *The butterflies of Ireland, A field guide* was the first book dedicated solely to Irish butterflies. This was followed by two excellent publications, *The butterflies and moths of Northern Ireland* (Thompson & Nelson 2006) and *Discovering Irish butterflies and their habitats* (Harding 2008), in combination giving geographical coverage to the whole island. Recent county publications have been the Lepidoptera of Counties Waterford (O'Meara 2001) and Wexford (O'Donnell & Wilson 2009).

The most exciting find of the 20th Century was the discovery of the Pearl-bordered Fritillary at Clooncoose in the Burren, Co Clare, by R.A. Phillips (1923). This was the first confirmed report of the existence of this species in Ireland. The 21st Century has been ushered in with the news that Ireland was home to two species of Wood White (Nelson *et al.* 2001) and not one as had previously been believed. The two species were then named *Leptidea sinapis* (Wood White) and *Leptidea reali* (Réal's Wood White). Réal first confirmed the species named after him in 1988. The two species are so similar in appearance that it is not possible to reliably distinguish them in the field. Museum specimens and samples from extant populations from a substantial number of sites in Ireland were dissected. *L. sinapis* was confirmed in the limestone pavement areas of Cos Clare and Galway and *L. reali* elsewhere throughout Ireland. The two species have been found within a few kilometres of each other but appear not to overlap in their distribution, whereas in Sweden and elsewhere on mainland Europe they had been reported as sympatric. However, very recent work by Dincă (*et al.* 2011) has shown that "*reali*" is really two cryptic species which are only resolvable on the basis of differences in their molecular biology. As a consequence, the proposed scientific name for the species in Ireland is now *Leptidea juvernica* (Cryptic Wood White).

An important action to promote the conservation of Lepidoptera has been the appointment by Butterfly Conservation of Maurice Hughes as Regional Officer for Northern Ireland c. 2001. Field work on Irish butterflies has continued over the past three decades with significant records by many recorders. A list of the names of those who contributed from 1995 is included in Appendix 11. The authors apologise to anyone who has been inadvertently omitted. Standing out among those who have tirelessly traversed the country over many decades are Ken Bond and Ian Rippey who both have made exceptional contributions to our knowledge. The highly organised and systematic survey of Co Donegal, led by Bob Aldwell and driven by Frank Smyth, in relentless pursuit of all species but strongly focused on the Marsh Fritillary in the latter years, is unmatched. This latter project has continued for more than a decade and is an exemplar for anyone interested in doing a thorough study of the butterflies of a county or a region.

In the final few years of the 20th Century the Butterfly Conservation's (UK) *Butterflies for the New Millennium* (BNM) project was the catalyst for The Dublin Naturalists' Field Club to engage in serious butterfly recording. The data collected facilitated distribution maps for the island of Ireland being included in the *Millennium Atlas* (Asher *et al* 2001). An update, *The State of Butterflies in Britain and Ireland* (Fox *et al* 2006) [SOBBI], was published five years later, followed by a 2010 Atlas (Fox & Asher 2010) with maps but no text. The concerted efforts over more than a decade have produced a much more detailed picture of the distribution of butterfly species in the island of Ireland. Field recording is continuing, building on this foundation.

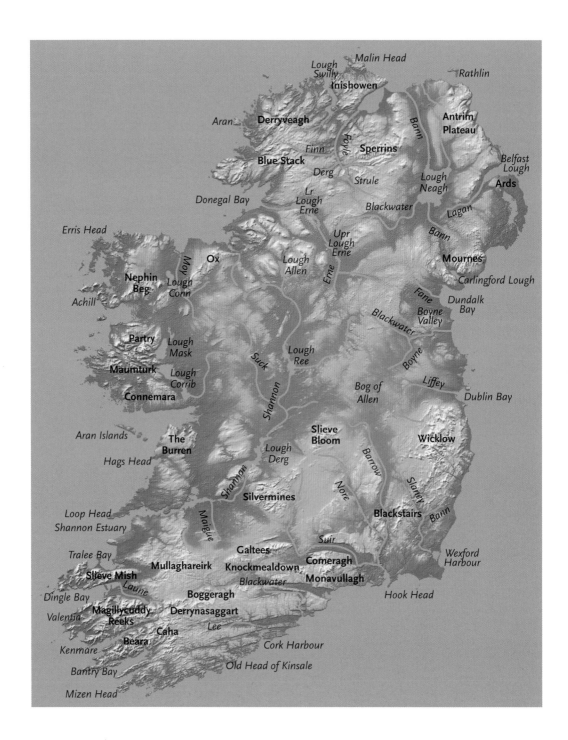

Ireland's Topography, Geology and Soils 2

IRELAND IS SURROUNDED to the north, west and south by the Atlantic Ocean and to the east by the Irish Sea. At the closest point it is 30 km from Britain. Its latitude extends from 51.5° to 55° north and longitude from 5.5° to 10.5° west. Its total area is approximately 83,000 km² and the greatest distance north to south is 486 km and the equivalent distance east to west is 275 km. The highest elevation is Carrauntoohill which is 1,041 metres above sea-level. The longest river is the Shannon (370 km) with its associated lakes. The largest freshwater lake in Britain and Ireland is Lough Neagh (383 km²) and other substantial water bodies in limestone areas include Loughs Corrib and Mask in counties Galway and Mayo, Upper and Lower Lough Erne in Fermanagh and the midland lakes. Much of the coast, especially the western seaboard, is very indented giving the island a relatively long coastline.

Ireland's general topography can briefly be described as an undulating central lowlands surrounded by an upland coastal fringe. Much of the landscape has been shaped by past glacial events. The basement rocks are crystalline, metamorphic and igneous which, in the Midlands, are generally covered and in the north and west are more exposed.

The central lowlands are largely floored by Carboniferous Limestone, with small areas of higher ground covered with either younger or older protruding deformed rock. The younger rock in Kilkenny and Leitrim contains residual coal measure deposits and older Silurian and Devonian sandstones are found around Lough Derg and in the Slieve Bloom mountains. The limestone rock is usually covered by glacial deposits, which are, topographically, most obvious in the form of eskers and drumlins.

In the west and north including Connemara and West Ulster, Ireland's oldest rocks – Pre-Cambrian metamorphic schist, gneiss and quartzite – are found together with granitic intrusions which dominate the higher ground and demonstrate a north-east south-west fold pattern that has been sculpted by the movement of ice sheets. In contrast, in the north-east, some of the youngest rocks are to be found with Tertiary basalt overlying chalk and younger sedimentary rocks. The Longford-Down massif comprising Silurian and Ordovician slates and greywacke sandstones extends from the Ards Peninsula southwest almost to the River Shannon north of Longford. It embraces much of Down, Armagh, Monaghan, Cavan and Louth. The area

The Bedrock Geology of Ireland

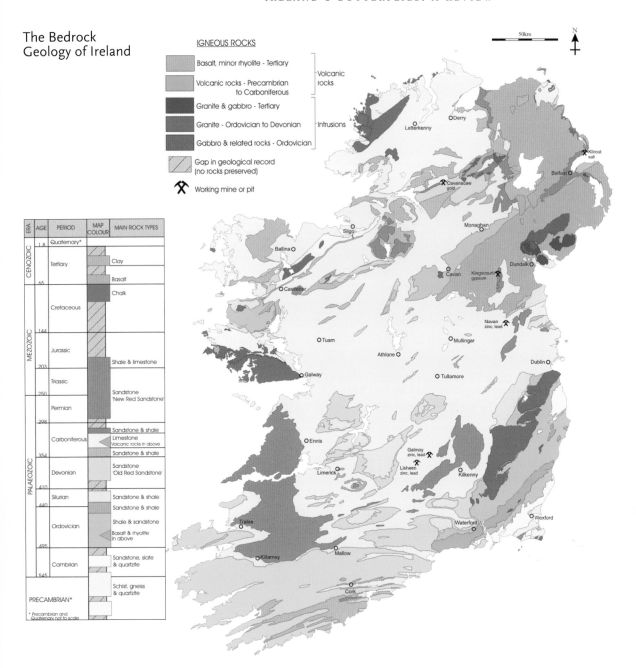

IGNEOUS ROCKS

- Basalt, minor rhyolite - Tertiary ⎫
- Volcanic rocks - Precambrian to Carboniferous ⎭ Volcanic rocks
- Granite & gabbro - Tertiary ⎫
- Granite - Ordovician to Devonian ⎬ Intrusions
- Gabbro & related rocks - Ordovician ⎭
- Gap in geological record (no rocks preserved)
- ⚒ Working mine or pit

50km   N

ERA	AGE	PERIOD	MAP COLOUR	MAIN ROCK TYPES
CENOZOIC	1.8	Quaternary*		
		Tertiary		Clay
	65			Basalt
MEZOZOIC		Cretaceous		Chalk
	144	Jurassic		
	203			Shale & limestone
		Triassic		
	250	Permian		Sandstone 'New Red Sandstone'
	298			Sandstone & shale
PALAEOZOIC		Carboniferous		Limestone Volcanic rocks in above
	354			Sandstone & shale
		Devonian		Sandstone 'Old Red Sandstone'
	410	Silurian		Sandstone & shale
	440			Sandstone & shale
		Ordovician		Shale & sandstone
				Basalt & rhyolite in above
	495	Cambrian		Sandstone, slate & quartzite
	545			
		PRECAMBRIAN*		Schist, gneiss & quartzite

* Precambrian and Quaternary not to scale

is mostly covered by glacial deposits, often in the form of drumlins and eskers. The drumlins mainly occur in a belt that stretches from County Down to Donegal and are best seen in the small rounded islands of Strangford Lough and of Clew Bay (Co Mayo). Esker ridges also extend across the Midlands. The Mourne and Carlingford Mountains and Slieve Gullion are largely granitic intrusions of similar age to the Antrim basalts.

Between Drogheda and Dublin the central lowlands, covered by glacial deposits, reach the Irish Sea. From Dublin to Dungarvan there is higher ground composed of shale and sandstone together with the granitic rock which dominates the Wicklow and Blackstairs Mountains. Cambrian rock stretches from Cahore Point to Bannow Bay and in the Carnsore area in the south-east granite is believed to have intruded into already metamorphosed Pre-Cambrian rock. The Copper Coast Geopark along the Waterford coast is mainly of Ordovician origin and has very interesting exposures.

In the south of the country from Dungarvan to Killarney and in the Dingle Peninsula, much of the earlier glacial deposits have been eroded leaving exposed Old Red Sandstone and slate. On the higher ground glacial features such as corries (cirques) are found. East of Killarney and Tralee is younger sandstone and shale originating from the Upper Carboniferous which extends northward through Clare almost to Galway Bay. North of Ennis extending into Galway the bare karst limestone of the Burren occurs with its unique mixture of Arctic Alpine and Lusitanian vegetation which is reflected in the greatest diversity of butterflies to be found in Ireland. The Aran Islands are remnants of the Burren limestone which were connected to Co Clare when sea levels were considerably lower during the cold phase of the Ice Age.

Since nearly all of Ireland, apart from the most southerly region, was denuded of its soil during the last Ice Age, the island's present day soils are generally of recent origin. These soils in Ireland have developed under conditions of high rainfall with evapotranspiration (evaporation and plant transpiration) as a proportion of precipitation estimated to be generally within the range of 25% to 50%. Where the parent material is permeable, podzols or brown earths are formed, but if the substrate is clay or silt then gleys occur.

The Carboniferous rocks of the central lowlands are covered with glacial deposits of clay and sand interspersed with bogs and lakes. These soils are mainly grey brown podzols and peats where the ancient lakes have been successively filled with fen and sphagnum. The Bog of Allen, which has been destroyed by the extraction of peat for electricity generation and for domestic fuel, was once one of the best examples of a raised bog in the Midlands. The soils of the north, west and south-west are mainly composed of poorly drained peats, peaty podzols and gleys. Peat soils of varied depth occur widely in all of the Irish lowlands where drainage is poor and where basin peat succeeded fens which originated in drier and warmer periods. In upland areas, and in lowlands with a high rainfall, peat occurs on top of soils that have been heavily leached resulting in hard pan formation. Generally this podzolisation, which is accompanied by an iron pan, is common from a height of 140 metres above sea level and upwards. In the lowlands much of this land has been drained to produce heavy clay soil pasture. In many western coastal areas such as Galway and Mayo the peat occurs as blanket bog on rock substrate, extending down to sea level.

In contrast, in the south and east the soils are generally more free drained brown earths and brown and grey-brown podzols. This soil distribution largely reflects the rainfall pattern with the poorly drained (and higher) ground receiving the highest volume of precipitation. Podzols are common in the sands and

General Soil Map of
Ireland 1980
© Teagasc

Great Soil Groups

Podzols

Brown Podzolics

Grey Brown Podzolics

Acid Brown Earths

Gleys

Shallow Brown Earths

Rendzinas & Liithosols

Basin Peats

Blanket Peat

Water

Urban

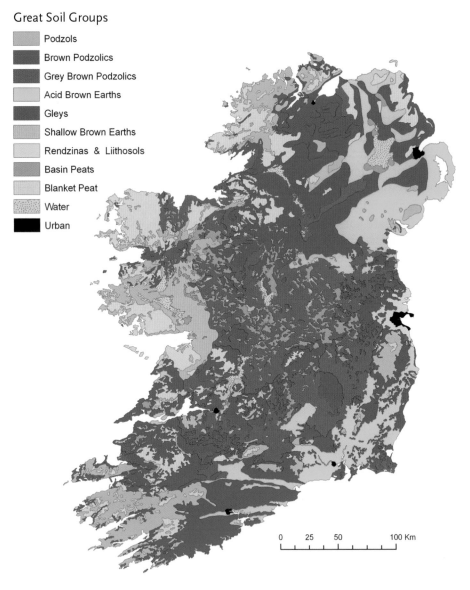

0   25   50   100 Km

gravels of the eskers and moraines that are plentiful mainly in the Central Lowlands. Similar soils also develop in sandy areas of glacial drift.

Brown earths have developed on loams derived from granitic drifts, for example, in counties Down, Armagh, Wicklow and Wexford, from micaschists in Tyrone and Londonderry and from some Devonian Old Red Sandstones. They may be formed on basaltic drift in Co Antrim and on the upper parts of drumlins in the east where the lower slopes are waterlogged.

Much of the central lowlands and the drumlin-drift belt from Donegal Bay to the Shannon Estuary have gley soils resulting in rushy pastures. Gleys become more common, replacing the brown earths on drumlins, as we move westwards where precipitation is higher.

Climate

3

I RELAND, with its constant exposure to Atlantic weather, is not overly suitable to a wide variety of butterflies. Our total of thirty or so species compares with in excess of fifty in Britain and 486 (Kudrna 2002) on the European continent. Climate is but one factor in our reduced numbers of butterflies. Size, isolation and a limited range of habitat are likely to be equally significant determinants.

Ireland's northerly latitude (between 51° and 55°N), its insular position near the track of constant Atlantic depressions, the prevailing south-west and westerly winds and its comparative lack of topographical diversity have resulted in a cool though uniform cloudy, windy and moist climate. Regional differences do exist. Ireland's climate is cool temperate, moderated by the North Atlantic Drift which flows north-eastwards from more tropical latitudes.

Temperature

Surrounded by salt water on all sides, and nowhere more than 110 km from the sea, temperatures over the whole island are seldom given to extremes whether seasonal or diurnal. In winter there is usually no more than 4°C difference between any part of the island, and in summer the difference is a mere 3°C. The Figure shows the July map constructed using temperature data for 1961-2000. Arguably, summer temperatures have more relevance in so far as butterflies are concerned, and the map shows the mean daily *maximum* during July, varying from only 17°C on the north coast to 20°C in the south and east. The mean daily *minimum* is about 11°C.

The decrease of mean daily temperature with altitude is about 1°C per 150

Daily Max 2 m Temperature (°C) Monthly Average July 1961-2000 © UKCIP

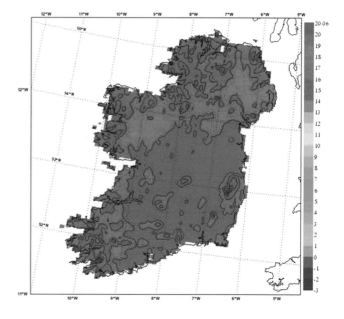

metres, so temperatures on our highest mountains can be 6°C cooler than at sea level. There are heat islands in and near the larger urban centres such as Dublin and Belfast which can raise local temperatures by 2-3°C. Historically, the extremes of temperature have ranged from -19°C in Sligo in January 1881 to 33°C in Kilkenny in June 1887.

Temperatures recorded at Met Éireann's meteorological station at Birr in the Midlands have been increasing in line with global trends and the graph shows the annual temperature difference from the 1961-1990 norm, alongside the ten-year average.

Temperature Trends at Birr (1995-2008)
© Met Éireann

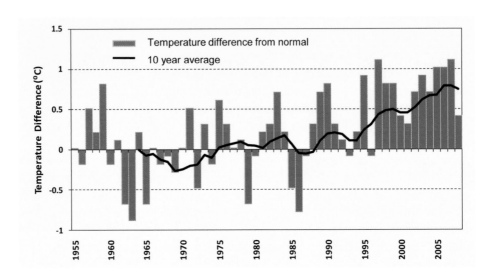

There has been a change in the extreme temperature indices for Ireland, of which the most obvious has been in relation to minimum temperature. For example, the frost day indices (the annual and seasonal account of days when the minimum temperature is less than 0°C) have changed very significantly over the decades at all meteorological stations, as exemplified by Shannon in the west and inland at Birr (McElwain and Sweeney 2006) with declines of 88% and 38% in the number of days with frost since records began at these locations 60 and 55 years ago, respectively. The graphs show clearly the downward trend which is most obvious for Shannon.

Number of Frost Days at Shannon © EPA

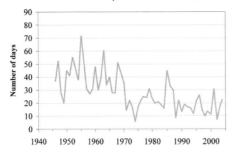

Number of Frost Days at Birr © EPA

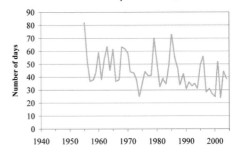

There has been, as might be expected, a corresponding curtailment of the length of the frost season (the number of days between the date of the first and last frosts). Also of interest is the general reduction in diurnal temperature range (the difference between the daytime maximum temperature and night time minimum temperature). This latter change has been attributed to an increase in cloudiness, especially at night. What precise influence this might have, for example, on the time taken for larvae which are nocturnal feeders to mature is not known. But it is not surprising that the combination of higher and more uniform diurnal temperatures has resulted in the earlier emergence of adult butterflies.

The evidence that global warming is taking place is overwhelmingly strong. Mean temperatures in Ireland have risen by 1.4°C between the 1960s and the 2000s. Ten of the warmest years in the last century in Ireland have occurred between 1995 and 2006. The Community Climate Change Consortium of Ireland (C4I) (McGrath & Lynch 2008) predicts that both January and July temperatures will rise by up to 1.5°C between 2021 and 2060. If this increase is maintained, the temperature in the middle of the present century will be very similar to that of La Rochelle in western France today, an obvious benefit to most butterfly species whose activities are limited by a minimum temperature for flight activity but detrimental to those which would have to seek shade during the hottest part of the day.

Rainfall

Total annual precipitation varies from about 750 mm in the Dublin area, and less than 800 mm in Co. Armagh and Strangford Lough, to over 2,400 mm in the highest mountains of the west and south-west. Precipitation is least in sheltered lowland eastern districts and greatest in the highest mountainous districts of the west. The driest season is March to July, and the wettest from August to February. From a butterfly's point of view it is not just the amount of precipitation that matters, but also its duration. There are about 150 days a year with 1 mm or more of rain on east and south-east coasts, and about 225 days a year in parts of the west. The total annual hours of rainfall lies between 550 and 850, about two hours a day on average, being less during the April-July period and more from October-January. The C4I report predicts that Ireland will become up to 20% wetter in January and 10-20% drier in July between 2021 and 2060

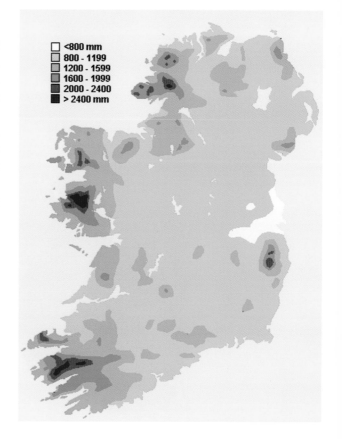

Average Annual
Rainfall in Ireland
© Met Éireann

<800 mm
800 - 1199
1200 - 1599
1600 - 1999
2000 - 2400
> 2400 mm

< 1200 hours
1200 - 1299
1300 - 1399
1400 - 1499
1500 - 1600
> 1600

Average Annual
Sunshine in Ireland

© Met Éireann

with a similar increase in extremes such as 2-day rainfall events.

Sunshine

As might be expected in a cloudy oceanic climate, annual sunshine totals are generally low, ranging from 1,200 hours inland in Co Tyrone in the north to 1,700 hours in Co Wexford in the south-east (26-36% of the maximum possible). Much of the country, except the south and east coasts, has less than 1,400 hours a year, but it is always sunnier near the sea. May and June are the sunniest months with about 5.5 to 7.0 hours a day, and December and January the dullest with only 0.9 to 2.0 hours per day. During the butterfly flight season (March to September) it always averages at least 3.0 hours a day, even in the least sunny areas.

Wind

The windiest areas are naturally around the north-west coasts, and the least windy in inland southern districts, average speeds ranging from 4-7 m/s, but gusts on the Donegal coast can reach 50 m/s. (1 m/s = 1.94 knots = 2.24 mph.)

Mean annual wind speed
(units in m/s) © Met Éireann

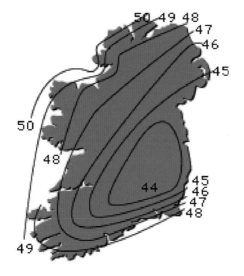

Maximum gust speed likely to be exceeded once in 50 years (units in m/s)© Met Éireann

In order to show which months were most conducive for butterflies from a climatic point of view, four parameters were used: temperature, sunshine, rainfall and windiness at Birr, Co Offaly, a central location with a complete set of weather records. The monthly averages of daytime (maximum) temperatures, sunshine hours, rainfall and windiness were ranked, and then totalled to give a favourability index, for each month of the butterfly flight period (March-October). The graph shows plots of the favourability index and of the number of species flying in each month from March to October.

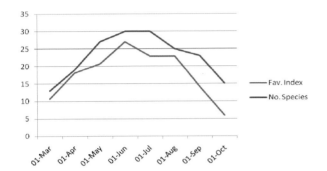

Favourability Index for the Butterfly Season

The favourability index peaks in June, declines slightly in July and August and then diminishes steeply. Thirteen species have been observed flying in March and the number of species reaches a maximum of thirty in mid-summer, declining to fifteen in October and then plummets. Overall, the chart shows a good correlation between the Favourability Index and the number of species flying.

Small Blue on Kidney Vetch

Red Admiral

4 Conservation

IN ORDER TO DEVELOP a coherent and effective plan for the conservation of Ireland's butterflies we need good quality data on their populations and distribution and a fuller understanding of their ecology, together with a clear and realistic vision of what can be achieved. To be successful, such a vision needs a will and a commitment for action which is shared by all – lepidopterists, land owners, state agencies, the general public and politicians. Policies for the conservation of butterflies can only be successful in the context of a coherent action plan to halt the loss of our national biodiversity.

We have had European Conservation Year, European Year of the Environment, The Rio Janeiro Earth Summit, Countdown 2010, Biodiversity Action Plans and Reports and, as we write, World Biodiversity Year, the Cancún meeting and the Nagoya Convention on Biological Diversity. Treaties and resolutions are very laudable in their own right and do make a certain contribution to public awareness of environmental issues but are usually confined to dusty shelves as they are aspirational rather than executive.

Some lepidopterists of more mature years will have clear recollections of the halcyon days when summers were apparently warmer and butterflies were more ubiquitous. Meteorological records refute the first of these recollections. With regard to frequency of butterflies, although high quality quantitative evidence is lacking, it is incontrovertible that the populations of Lepidoptera and other invertebrates have substantially declined.

Major changes in the Irish countryside and its management have taken place in the past 40 years since our accession to the European Union (European Economic Community). Driven by the Common Agricultural Policy (CAP), intensification of farming has impacted severely on the availability of suitable habitat for butterfly species. The drive for increased productivity has resulted in drainage, scrub clearance, reseeding of pasture, afforestation (with non-native species) and the application of large quantities of fertiliser, insecticide and herbicide. Stocking densities for both bovine and ovine species have increased. High density grazing by sheep, which consume almost all plant material available, is particularly destructive. The increase in Ireland's human population has resulted in further pressures due to quarrying and the construction of buildings and roads leading to further environmental loss. Recreational demand for leisure facilities such as golf courses has resulted in irreversible spoilage of prime coastal and inland areas. Unfortunately, sheltered south facing sites are equally attractive as places of habitation for both humans and butterflies. The latter always lose out in the unequal competition.

The European Union Habitat Directives have two major designations or categories for the protection of what it considers to be important areas for wildlife. They are termed *Special Protection Areas* (SPAs) for birds and *Special Areas of Conservation* (SACs) for other organisms. Designation has the objective of protecting at least a portion of the most seriously threatened habitats and species across the Union. Collectively, these two entities are referred to as Natura 2000 sites. Each member state is obliged to designate sites within its own jurisdiction. The failure to date to fully comply with the Directive and to designate and protect Natura 2000 sites in the RoI is extremely disappointing and EU enforcement attempts have not yet been effective. Even where sites have been designated, derogations from implementation have allowed habitat destruction to continue and to accelerate, unimpeded. The National Parks and Wildlife Service Report *The status of EU Protected Habitats and Species in Ireland* (Anon. 2008a) is a very stark and pessimistic assessment in relation to national conservation achievements to date and future prospects. The following assessment terms used in the Report "favourable" (good), "unfavourable_inadequate" (poor) and "unfavourable_bad" (bad), are appraisals related to reference values no less than those existing when the Habitats Directive came into force in 1992. Some extracts from this report are given in the accompanying Table.

Habitat	Habitat Area	Future Prospects
Vegetated sea cliffs	good	poor
Fixed/*grey dunes	poor	bad
Humid dune slacks	poor	bad
Machair*	poor	bad
Orchid rich/calcareous grassland*	bad	bad
Raised bog (active*)	bad	bad
Limestone pavement*	poor	poor
Old oak woodlands	bad	bad

*EU priority habitats

Even in the unlikely event of co-ordinated, systematic and appropriate action, mitigation of the rate of disappearance of species rather than reversal is likely to be the best achievable outcome, with a very substantial and progressive continuation of loss of biodiversity. Incremental damage is cumulative and likely to be irreparable.

The Distribution Atlas of Butterflies in Ireland (Ní Lamhna 1980) contains records from approximately 900 10-km squares. Coverage was low for the Inishowen Peninsula, mid-Donegal, the border areas and north Tyrone, south Monaghan, Sligo, Mayo, north-east Galway and south Clare. Nevertheless, records for 2-5 species were obtained from 220 squares, 6-10 species in 224 squares, 11-20 species from 348 squares and a minimum of 20 species in 55 squares.

The table below presents a simple comparative analysis of the number of 10 sq km records for the three five-year periods of 1995-1999, 2000-2004 and 2005-2009. Any apparent gains or losses should not be rigorously interpreted. While there has been a comparable amount of recording effort in these three periods, the timing of visits to sites has not been synchronised. A substantial number of the 'losses' are attributable to either a lack of return visits to known sites or different seasonal timing. Similarly, a portion of the gains are attributable to the discovery of previously existing but unknown sites. An increase in the number of recorded squares should not be construed as a distribution or population increase. Specifically, there have been many gains in Donegal where a sustained and systematic study has been in progress for a decade. The Donegal survey has shown that persistent and careful checking for species such as the Green Hairstreak, Holly Blue and Marsh Fritillary, in areas of suitable habitat, may eventually locate these butterflies. It can be assumed that similar approach in many other counties would yield significant gains.

Species

Species	No. 10 km records 1995-1999	No. 10 km records 2000-2004	*No. 10 km records 2005-2009
Essex Skipper	0	0	5
Dingy Skipper	58	58	76
Wood White (both species).	237	202	280
Clouded Yellow	110	303	193
Brimstone	116	127	104
Large White	595	488	511
Small White	532	437	449
Green-veined White	887	811	773
Orange Tip	689	636	637
Green Hairstreak	118	157	208
Brown Hairstreak	16	12	15
Purple Hairstreak	19	30	39
Small Copper	374	360	365
Small Blue	45	54	60
Common Blue	436	429	428
Holly Blue	110	164	252
Red Admiral	558	538	534
Painted Lady	358	530	579
Small Tortoiseshell	633	635	642
Peacock	656	640	635
Comma	2	8	17
Pearl-bordered Fritillary	6	3	8

Dark Green Fritillary	100	97	107
Silver-washed Fritillary	167	216	218
Marsh Fritillary	88	75	136
Speckled Wood	775	719	701
Wall Brown	293	255	170
Grayling	151	125	123
Gatekeeper	48	56	34
Meadow Brown	712	756	695
Ringlet	568	671	592
Small Heath	284	256	322
Large Heath	51	85	105
No. 10 km sq visited	980	980	951
No. Species /square	9.8	10.1	10.5

No. of 10 km square records for three successive 5-year periods

*In the main compiled from records received up to 1/3/2010, with a small amount of data from 2010 season

Butterfly Conservation (NI) is continuing with the *Butterflies for the New Millennium* and the *Butterflies of the Wider Countryside* recording schemes. The Dublin Naturalists' Field Club and its volunteers are progressing their recording in the Republic of Ireland (RoI). In Northern Ireland (NI) a butterfly monitoring scheme using transects (Pollard Walks), has been in place since 1979 when the first one was commenced in the Murlough Reserve by Jo Whatmough of the National Trust. In the transect method, data is accumulated by weekly counts of butterfly populations along fixed routes from April to September each year, in suitable butterfly weather. The minimum temperature and other requirements to make the method valid are extremely challenging in Ireland's very variable weather. Such systematic long-term monitoring by expert recorders can yield valid information about trends in population when averaged over a significant number of sites. In 2008 the National Biodiversity Data Centre in Waterford, commenced a similar pilot scheme in the RoI. It is likely to be a number of years before there is sufficient data from experienced recorders to pronounce authoritatively on population trends.

It is now widely acknowledged that insects are very suitable for use as biodiversity indicators. Butterflies are very sensitive to alterations in their habitat and climate change, especially temperature. They are considered to be good representatives of the biodiversity of the whole 'insect group' which comprises half of all terrestrial organisms and more sensitive than birds as indicators of change. They are highly visible, easy to identify and amenable to monitoring using tried and tested methods. The short life cycle of butterflies, having one or more broods per annum, means that population trends can be determined and quantified in years rather than in decades for longer living organisms. Can we afford to delay any action until it is again reconfirmed that our climate and natural environment are indeed changing and are having a detrimental affect on wild life?

In the millennia since the last Ice Age, butterflies have had an opportunity to adapt to fluctuations and slow changes in climate. But it is generally acknowledged that global warming is now happening at a rate that is challenging, and in some instances, exceeding the capacity of insects to adapt by evolving or moving. In the northern hemisphere, some butterfly species are expanding their range and moving in a polar direction as temperatures rise. In Britain, for example, the Comma is expanding northwards and a small but an increasing number of sightings in Ireland confirms that it has established itself here at low density.

Climate modelling is an infant science but using up-to-date modelling methodologies, it has been predicted that regions such as the northern Mediterranean will become too hot and dry for many species (Settele *et al.* 2008). Some species may successfully spread northwards while others may not. Wilson *et al.* (2005) have shown that in Spain a number of species have adapted to higher temperature by shifting their territory an additional 100 metres above sea level for every one degree rise in temperature. Unfortunately larval food plants generally cannot adapt as rapidly and the opportunity for butterflies to retreat to higher ground and higher latitudes in the Northern Hemisphere is quite limited.

It has been predicted that the Large Heath, a habitat specialist which has very specific requirements, may become extinct in Britain and Ireland towards the end of the century. Unfortunately, the loss of most of its bog habitat due to human exploitation has already happened. Ireland may indeed make some gains in the form of habitat generalists such as Clouded Yellow, the Red Admiral and Comma becoming firmly embedded as permanent residents. The Geranium Bronze butterfly *Cacyreus marshalli*, a Pelargonium specialist, could possibly gain a toehold in parks and gardens in warmer areas. The various climate change models are still lacking in refinement and may well underestimate the magnitude of change and alteration in precipitation and other weather parameters. On the other hand, it is now being predicted that changes in sunspot activity may superimpose upon us 'locally' a temporary Maunder's Minimum Little Ice Age similar to that of 1645-1715.

To date very little has been done to protect existing habitat, to implement appropriate management plans and to halt and reverse the fragmentation of habitats and sites in RoI. But there is scope, within a reformed CAP, to refocus the under-achieving Rural Environment Protection Schemes (REPS) in a genuine effort to halt the loss of biodiversity. The REPS scheme, under the auspices of the Department of Agriculture in the RoI, had a participation of 60,000 when it was 'closed' in 2009. In NI there are now five Environmentally Sensitive Areas (ESAs), covering 20% of agricultural land and long-term monitoring is being carried out to evaluate ESA designation on the biological components of the environment and its impact on the landscape. From a conservation perspective extensive farm management, with low livestock rates and reduced fertiliser use, is clearly preferable to intensive management with high livestock levels. From an environmental perspective, natural meadows are superior to ryegrass monocultures. One late cut of silage is less damaging then multiple harvesting. As oil prices soar, the widespread use of herbicides and pesticides derived from this source could readily be halted without a serious loss in income and agricultural productivity. Understandably the Nitrates Directive, which restricts the amount of fertiliser that may be applied, has caused difficulties for farmers who were incentivised for so many years to intensify and increase production. Landowners, as the stewards of our environment, should be encouraged and rewarded, rather than penalised, for their ownership of sensitive areas of biodiversity.

Intelligent planning and management of roadside verges, parks, canals and riverside corridors could easily be substituted, with economic benefit, for current environmentally destructive regimes. The incorporation of aberrations such as alien 'wildflower meadow' mixes on our roadsides could readily be avoided. There is scope to encourage native biotopes through thoughtful design and management. Blanket afforestation of marginal land with a high nature value, could be replaced by the planting of highly fertilised farmland of low nature value, without the use of any fertilisers. The avoidance of obsessive tidiness by manicuring of grass in public areas, is a strategy that local authorities could readily adopt at a lower financial cost to the taxpayer. A less interventionist approach would help butterfly and invertebrate conservation. Brownfield sites, including derelict urban and industrial areas and worked-out quarries, could be very valuable refuges for wildlife, rather than being used as waste disposal sites. Most urban gardens are small but there are few of us that could not make at least a token contribution in encouraging butterflies and other insects by providing nectar sources for the adults and food plants for larvae.

Butterfly Conservation Europe's key recommendations for the future of the CAP are summarised below:

- Establish a sustainable land management and rural development policy
- Ensure that sufficient funding is dedicated to securing public good
- Deliver good management of Europe's protected areas
- Support high nature value farmland
- Ensure environmental schemes deliver their objectives
- Put policies in place to adapt to and mitigate climate change.

The recently revised *European red list of butterflies* (van Swaay 2010) lists only one species resident in Ireland, the Large Heath, which is classified as *vulnerable* in a pan-European context but considered *not threatened* within the 27 EU member states. But to concentrate only on the conservation of 'scarce' species or those on red data lists would be very short-sighted. Butterfly species, whose populations are quite stable at a European level, may be nationally, regionally or locally scarce or diminishing in numbers. Species can move towards extinction through incremental erosion of suitable habitat or rapid change in climate. Small isolated and fragmented 'protected areas' are not a solution any more than zoos are the answer to the extinction of larger animals.

The state agencies in the two jurisdictions of Ireland, the Northern Ireland Environmental Agency, (NIEA) and the National Parks and Wildlife Service (NPWS) have had little visible success to date in the protection of butterflies. There are eight species on the *Priority List* for Northern Ireland: Small Heath, Large Heath, Small Blue, Dingy Skipper, Marsh Fritillary, Grayling, Wall Brown and Cryptic Wood White (as Reál's Wood White). The Small Blue is now believed to be extinct at its last known Fermanagh site. The Marsh Fritillary has disappeared from some National Nature Reserves and both the Wall Brown and Dingy Skipper are now very restricted in distribution in Northern Ireland. In the Republic of Ireland the Marsh Fritillary (An Appendix II Species under the Bern Convention and an Annex II Species under the Habitats Directive) is the only butterfly species on the *List of Protected and Rare Species*. Under the Directive it is incumbent on each member state to designate a proportion of its most important habitats as SACs. The NIEA has been active in the legal designation of some newly discovered Marsh Fritillary sites. A number of designated sites in NI have specified butterflies listed as being key features, of primary importance to the integrity of the site. Examples of sites are Monawilkin in Co Fermanagh and Murvagh in Co Down. Hopefully, more specific butterfly led designations will follow. Recently the NPWS has commissioned a limited survey of the Marsh Fritillary, stimulated by a reminder from the European Commission of the State's obligations under the Habitats Directive.

The International Union for Conservation of Nature (IUCN) is the world's main authority on the conservation status of species. A series of Regional Red Lists are produced by countries or organizations, which assess the risk of extinction to species within a political management unit using the IUCN criteria and guidelines.The recent production of All Ireland Red Lists for groups of organisms that include bees, water beetles and butterflies is encouraging. There are somewhat mixed views about the intrinsic value of Red Lists for invertebrates given the singular failure of the concept to conserve other groups of organisms in Ireland and the fact that that if an organism is not technically 'protected' then it is seen as being of even less significance. The importance of the preservation of our biodiversity and the biogeographical integrity of species within Ireland is still alien to many. An increased awareness of our natural heritage needs to be followed by effective actions to conserve it. An authentic political commitment is a prerequisite to success in conservation.

Mating Dark Green Fritillary

Green Hairstreak

Butterflies as Insects

5

T HIS SECTION is divided into two parts. The first part contains a general description of the butterfly, its characteristics, life cycle and behaviour. The second part is a more detailed account of the anatomy and physiology of the butterfly as an insect where a certain elementary scientific knowledge is assumed. It endeavours to answer some of the unanswered puzzling questions that often spring to the enquiring mind, such as, do butterflies have blood and what controls the transformation of a caterpillar into a pupa and then into a butterfly?

PART I

Although very diverse and numerous, insects are quite similar in overall morphology (structure and form) both internally and externally. Butterflies and moths belong to the order of insects called Lepidoptera which are clothed in a dense covering of tiny scales on their membranous wings, body and appendages. The word Lepidoptera is derived from the Greek words, *lepis* (scale) and *pteron* (wing). They are a species-rich order widely found in nearly all geographic regions and diverse habitats.

STRUCTURE OF BUTTERFLIES

Insects are organisms which belong to the phylum Arthropoda which is the largest phylum in the animal kingdom. The chief characteristics of this phylum of invertebrates are the jointed-limbs, hard exoskeleton (external skeleton) and segmented body. In insects, the body is divided into three sections, the head, thorax and abdomen.

Irish butterflies belong to the family with club shaped antennae called Rhopalocera and most of our moths belong to the family with variously shaped antennae (such as comb-like or plumose) called Heterocera. So the existence of a 'club' on the end of the antenna is a very good feature for recognising a butterfly. It is acknowledged by lepidopterists that the distinction between butterflies and moths is very contrived, but in relation to the Lepidoptera found in Ireland it is a very convenient distinction.

The butterfly's head contains the brain, sucking pump and the feeding and sensory structures. Attached to the head of the butterfly are a pair of long, slender, segmented antennae which function almost exclusively as sensors and are clothed with scales. They may detect motion, orientation, scent, humidity and various other chemicals. For example, butterflies use their antennae to detect which plants are producing nectar and males can sense pheromones from females of the same species. Near the base of the antenna is a sensory organ called Johnston's organ which has receptors that are sensitive to stretch. The organ senses orientation and balance during flight, enabling the butterfly to finely adjust direction, and it is also believed to play a role in the detection of magnetic fields during migration. If a butterfly loses an antenna, it may he unable to fly in a direct line and end up flying in circles.

Butterflies have a pair of large, spherical multifaceted compound eyes that dominate the head. Hairs are often present between the facets (Fig. 1). Butterflies have binocular vision and because of the size, shape and position of the eyes they have a very wide field of vision. Each eye is made up of as many as 17,000 individual light receptors or visual units called ommatidia. Each ommatidium consists of a cornea and a crystalline cone which together behave as a powerful non-focusing lens. Light enters each ommatidium through the cornea and travels through the crystalline cone and rod until it reaches a cluster of light-sensitive retinal cells near the back of the eye which are sensitive to a particular part of the light spectrum. Nerve fibres from the retinal cells converge onto the optic nerve which conveys the information to the brain. The image produced is an upright mosaic picture of the field of view.

Humans can detect light in the 390 to 750 nm (violet to red) region of the light spectrum. Butterflies are sensitive to wavelengths from 254 to 600 nm (ultraviolet to orange-yellow). Their light receptors have peak sensitivity in the ultraviolet, blue and longer wavelengths (green – yellow – orange) region.

Because of their ability to see in both visible and ultraviolet light, butterflies can see patterns on flowers and other butterflies which are quite different

Fig.1
The "hairy" eyes of the Small Tortoiseshell

Fig 2
Pearl-bordered Fritillary

to those seen by humans. Butterflies are also capable of detecting polarised light which helps them determine the position of the sun. Although the overall image seen by butterflies may be of poor resolution, it gives acute perception of any movement which may signal a threat to them.

The butterfly's feeding tube or proboscis consists of a long pair of interlocking channels between which they can sip floral nectar. The proboscis can be coiled-up below the head when not in use or extended to enable the butterfly to reach into flowers. There are small muscles that assist this coiling and uncoiling. Olfactory receptors near the tip and in the food canal of the proboscis enables the butterfly to detect suitable nectar and minerals. The length of the proboscis varies from species to species and in the instances of the Small Heath and the Peacock they measure 7 mm and 17 mm respectively. On each side of the proboscis and extending forward in front of the face are a pair of labial palps which are covered with scent detecting sensory scales.

Butterflies are attracted to plants either by scent and/or by colour. Males and females of the same species may have different flower preferences related to differences in their nutrient requirements for their respective roles in reproduction. The existence of suitable larval food plants is essential for their caterpillars but there is also evidence which indicates that, when a butterfly's habitat becomes fragmented, the supply of suitable nectar producing plants is also critical for the survival of the species.

There are obvious advantages for a butterfly when its larval food plant is also a major source of nectar, as in the instance of the Small Blue, where Kidney Vetch provides food for both adult and larva. This may, possibly, explain why this butterfly has an ability to survive in small colonies. However, a single larval food plant limits its distribution to the plant's range.

In the process of obtaining food, butterflies may transfer pollen to the stigma of another flower of the same species resulting in fertilisation. Some of the native flowering plants that are partially adapted for butterfly pollination are the Pyramidal and Fragrant Orchids, Hemp Agrimony, Ragged-robin and Water Mint. Non-native plants such as Red Valerian and members of the Dianthus family have been identified as being pollinated by butterflies. In other plants, such as Bird's-foot-trefoil, the pollination function remains with the bees.

The butterfly's head is attached to the thorax by a membranous neck which allows for movement. The thorax is the centre of locomotion because attached to the thoracic exoskeleton are two pairs of wings and three pairs of legs and the associated muscles (Fig. 24).

There are two main types of scales contributing to the colour of butterfly wings, pigmented scales and structural scales. Pigmented scales give rise to a variety of colours by the absorption and reflection of light due to the presence of melanins and a variety of other chemical pigments. Structural scales are responsible for many of the brighter or more iridescent colours because a complex arrangement of tiny scales gives rise to colours due to multiple reflections, diffraction and the interference of light.

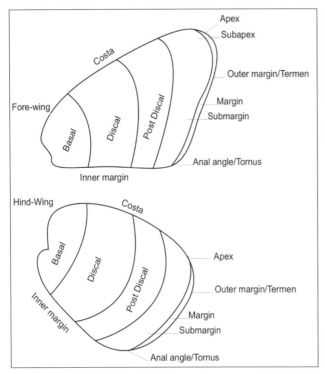

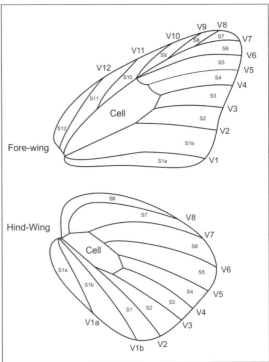

Fig. 3
Wing areas.

Fig. 4
Wing venation.

Many males have specialized scent scales usually concentrated in patches on the upper surface of the forewings or on wing folds called androconia. At the base of the androconia are tiny glandular structures that produce scent (pheromones) for attracting suitable mates. These modified scales may also be scattered among scales on the wings, body or legs or, in some butterflies, on specialized paired brushes located at the tip of the abdomen.

Patterns such as ocelli (false eyes) on wings are considered to be either deterrents or distracters for would-be predators. Colour and patterns on butterfly wings enable individuals to recognise their own species from a distance, differentiate the sexes for reproductive purposes and ward off predators. They also have a role in camouflage which is very apparent when looking for the Green Hairstreak when perched on Bilberry or Bramble and the Grayling on gravelly substrates. All Irish butterflies, except the Skippers, fold their wings over their backs in an upright position when at rest. Skippers fold their wings tent-like over their bodies. Figs. 3 and 4 illustrate the terminology used to identify spaces and veins on the butterfly's wings

Adult butterflies have three pairs of legs that are developed for walking and perching. Each leg is made up of five parts: coxa, trochanter, femur, tibia and the segmented tarsus which has claws at its distal end often referred to as the pretarsus. The inner surface of the tibia of the forelegs usually bears a spur-like appendage that is used for cleaning the proboscis and antennae. (Figs. 2 and 5)

The legs and especially the tarsal segments of the forelegs (foretarsi) have chemoreceptors which enable the butterfly to analyse ("smell" and "taste") food plants on which they land. A female butterfly can determine if a plant is suitable to lay her eggs upon by identifying chemicals released from the plant after scratching the leaf surface with her legs. Although cues such as sight, smell, and taste are important, chemical stimuli from the host plant play a very important role at the final stage of egg laying, as the choice of oviposition site is crucial to the survival of her offspring. The chemoreceptors are sensitive to certain chemicals from the host plants that are genetically determined for each butterfly species.

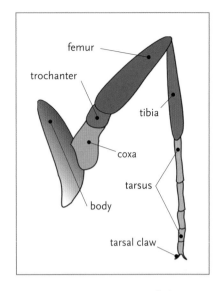

Fig.5 Butterfly leg

In some butterfly families such as the Nymphalidae (the brush-footed butterflies) the forelegs are greatly reduced to brush-like stumps and incapable of functioning for locomotion but function as modified chemoreceptors. The forelegs of the males of these butterflies lack the distal part of the tarsus, while the females have forelegs reduced in size without loss of any parts. These vestigial forelegs are kept tucked up near their heads (p.52).

The butterfly's abdominal exoskeleton is elongated and is broadly attached to the thorax. It consists of ten segments (seven or eight are easily seen), with the last segment containing the sexual organs. The abdomen contains the butterfly's heart, malpighian tubules (uses include excretion), reproductive organs (including claspers and ovipositor), spiracles and most of the digestive system. The segments are linked by membranous folds and allow the abdomen to bend which is essential for mating and egg laying.

CLASSIFICATION OF BUTTERFLIES

Butterflies are usually classified into families and the indigenous Irish butterflies can be considered to fall into five families:

- Hesperiidae (Skippers)
- Pieridae (Whites)
- Lycaenidae (Blues, Coppers, Hairstreaks)
- Nymphalidae (Vanessids, Fritillaries)
- Satyridae (Browns). Some taxonomists classify the Satyridae as a subfamily of the Nymphalidae.

Families

The Hesperiidae are considered to belong to the most primitive of butterfly families and two species, both small in size, are established in Ireland: the rather inconspicuous native Dingy Skipper and the orange-coloured Essex Skipper, a recent immigrant or introduction. The Skippers have more widely spaced antennae which are terminally hooked and they fold their wings moth-like. The word 'skipper' derives from their characteristic flight trajectory.

The Pieridae are predominantly white or yellow (to orange) with black markings and among their number are the erratic migrant Clouded Yellow, our native Orange Tip and the very common Green-veined White. The Large

White and the Small White, often referred to as Cabbage Whites, are pests on brassicas. The latter species is found worldwide. Finally, there are two native species of Wood White.

The Lycaenidae are small in size with fluted hindwings and include three Hairstreaks, three Blues and one Copper, with the males generally having the more vibrant colours. They range from the tiny low-flying Small Blue, to the Purple Hairstreak which infrequently descends to ground level from its oak canopy.

The larvae and pupae of the Lycaenid species are often attended by ants which milk them for their secretions. Most Lycaenids secrete a nutritious liquid, from the Newcomer's gland present on the dorsum of the seventh abdominal segment, containing amino acids which are attractive to ants. In return, the ants may carry the pupa into their nests below ground, gaining protection for them from other insects that would not enter the ant's nest.

The Nymphalidae contain our familiar native Small Tortoiseshell and Peacock (collectively described as Vanessids) and four Fritillaries (Marsh, Silver-washed, Dark Green and Pearl-bordered). There are two regular migrants, the Red Admiral and the Painted Lady and the very rare vagrant Camberwell Beauty. A characteristic feature of the Nymphalidae is that they have, at some stage of their evolution, lost the ambulatory use of their front legs and are often classified as brush-footed butterflies.

The Satyridae (Browns) number eight and are fairly sombre in colour with a mixture of browns, yellows or greys and generally have a range of ocelli (false eyes) on their wings. Their assortment of colours assists them in camouflage. They have reduced front legs and so are often considered to be a sub-group of the Nymphalidae. The base of the satyrid forewing is swollen and contains special hearing organs. The eight species are comprised of the Speckled Wood, Wall Brown, Grayling, Gatekeeper, Meadow Brown, Ringlet, Small Heath and Large Heath. Their larval food plants are grasses except in the case of the Large Heath whose preference is Hare's-tail Cotton-grass.

The vagrant Monarch (Milkweed) very occasionally arrives on our shores from North America, transported by residual autumn hurricanes. A member of the Danaidae, its larval food plants are the Milkweeds which are not found in Ireland.

BUTTERFLY LIFE CYCLE

Butterflies are holometabolous which entails the insect experiencing a complete form of metamorphosis in which it passes through four separate stages of development as egg, larva, pupa and imago (Fig.6).

The Egg

Mating and egg laying are carried out by the adult butterflies. Within the egg the embryo develops into a tiny fully formed larva.

The outer membrane or egg shell is soft during development but hardens shortly after oviposition, assuming a specific shape consistent for the species.

Fig.6
Butterfly life cycle

1st instar
2nd instar
3rd instar
4th instar
5th instar
LARVA
EGG
PUPA
BUTTERFLY

The shell may be smooth or strengthened by raised longitudinal ribs or transverse ridges or both (Fig. 7). At one end there is a tiny opening called a micropyle through which the sperm enters, and this opening is surrounded by a rosette of radiating ridges. Usually the eggs are glued to the substrate by a secretion of the female accessory glands that has been applied to the egg within the oviduct.

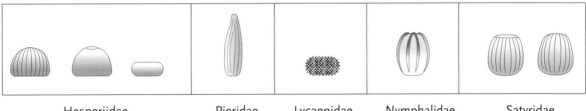

| Hesperiidae | Pieridae | Lycaenidae | Nymphalidae | Satyridae |

The female of most species deposits her eggs directly onto the larval food plant or in very close proximity. Some have very specific locations, for example the Orange Tip lays her egg on the pedicel (flower stalk) of the Cuckooflower whereas the Green-veined White chooses the underside of leaves of the same plant. The Silver-washed Fritillary uses her feet to detect a patch of violets and then lays her eggs on the north side of a nearby tree trunk. This is essential advanced planning for her caterpillars which will require food in the following year. Insects are good botanists and extremely expert in identifying the correct food plants.

Fig. 7
Egg shapes

Larvae

When the larva first hatches from its egg it is referred to as a first instar larva. The caterpillar's main purpose is to eat. Many species of caterpillars begin by first eating their egg shell which contains plenty of nutrients. Other species begin by eating the tender, small parts of leaves.

As the larval skin cannot grow with the larva it must make a new, larger skin. The larva does this by first growing a new skin underneath the outer skin. When completed it sheds the old skin and the newer, larger skin gives the larva room to grow. This process is called moulting and the stages between these moults are called instars.

Larvae of butterflies are usually quite specific in relation to their dietary requirements. Some species chew large quantities of low calorie leaves while others feed on the more nutritious seed pods/fruits of the chosen plant.

Larvae are approximately cylindrical in shape with a rounded head, apart from the Lycaenidae which are often described as slug-like in shape.

As for all insects, the body is divided into three sections: the head, the thorax and abdomen. Internally, the caterpillar is arranged much like the butterfly although the digestive system is much more prominent in the caterpillar. The reproductive organs located towards the rear of the body are undeveloped.

Fig. 8a
The caterpillar

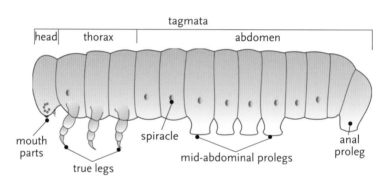

The caterpillar's head is well defined and sclerotised (hardened). On the head there are six pairs of simple eyes called ocelli or stemmata which detect different intensities of light, a mouth with powerful mandibles for chewing and glands used for producing silk which is extruded through a spinneret on the labium or lower lip. This silk is used to support the caterpillar, make webs and cocoons and eventually support the pupa.

Fig 8b
The caterpillar head

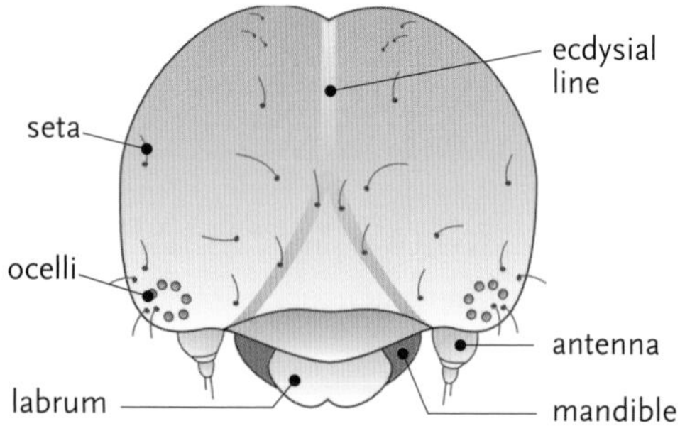

The thorax consists of three segments and each of the thoracic segments carries a pair of "true" legs with claws. They are used primarily for holding and manipulating the food on which they feed. There are ten abdominal segments. Segments three to six each have a pair of abdominal prolegs and segment ten has one pair of anal prolegs. Each proleg is equipped with a circle of tiny hooks called crotchets

44

that aid in grasping and walking. Crotchet-bearing abdominal prolegs distinguish Lepidoptera from other insect larvae (Fig. 9).

On each side of the body of the caterpillar there are spiracles through which respiratory gases enter and exit the body. One pair is present on the prothoracic segment and eight pairs on the first of the eight abdominal segments. Its body is covered with a range of spines, bristles or hairs which vary from species to species and generally have either a sensory or a defensive purpose. When fully fed and developed the caterpillar empties its gut, stops feeding and goes in search of an appropriate location for pupation. At this time single larvae may be seen 'wandering' in search of a suitable location to pupate.

Fig.9
Black crotchets
(hooks) on prolegs of
Silver-washed Fritillary

Pupae

The larva transforms itself into a pupa by anchoring itself to a substrate and moulting for the last time. When a butterfly larva has located a pupation site it usually spins a small bead of silk on e.g., the underside of a leaf or on a stem and anchors itself by its cremaster (anal claspers).

In many species the pupa hangs in a head-down position by its cremaster. In other cases, such as the pupa of the Pieridae and Lycaenidae families, it may also spin a silken girdle around its waist to secure it to the leaf or stem in a head-up position. Some species may pupate lying in vegetation or underground in a cocoon. Breathing takes place through laterally located spiracles, one pair in the thorax and one pair in each abdominal segment.

Fig.10
Small Tortoiseshell
beginning to pupate

Within the pupal case the caterpillar is transformed into an adult butterfly. The internal organs undergo considerable reorganisation to cope with the different requirements of the adult and finally, when the changes are complete and weather conditions are satisfactory, eclosion occurs and the adult emerges.

Adults

Metamorphosis to the adult occurs during the pupal stage. When ready to emerge the fully grown butterfly makes a small hole in the pupal case and inhales deeply splitting the case and allowing the adult to emerge.

The newly emerged adult butterfly moves to a suitable location and pumps fluid through its wing veins to inflate them. When inflation is complete, the wings are dry and the insect's body sufficiently warm, it is ready for its first flight. But first the fresh adult must pass a pinkish liquid called meconium which contains the excretory products that are stored in the malpighian tubules.

Males usually quickly find the newly emerged female. After fertilisation the female's egg-laying task is paramount, and her search for larval food plants begins. Butterflies, especially the smaller ones, have limited reserves of food and use their proboscises to imbibe nectar containing sucrose and amino acids or sap from a range of plants. The Peacock and Red Admiral sometimes feed on tree sap or on ripe fruit.

Males, and females to a lesser extent, visit wet soil, dung, urine, dead animals or soil in search for minerals and amino acids. Puddling is the general term used to describe this behaviour and is exemplified by males congregating and imbibing on the edges of muddy pools. This is a more frequent happening in hotter climates than in Ireland. Species associated with trees may feed on the honey dew secreted by aphids.

The life span of the adult is typically of the order of a couple of weeks for many species but may be as short as a few days. With favourable weather conditions some butterfly species can have two or even three generations per year. For the hibernating species, life is more extended and, in the instance of the Brimstone, (our longest living butterfly) the generations sometimes overlap and the longest survivors can be 11 months old.

In order to maintain a steady population, sufficient eggs must be laid to provide a viable next generation. A female laying two hundred eggs can be considered successful if, on average, two of her progeny emerge from their pupae, mate and lay another batch of fertile eggs. Weather is one natural factor that exercises a control on butterfly populations but, in general, mortality, has three main causes – predation, parasitisation and disease.

PREDATION AND PARASITES

Predation in the early stages (egg or larva) are believed to cause up to 80 per cent mortality. Eggs and smaller larvae are eaten by a variety of arthropods especially nocturnal beetles and spiders (Fig 11). Wasps have been known to remove whole batches of Small Tortoiseshell and Small White caterpillars in high summer to feed their own larvae. Larger larvae are taken mainly by birds. Pupae are believed to be at risk mainly from birds and small mammals in some climes. There have been numerous reports of adult butterflies being devoured by birds such as flycatchers and, to a lesser extent, by dragonflies. Spider webs also take their toll on low-flying butterfly species. Most predation appears to happen at night. Cannibalism may happen amongst small larvae such as the Orange Tip where there is strong competition for food.

Fig 11
Large White butterfly
trapped in spider's web

An insect that completes its larval development within the body of another insect, eventually killing its host, is termed a parasitoid. Most parasitoids are wasps and flies and are considered to be the main cause of death in the developing butterfly and hence exercise an important control on population size. Attack may happen at either the egg, larval or pupal stage depending on the specific organism (Figs 12a, 12b and 13). Some parasitoids are host-specific while others are generalists. In Britain, in specific populations of Marsh Fritillary, up to 80% of larvae have been reported to be parasitised by the braconid wasp *Cotesia bignelli* which is also widespread in Ireland. Some argue that this is the prime cause of local extinction of Marsh Fritillary colonies, although the requirements of this species are now known to be complex and parasitism is just one factor affecting any population.

One of the more frequently observed incidents of parasitism relates to the Cabbage Whites (Large and Small White). The braconid wasp *C. glomerata* uses its ovipositor to inject eggs into the body of the caterpillar. The eggs hatch and the parasitoid larvae feed and grow within the caterpillar without causing any fatal damage. The yellow parasitoid larvae finally emerge from the caterpillar body, wrap themselves with silk and commence pupation. The predated caterpillar then displays an extraordinary form of altruism, which is believed to be caused by a virus transmitted by the parasitoid to its host. It proceeds to further wrap the yellow pupae in another protective web of silk and stands guard for several days to ward off any approaching (hyper)parasitoids, before finally expiring. Because of their often specific dependency on a single host, which have with their own population fluctuations, parasitoidal insects are themselves very vulnerable to extinction.

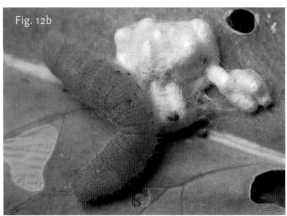

Fig. 12a
Larvae of *Cotesia glomerata* emerging from their host a Small White caterpillar

Fig. 12b
Dying Small White caterpillar and silk cocoon with pupating *Cotesia glomerata*

ADULT BUTTERFLY BEHAVIOUR

Male butterflies normally emerge a few days in advance of the females and await their appearance for a mating opportunity. A female butterfly endeavours to enhance the survival of her offspring to maturation by choosing 'good' sites for egg laying. Similarly, the male will endeavour to mate as frequently as possible to maximise his progeny. Adequate food supply (nectar and larval food plant), suitable egg laying sites and shelter for the over wintering stage are all critical for the butterfly.

Unlike nocturnal moths, many of our temperate butterflies are ectotherms reliant on their environment to maintain body temperature, and require internal (thoracic) temperatures of 30-40°C for efficient flight. Butterflies sometimes warm up through wing muscle activity (shivering) but usually by basking in the sun. Sustained flight in butterflies is made possible by the conversion of 90% of wing muscle energy to heat. Basking occurs in sunny sheltered areas on plant leaves or other surfaces such as bare ground, varying with species and habitat. The microclimate near a surface sometimes achieves a temperature 20°C above the ambient, so some butterflies are capable of flight in cold but sunny weather. Butterflies have three strategies for basking: (i) spreading out of wings, (ii) tilting of the body and closed wings towards or away from the sun and (iii) opening their wings partially in a V so that the body is directly available to the sun's rays at the bottom of the V. Pigmentation and wing surface area have an important role in the capacity of a butterfly to gain energy quickly. In the middle of the day in very hot weather butterflies may seek refuge from direct sunlight to prevent overheating.

Most species of butterfly visit flowering plants in order to acquire nectar. Others such as the Purple Hairstreak feed on the honey dew discharged by aphids on trees. In some species, the male may transfer a considerable amount of nutrients to the female in sperm packages when mating. These nutrients assist in the development of eggs. In other species, the female herself acquires essential nutrients through foraging. Short-lived species acquire most of the food requirements for adulthood during the larval stage. In hot or dry weather the insects can acquire additional water directly from their environment or by imbibing plant nectar through their proboscises, when it is least concentrated, early in the morning

Mate Location Behaviour

In species where there is a single generation per annum, butterflies have a programmed strategy to ensure survival with adult emergence taking place over a period of time which can be up to four months for the Meadow Brown. This strategy helps to limit their vulnerability to adverse weather conditions which may not be conducive to successful breeding. Males emerge from pupation before females in order to maximise their mating opportunities. Broadly speaking, males have two specific strategies to locate females, namely perching and patrolling. Perching males, for example the Green Hairstreak, sit in sites suitable for the interception of passing females. Patrolling males, such as the Silver-washed Fritillary, actively search for females. The latter behaviour may be over a relatively large area, or sometimes it is more territorial with frequent return to the original perch. Very mobile species such as the Small Tortoiseshell and Peacock change perches through the season. The Peacock is fiercely territorial and will mob any passer by. The Purple Hairstreak and Small Heath indulge in "lekking" or "hill topping", where males aggregate in groups and competitively woo females which approach them.

Fig. 13
Marsh Fritillary larva with parasitoids

Ringlet

Brimstone

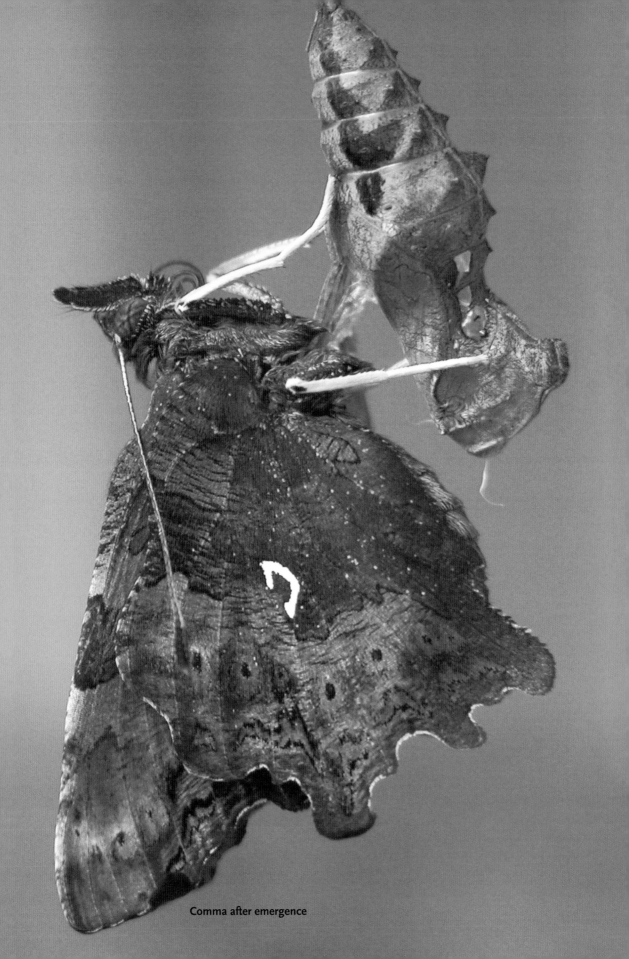

Comma after emergence

Green-veined Whites

PART II

(i) EXOSKELETON (INTEGUMENT) STRUCTURE

In most insects the integument or exoskeleton forms a tough, strong but flexible outer covering that surrounds the surface of the insect, permitting freedom of movement while conferring a high degree of protection and defence.

The basic structure of the Lepidoptera exoskeleton and many of the biochemical and physiological processes are common to insects in general. Butterflies, like all insects, have an external skeleton (or exoskeleton) to which muscles are attached.

Adult insect bodies have three basic divisions or tagmata:

- The head, with sensory antennae, compound eyes, ocelli and mouthparts.
- The thorax, which has the wings and three pairs of jointed legs.
- The abdomen, with spiracles and genitalia.

Each tagmata is formed of segments which are sclerotised in areas to form plates. These plates called sclerites, which are connected by flexible membranes that allow for the movement of joints and segments, form the insect's exoskeleton. Sclerites vary in name according to the location.

The first six segments of the adult insect's exoskeleton form the head and fuse fully together. Structurally, the thorax is composed of three body segments: prothorax, mesothorax, and metathorax. These three segments are fused to form a rigid structure that contains the musculature for the legs and wings. Each segment has a dorsal sclerite called the notum, a ventral sclerite called the sternum and the side of each segment is called the pleuron.

Usually eight abdominal segments are visible in the lepidopteran adult (ten are visible on the larva) and the remainder which form the genitalia are partially visible. Each segment of the abdomen consists of a dorsal sclerite called the tergum and a ventral sclerite called the sternum. The tergum and sternum are joined to one another laterally by a pleural membrane. The front margins of each segment can often slide inside the sclerites of the preceding segment, allowing the abdomen to expand and contract in response to the actions of skeletal muscles.

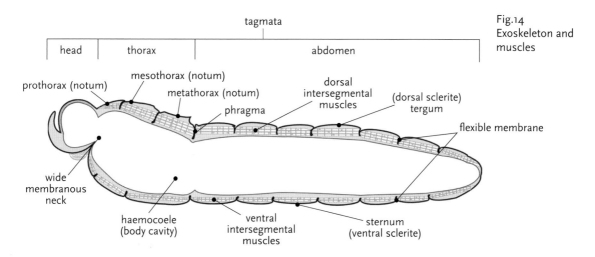

Fig.14
Exoskeleton and muscles

The insect's exoskeleton is not just a protective outer covering, it is a living organ that:

- Provides structure, maintaining anatomical integrity.
- Protects against infection.
- Prevents damage by mechanical and chemical injury.
- Inhibits water loss.
- Provides areas for the insertion of muscles of locomotion.
- Forms a sensory interface with the environment.
- Provides cuticle continuous with that of the outer body which lines the trachea. It also lines and protects the foregut and hind gut, exocrine gland ducts and part of the reproductive tract.
- Forms the wings in adult insects.

The exoskeleton consists of three parts:

- **The Cuticle** (outer layers) and its accompanying setae and scales, which are a particular characteristic of Lepidoptera.
- **The Epidermal Cells**, which are the living part of the exoskeleton and secrete the overlying cuticle with the exception of the cement layer. Epidermal cells can be modified to form various specialised cells such as exocrine gland cells, oenocytes and setal hair cells. The latter can form hair-like organs called setae which connect with the outside by projecting through pores in the cuticle. In the butterfly they are further modified to become the colourful wing scales (Fig. 16).
Exocrine glands produce compounds, such as pheromones, that initiate their effect external to the insect, through tiny pores in the integument.

Fig. 15
Pore canals of the
epidermal cells

Fig.16
The three layers of
the exoskeleton with
seta and gland cell

- **The Basement Membrane**, which acts as a selective membrane allowing nutrients and hormones to reach the epidermal cells from the haemolymph (blood), and also allows passage to tracheae to supply oxygen and nerves to supply sensory setae (Figs. 15 and 16).

Oenocytes, which are derived from epidermal cells, are present on the inside of the basement membrane and in the haemolymph of Lepidoptera. Their function is to synthesise and secrete cuticular lipids.

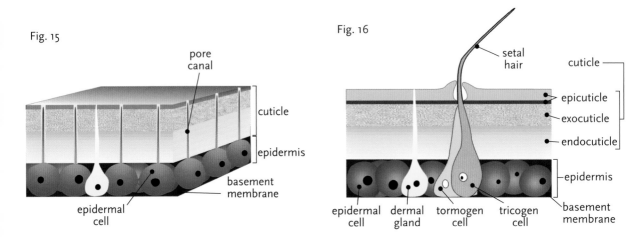

Fig. 15

pore
canal

cuticle

epidermis

basement
membrane

epidermal
cell

Fig. 16

setal
hair

cuticle

epicuticle

exocuticle

endocuticle

epidermis

basement
membrane

epidermal   dermal   tormogen   tricogen
cell   gland   cell   cell

In addition, pore canals provide an avenue for the transport of various materials, including wax and cement. These are minute channels formed around cytoplasmic extensions of the epidermal cells and run through the cuticle ending below the epicuticle. Inside the canal are wax filaments that extend to the epicuticular layer.

Pore canals are particularly developed in sclerites and may be almost lacking in membranous larval trunks.

Insects do not have an internal skeleton although infoldings of the exoskeleton, called apodemes, form in the head of adults and larvae and in the thorax of adults. They provide extra strength and sites for the attachment of muscles.

The Cuticle

The cuticle is a relatively thin layer of non-cellular material which lines the external surface of the body as well as lining the tracheae, the anterior and posterior sections of the alimentary canal and parts of the reproductive system. It is mainly composed of water-insoluble chitin which forms a soft and flexible substance. Its consistency is quite similar to our familiar white mushroom, as the walls of the mycelium which make up its solid substance are also composed of chitin. The hardness is due to sclerotisation or tanning and occurs when the epidermal cells release chemicals into certain areas of the exoskeleton forming body wall plates or sclerites (Fig.14).

The cuticle is flexible, elastic and white when first formed and stays that way in many larval forms. However, in most adults it undergoes chemical processes which result in sclerotisation.

The cuticle can be divided into:

- **The Epicuticle**
  The outermost component of the cuticle is the epicuticle which is a thin, organised non-chitinous layer of largely sclerotised lipoprotein called the cuticulum and is present in all insects. It has an outer waterproofing wax layer which protects the insect from water loss.
  The epicuticle is stiff and inflexible and because it is relatively inextensible it inhibits the expansion of the insect between larval moults and in the adult insect.
- **The Procuticle**
  Beneath the epicuticle is the main structural part of the cuticle called the procuticle. The procuticle is much thicker than the epicuticle and slightly extensible (Fig.16).
  It divides into two layers:

  - **Exocuticle**
    Consists of layers of protein intermixed with chitin. Chitin is a complex polysaccharide that gives the cuticle its strength and stability. This area becomes hard and rigid because it undergoes sclerotisation. During a moult this region is not broken down by enzymes and, with the epicuticle, is what remains in the form of the larval exuvia.
  - **Endocuticle**
    Consists of a large number of layers of chitin in a protein matrix and is the thickest part of the cuticle. Unlike the exocuticle it does not undergo sclerotisation so is extremely soft, tough and flexible.

Cuticle hardness is determined by the ratio of exocuticle and endocuticle, with hard cuticles predominantly made of exocuticle. The precise nature of these layers varies from place to place in the exoskeleton according to the species and stages of the life cycle.

In the adult Lepidoptera the cuticle forms soft and flexible membranes between the body sclerites, whereas most of the larval cuticle is soft and flexible with the exception of its sclerotised head and mouthparts and a few areas of the body such as the prothoracic shield, anal plate and crotchets.

(ii) MOULTING

Lepidoptera undergo complete metamorphosis by going through a distinct four-stage life cycle with the larval and adult stages differing considerably in their structure and behaviour (Fig.6). The larvae of both butterflies and moths are also called caterpillars.

- During the egg stage the larva is formed. When hatched the larva feeds, grows and must moult as the inextensible epicuticle gets too small. Beginning with the emergence from the egg and between subsequent moults, each new larva formed is referred to as a larval instar and numbered accordingly.

  At some point during each instar stretch receptors, nutritional status and body weight of the insect cause the brain to initiate these moults. Larval growth occurs during a specific number of instars and butterflies usually have attained optimum larval growth and development after five instars.

- As the larval cuticle is not very extensible, the larva forms a new highly folded cuticle under the old one, increasing the epidermal cell layer by cell division (mitosis). When formed, the old cuticle is sloughed off (ecdysis) and the new larger exoskeleton can then be inflated, hardened and pigmented. Because of the configuration of the folding of the new cuticle the larva grows mainly in length so it is unlikely that one will see a short fat larva.

- In the embryo, wing imaginal discs are present as precursor wing cells and form sac-like structures inside newly hatched and growing larva.

  Wing imaginal discs of Lepidoptera commence proliferation inside the larva early in the developmental period whereas the imaginal discs for eyes, legs, proboscis and antennae develop and proliferate during the final larval instar.

  These adult-specific structures, such as the wing imaginal discs, found on the second and third thoracic segments of the larva, are unaffected by these moulting events until the final larval moult.

- The development of these imaginal discs is a feature unique to the holometabolous insects (insects that undergo complete metamorphosis). Development through embryo, larva, pupa, and adult stages does not simply involve developing and enlarging existing structures.

  Metamorphosis involves the elimination of larval-specific structures, the remodelling of other tissue cells to suit adult purposes and the multiplication and differentiation of special groups of imaginal disc cells containing the genetic material of the future adult.

  Imaginal disc cells develop in response to stimulation by the moulting hormone ecdysone together with insulin hormone.

- During pupation, transformation into the butterfly takes place by further differentiation and growth of the imaginal disc cells in response to stimulation by the hormone ecdysone. This is accompanied by the breaking-down of the remaining larval tissues.

Stages of Moulting

Moulting is controlled by neurosecretory cells in the brain. When the immature larval exoskeleton has grown sufficiently to require a larger one, sensory input from the body stimulates neurosecretory cells in the brain to initiate its formation (see Endocrine System).

i.

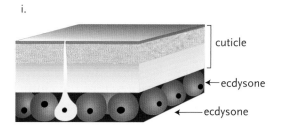

The larval moulting begins when moulting genes in cuticular epidermal cells are stimulated by exposure to ecdysone into forming a new cuticle.

ii.

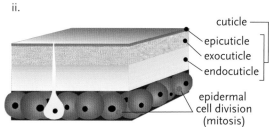

The activated epidermal cells undergo division (mitosis). This is the principal growth period in the formation of a new enlarged cuticle for the next instar. Each epidermal cell undergoes a single division per instar.

iii.

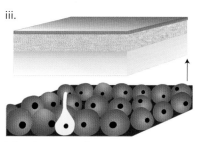

The larva undergoes a process termed apolysis when the existing structural cuticle becomes detached from the soft underlying epidermal cells.

iv.

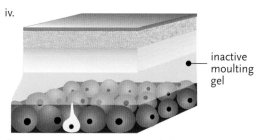

The ecdysial space created between the epidermal cells and the endocuticle is filled with a moulting gel containing the inactive enzymes chitinase and protease.

v.

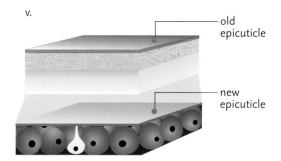

During this time a new epicuticle (cuticulum) is secreted by the epidermal cells. This layer now protects epidermal cells from digestion by enzymes in the moulting fluid.

vi.

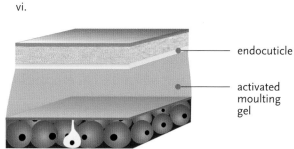

The enzymes chitinase and proteinase in the moulting fluid become activated and begin to digest the old endocuticle.

vii.

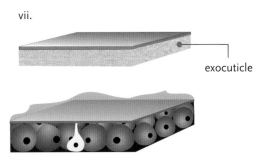

exocuticle

Digestion of the endocuticle continues until the exocuticle is reached. As it is sclerotised the exocuticle is not affected by the digestive enzymes. Any remaining moulting fluid is reabsorbed.

viii.

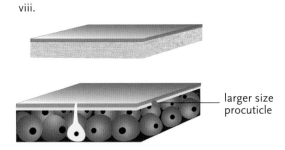

larger size procuticle

Epidermal cells lay down the larger new procuticle, re-using much of the chitin-protein breakdown products from the old endocuticle in the process.

ix.

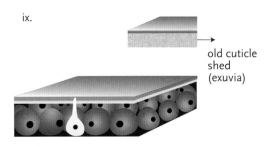

old cuticle shed (exuvia)

The wax layer of the new cuticle is secreted and deposited by the epidermal cells on the enlarged exoskeleton.

The insect can now remove itself from the old cuticle by breaking along the ecdysial lines which are areas in the cuticle that normally have little exocuticle. As there is no longer any endocuticle these lines become weak points so the cuticle can be shed (Fig. 8b).

Ecdysis occurs when the old exocuticle and epicuticle are sloughed off.

The shed cuticle is called the exuviae and the process of moulting is called ecdysis. The exuviae incorporates that part of the exoskeleton that lines some organs.

x.

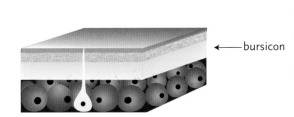

bursicon

Bursicon hormone is released from the neurosecretory cells of the brain and stimulates sclerotisation in the procuticle of the new exoskeleton.

Finally, when the wax layer is in place, the moult is complete and the cycle can start over again at the next moult.

(iii) SETAE AND SCALES

The exoskeleton has to be able to communicate information from the external environment to internal organs without weakening its structure.

Lepidoptera convey this information through the formation of setae. Some epidermal cells of the exoskeleton become specialised and produce hollow hair-like structures which extend through pores in the cuticle. These specialized cells are called trichogen cells and the hair-like structures they produce are called setae. A nerve may extend into the hollow shaft of the seta forming a sensory device called a sensillum. They serve many purposes including defence, locomotion, pheromone dispersal, sexual display and camouflage (Figs. 17a and 17b).

A typical seta is composed of four different types of cells:

- The trichogen cell secretes the tapered or hair-like protuberance.
- The tormogen cell, another modified epidermal cell, forms the socket.
- A sensory neuron (nerve cell) innervates the seta, and its axon extends inward to form a nerve connected to the central nervous system.
- A thecogen cell, which surrounds the nerve cell, and acts as an auxiliary cell by secreting the dendrite sheath of the nerve.

The most common types of setae are the mechanoreceptors and chemorecep-tors which are distributed widely over the insect's body. These socketed, tactile sensilla are called trichoid sensilla and respond to any form of mechanical or chemical stimuli on the insect's body.

Many of the sensory organs of the insect's exoskeleton are modifications of the mechanoreceptor such as chemoreceptors and campaniform sensilla. Campaniform sensilla are dome-shaped structures in the cuticle and are located throughout the body especially near joints. They monitor joint

Figs. 17a and 17b
Seta and Trichoid
sensillum

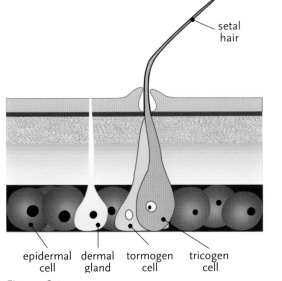

Fig. 17a Seta

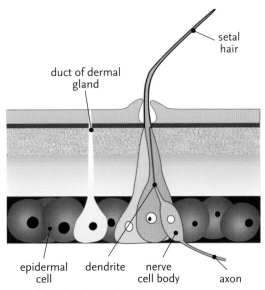

Fig. 17b Trichoid sensillum

movement and position and respond whenever mechanical stress causes the exoskeleton to bend. Those present in the wings enable the insect to control flight movement.

Although most setae develop as sensory receptors, some become secondarily non-innervated and lose their sensory function. Instead these non-sensory setae are used by the insect for preening, sexual display and aerodynamics.

One major modification in Lepidoptera is that setae may be flattened to form broad scales which are often highly coloured. These scales clothe the wings, the head including part of the antennae and palpi, the thorax including the legs and the abdomen and parts of the external genitalia.

Another modification are the specialised setae that form the androconial organs located along the forewing veins of the male butterfly and used for pheromone dispersal.

Fig. 18
Long setae of the
Small Tortoiseshell

Structure of Sensilla
- Hair-like sensilla: mechanoreceptors, chemoreceptors, olfactory sensilla.
- Dome-like sensilla: mechanoreceptors that detect stresses and deformation of cuticle. These are usually proprioceptors that sense the position of the body parts in relation to each other.
- Chordotonal organs: mechanoreceptors attached just below the surface of the cuticle which perceive internal strain and body movement. They are located on legs and wings of adult insects and on the body wall of larvae.

Function of Setae and Scales:
- They form the tactile setae that are present on most parts of a butterfly's body and are scattered fairly evenly over the larva's body. Mechanoreceptors and chemoreceptors are particularly concentrated on the antennae and legs of butterflies.
- They form the colourful wing scales and the cryptic wing scales of the adult butterfly.
- Male butterflies disperse pheromones using specialized setae (androconia) located along the forewing veins.
- Broad setae on the inner surface of the tibia of the foreleg are used to clean the antennae and proboscis (Figs 2 and 5).
- Tibial spurs on the legs contain scale-like tactile hairs and chemosensory sensilla that detect suitable chemicals in host plants for the purpose of feeding and discovering oviposition sites.
- There are several collections of specialised setae and nerves that help the adult butterfly detect wind, temperature and the position of body parts during flight (proprioceptors).
- Elongated setae that form the tactile fringe of the wings are an important aid to flight (Fig 19).

- Setae and vein structures strengthen the wings of butterflies (Fig. 21).

In summary, mechano- and chemo-reception, camouflage, defence and phero-mone dispersal are the main functions of these diverse and numerous setae.

Fig. 19
Wing fringe of
Small Blue

Setae are relatively obvious and long in tactile structures, where they extend through sockets in the exoskeleton and project above the cuticle. Whereas for taste, smell, temperature, humidity, stretch or other senses they may appear as minute domes, pits or pegs on the cuticle. The wing scales, which are modified setae, are tiny, regularly overlapping pieces of flattened chitin.

Fig. 20
Setae and spines on
legs of Large White

(iv) WINGS

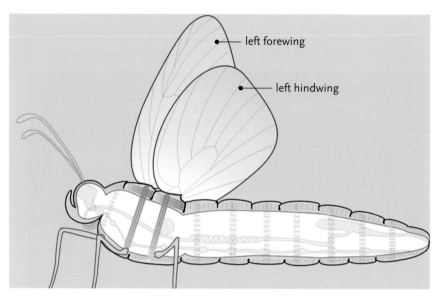

- The insect's thorax is structurally composed of three body segments, the prothorax, the mesothorax and the metathorax and is almost exclusively adapted for locomotion. One pair of legs is attached to each thoracic segment and a pair of wings is attached to each of the second and third segments (Fig. 24).
- Insect wings are formed by an extension of the thoracic cuticle and are not modified forelimbs as seen in birds and bats. They only become functional during the adult stage of the insect's life.
- Most insects, including butterflies and moths have two pairs of wings. Lepidopteran wing-coupling allows the fore and hind wings to beat together. Most moths use wing-coupling bristles called a frenulum on the underside of the wings.

  Butterflies do not have this arrangement. Their wings are held together because the front pair overlaps the hind pair to a considerable extent.

  In addition, they have an enlarged area at the base of the front margin of the hindwing known as the humeral lobe. The wings are not actually joined but this enlarged overlapping area grips the underside of the forewing permitting the wings to move in unison, a feature found only in butterflies.
- Butterfly wings are an extension of the body exoskeleton. They consist of a thin membrane formed by two layers of exoskeleton that are tightly opposed except in areas which are supported by 'veins' where they remain separated (Fig. 21).

  'Veins' form channels through which ventilatory tracheae and nerves supply each wing and because the channels are continuous with the body cavity (haemocoele), haemolymph circulates throughout the wings. The

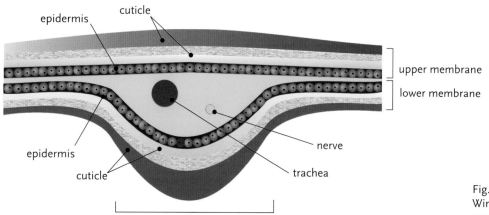

epidermis

cuticle

upper membrane

lower membrane

epidermis

cuticle

nerve

trachea

wing vein

Fig. 21
Wing membranes,
nerve and trachea
forming a wing 'vein'

cuticular layer is thicker and more sclerotised over the veins which contributes to the strength and rigidity of the wings.

- The wings are clothed with scales which normally contain colour pigment.

A typical scale fits into a socket by way of a stalk.

Fig.22 (a)

Fig.22 (b)

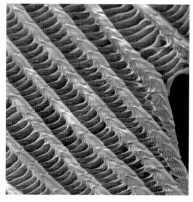
Fig.22 (c)

The body of the scale is composed of an upper and a lower layer called laminae with the internal space between (lumen) subdivided by internal supports.

The lower lamina (the surface that lies next to the wing membrane) is smooth. The upper lamina is more complex and usually covered with longitudinal ridges with interconnecting transverse ridges (Fig. 22).

- Wing patterns can be formed by pigment deposited in the scale cuticle, usually a single colour for each scale.

Additionally, structural colours can be produced by the microstructure of the scales. The regular longitudinal ridge spacing may produce colours by diffraction, breaking up light into its constituent colours. Also, these

Fig.22
(a) Peacock wing
    scales x50 (SEM)
(b) Wing scales x200
(c) Wing scale showing
    the upper lamina
    with longitudinal
    and transverse
    ridges x5000

diffractive scales can exhibit a high degree of iridescence as light reflected from a series of superimposed surfaces, such as the overlapping laminae, produces interference colours. This type of structural colour results in the bright hues often seen in adult butterflies.

Fig.23
Green Hairstreak butterflies, showing iridescence in direct sunlight (right).

The lepidopteran wing scales serve a variety of functions:

- Many wing scales are waxy and easily detach and this may enhance the insect's chance of escaping from predators and webs.
- The scale structure with its close-set exposed surface ridges allow water to run off, preventing pooling while cleaning the surface of the wings.
- Lepidoptera have the capability, due to the presence of the upper and lower wing scale, of developing very different upperside and underside wing patterns and colours which may vary from vivid or aposomatic colouration (warning colours) on one side to dull or cryptic colouration on the other.
- These features aid in communication, camouflage, mimicry and warning.
- Wing scale covering has been said to influence aerodynamics by contributing to lift during flight enabling longer periods of gliding.
- They play a role in thermoregulation through the absorption of solar radiation and insulation.

Wing movement
- Insect wing movements fall into two categories:
    - Movements of flight
    - Movements of flexion and extension (muscles producing folding after flight or extension prior to flight).

These movements are accomplished by five paired sets of muscles.

The ability to fold wings over the body is lost in many Lepidoptera, most notably butterflies.

Muscles that produce the wing beat in insects, with the exception of dragon-

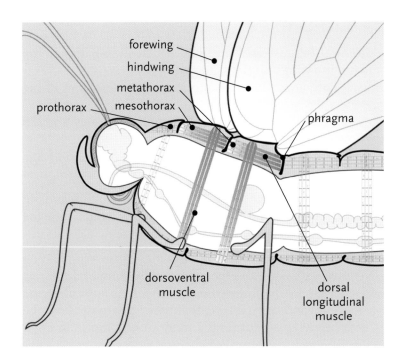

Fig. 24
Showing the dorsoventral muscles and the dorsal longitudinal muscles of thorax (red).

flies and mayflies, are not attached directly to the wings but move the wings indirectly by changing the shape of the thorax. Both the upstroke and the downstroke are produced in response to contraction of muscles attached to the thoracic cuticle.

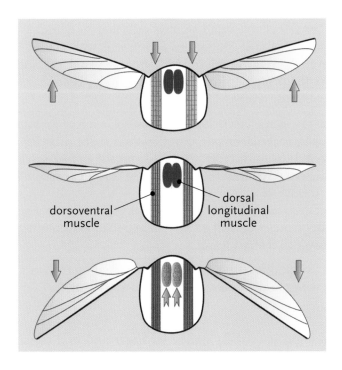

Fig.25
Movement of wings in flight. First figure shows the dorso-ventral muscles in action. Third figure shows the dorsal longitudinal muscle in action (after Snodgrass).

- Main muscles that act on the thorax producing wing beats are

  - The dorsoventral (tergosternal) muscles which slightly flatten the thorax and flip the wings up (Figs. 24 and 25).
    These muscles are attached to the top and bottom surfaces of the meso- and meta-thoracic segments.
  - The dorsal longitudinal muscles which deepen the thorax and flip the wings down.
    These muscles are attached to phragma, which are cuticular invaginations of the meso- and meta-thoracic segments.

  Action of these muscles cause the base of the wings to move in and out of lateral fulcrum points (joint) while flipping the wings into the upstroke and downstroke of the wing beat cycle.

- Muscles that attach directly to the base of the wings cause wing folding and may also control extension and the pitch and twisting of the wings which are necessary for the finer movements of flight. As butterflies and insects wings move up and down during flight they also twist about the vertical axis with the wing tip forming a more or less figure of eight pattern.

- During flight, both the up stroke and down stroke muscles must contract in alternating sequence. Two different mechanisms can control this muscle action in insects, producing synchronous control (produced by nerve impulses) and asynchronous control (produced by muscle pacemakers).

  Butterflies have neurogenic (synchronous) control of their flight muscles, meaning that each contraction is triggered by a separate nerve impulse. Because of the refractory period of nerve cells there is a limit to their rate of stimulation. Therefore, butterflies and insects with neurogenic flight muscles have relatively low wing beat frequencies in the region of 10-50 beats per second (rough estimate of beats of honey bee 180-203bps and large white butterfly 9 bps).

  Insects with myogenic (asynchronous) control, such as flies and wasps, have developed pacemaker properties in their flight muscles and after being triggered to contract by a signal from the nervous system they continue to alternate contractions if stretched beyond a certain threshold, until they receive a signal from the nervous system to stop. The frequency of the wing beat may be as high as 500-1000 beats per second. Such high frequencies permit greater lift and manoeuverability allowing insects to hover or fly backwards.

- Much work has and is being done on understanding the aerodynamics of flapping wings and vortices produced during flight.

Fuel for Flight

In many species flight is initially fueled by sugar and prolonged flight is accompanied by the use of fat as fuel, the switch being triggered by adipoki-netic hormones.

But nectar-only feeding butterflies and moths are unable to use sugar (trehalose) directly. They must first convert it into fat before it can be used as a sourse of energy.

Fats provide more energy per weight and can easily be stored in the form of droplets whereas sugar requires water to keep it in suspension during storage, therefore fats are the most economical and efficient energy source for flights of long duration.

(v) ENDOCRINE SYSTEM

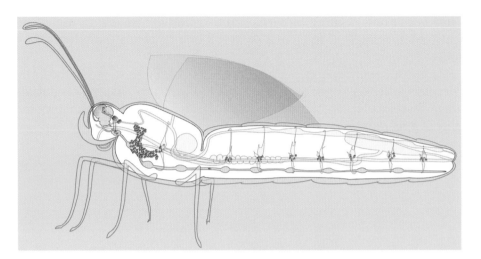

Two forms of communication in an animal integrate body function in order to adjust and correlate the activities of the various body systems, thus enabling them to adapt to the changing demands of the external and internal environment.

The Nervous System transmits electrical signals that either interpret information or initiate a quick response in specific tissue. The Endocrine System transmits chemical signals, in the form of hormones. Compared to the nervous system the endocrine system regulates slower processes and often in *various tissues*.

The endocrine system is a collection of glands that work interdependently and produce hormones that regulate the body's growth, metabolism, sexual development and function. Each of these glands produces hormones that target a particular area of the insect's body and are released and transported in the haemolymph to the target cells where their modifications may be stimulatory or inhibitory.

Endocrine hormones play an important role in the control of:
- Metamorphosis
- Moulting
- Reproduction
- Diapause
- Metabolic activities such as respiration and excretion
- Behaviour
- Programmed cell death (during metamorphosis).

Sources of endocrine hormones in insects include:
- The Neuroendocrine System of
  - The Brain, especially the pars intercerebralis and pars lateralis

- ■ The Ventral Nerve Cord
- ■ Corpora Cardiaca
- ■ The Epitracheal Glands.
- ● The Corpora Allata
- ● The Prothoracic Glands
- ● Endocrine Glands found in the gut, fat body and reproductive organs.

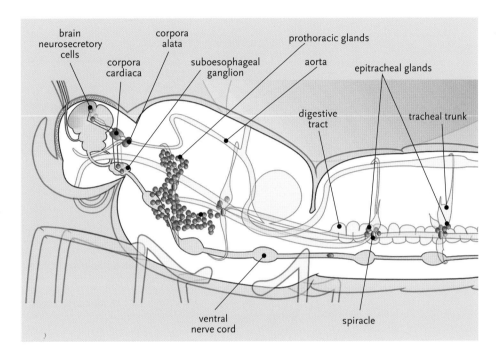

Fig. 26
The endocrine system
(detail)

The Neuroendocrine System

The neuroendocrine system consists of nerve cells that produce neurohormones from neurosecretory cells located mainly in the brain, corpora cardiaca and ventral nerve cord, although they can be found in other tissues throughout the body such as the epitracheal glands and the fat body, and serve as a link between the nervous system and the endocrine system.

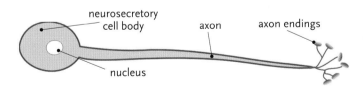

Fig. 27
The neuroscretory cell
is a specialized cell
that is both nervous
and secretory

Neurohormones are regarded as master regulators as they control most physiological and metabolic processes including the regulation of secretion of other hormones that control metamorphosis, moulting and reproduction. They also regulate respiration, excretion, the synthesis of blood lipids, carbohydrates and proteins and control energy metabolism related to flight.

Most of the known insect neurohormones are found in the neurosecretory cells that terminate in what is termed the Brain-CC-CA complex. This complex is formed by paired neurosecretory groups of cells in the brain and the suboesophageal ganglion plus the corpora cardiaca and corpora allata glands.

Fig. 28
The brain-CC-CA complex. The main neurohormonal release sites and storage organs of the insect's brain (red).

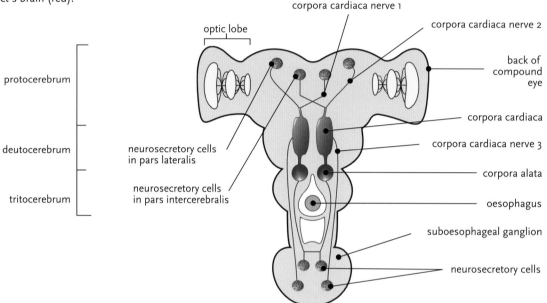

Corpora Cardiaca

Corpora cardiaca is a pair of endocrine structures located on the walls of the aorta just behind the brain which store brain hormones. In addition, they contain neurosecretory cells that synthesise and release hormones that, with brain hormone, indirectly control the production of moulting hormone when immature insects require a larger exoskeleton.

When immature insects require a larger exoskeleton, sensory input from the body stimulates neurosecretory cells in the brain into producing brain hormone which in turn triggers the corpora cardiaca into releasing their stores of prothoracicotropic hormone (PTTH) into the circulatory system (in some insects, including Lepidoptera, the corpora allata secretes the PTTH). This hormone acts on the cells of the prothoracic gland stimulating them to produce ecdysone (moulting hormone).

Another hormone, secreted and stored by the corpora cardiaca is the adipokinetic hormone. It regulates the mobilisation of fats and carbohydrates required during flight from stores in the insect's fat body and also boosts the immune system.

The Corpora Allata

The corpora allata is a small pair of endocrine glands structurally associated with the corpora cardiaca and lie just behind it but are not part of the neuroendocrine system.

In Lepidoptera PTTH is produced primarily in the corpora allata.
Cells of the corpora allata gland also synthesise and secrete juvenile hormone (JH) prior to each moult (see Moulting).

Neurosecretory cells in the brain regulate the activity of the endocrine glands in the corpora allata by:

- Stimulating them to produce JH during larval instars.
- Inhibiting them during transition to adulthood.
- Reactivating them once the adult is ready for reproduction.

Prothoracic Gland

In insects the largest and most obvious of the endocrine glands are the prothoracic glands which are a grape-like group of cells surrounding the trachea in the first thoracic segment (Fig.26).

The prothoracic glands produce and release ecdysteroids, a group of steroid hormones that includes the moulting hormone ecdysone. Ecdysone stimulates synthesis of chitin and protein in epidermal cells required for the formation of the exoskeleton and, in conjunction with the juvenile hormone trigger events that culminate in moulting. The principal function of the moulting hormone is to stimulate a series of physiological events that leads to the formation of a new exoskeleton.

Larval moulting (ecdysis) entails a complex feed-back mechanism:

- When the larva outgrows its exoskeleton stretch receptors, nutritional status and body weight are the stimuli that trigger the release of brain hormones from the pars intercerebralis of the brain.
- These brain hormones stimulate the production of PTTH in the corpora allata.
- PTTH in turn stimulates the prothoracic glands to produce ecdysone.
- Pulses of ecdysone initiate moulting and the whole process is greatly modulated by juvenile hormone (JH). JH determines when the adult insect emerges from the pupal case and the larva from the egg (eclosion).
- In the presence of the correct level of JH, ecdysone promotes larva-to-larva moults. With reduced amounts of JH, ecdysone promotes pupation. Complete absence of JH results in formation of the adult.
- Prothoracic glands atrophy in adults as they no longer moult.

The Epitracheal Glands

The epitracheal glands are groups of neurohormone secreting cells associated with the trachea and are part of the neuroendocrine system. They produce ecdysis triggering hormone (ETH) in Lepidoptera which regulates moulting behaviour (Fig.26).

Ventral Ganglia of the Nerve Cord

Towards the end of each moulting stage the neurosecretory cells of the ventral ganglia begin secreting eclosion hormone which influences larval ecdysis and eclosion up to the adult stage. The rising level of eclosion hormone in the haemolymph stimulates the neurosecretory cells of the brain and ventral ganglia to produce bursicon after each ecdysis. Bursicon is a hormone that produces and accelerates sclerotisation of the new cuticle.

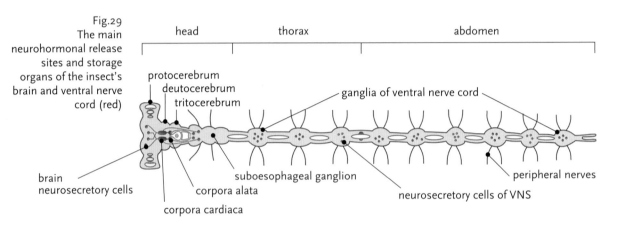

Fig.29
The main neurohormonal release sites and storage organs of the insect's brain and ventral nerve cord (red)

(vi) NERVOUS SYSTEM

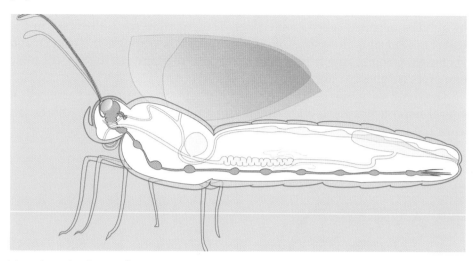

Together the butterfly's nervous system and endocrine system control insect behaviour.

It is not possible to point to a particular part of the central or peripheral nervous systems that might comprise the regulatory system in insects but it is known that insects have a number of related regulatory mechanisms such as 'higher' brain centres, motor and sensory neurons, neurosecretory neurons and neurohormonal organs that function to achieve such control.

The insect's nervous system can be divided into:

- The Central Nervous System
- The Peripheral Nervous System
- Stomodaeal Nervous System (Autonomic Nervous System)
- The Coelopulse Nervous System (Autonomic Nervous System).

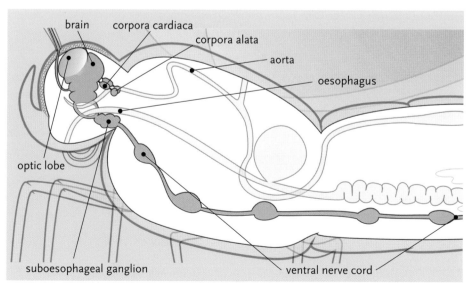

Fig 30.
Insect brain and part of the ventral nerve cord (detail)

The Central Nervous System

Insects have a central nervous system consisting of a series of ganglia linked by bundles of axons called connectives. These ganglia form the brain in the insect's head and the nerve cord which extends through the thorax and abdomen. Ganglia supply nerves to successive segments of the insect's body and process sensory information (Fig. 34).

The basic component of the nervous system is the neuron or nerve cell. A typical neuron has a cell body containing a nucleus and two long fibres (an axon and a dendrite).

Fig. 31
Motor and sensory
neurons

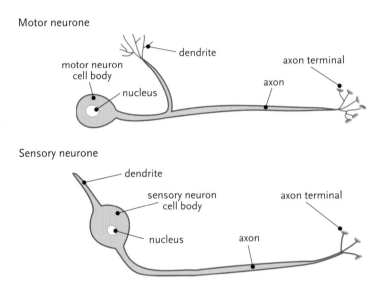

A ganglion is a large collection of neurons where the cell bodies lie at the periphery and the axons and dendrites, lie at the centre. The centre region is called the neuropil and is mainly an area where one nerve connects with another (synapse) (Fig. 32).

Fig. 32
Neurons in right side
of ganglion

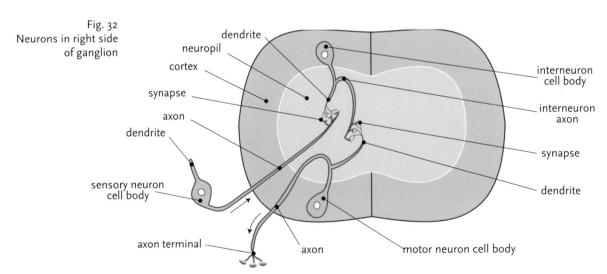

76

The Brain

The insect's brain consists of three major lobes, each containing pairs of ganglion that supply nerves for specific functions.

- The Protocerebrum: the first pair of ganglia includes the optic lobes and receives input from the compound eyes and ocelli and is thought to be mainly associated with vision. The protocerebrum also contains the 'higher' brain centres.

  The brain of butterflies is said to be characterised by the presence of very large optic lobes and a small deuterocerebrum. In addition, butterflies of both sexes have two pairs of extraocular photoreceptors on the genitalia which are essential in females for oviposition and play an essential role in achieving copulation in males.

Fig 33
The Brain

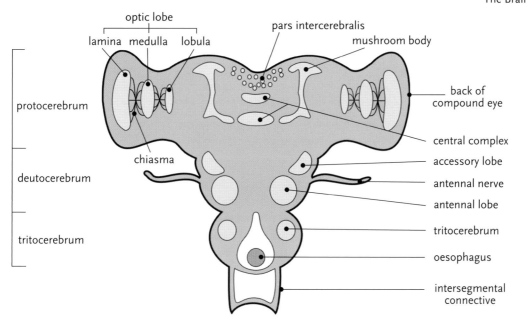

'Higher' Brain Centres: The insect's protocerebrum contains many complex and little understood neuropils. Two anatomically distinctive neuropils, the mushroom bodies and the central complex, have been widely investigated for their apparent role in controlling more complex behaviours. Corpora pedunculata or mushroom bodies are paired lobes of neuropils present in the protocerebrum and extend into the deutocerebrum of all insects. Mushroom bodies are known to be involved in learning and memory particularly for smell, sensory integration and context recognition. They are currently the subject of research.

- The Deutocerebrum: the middle pair of ganglia process information collected by the antennae. Antennal sensory neurons detect odour, taste, tactile sensation and environmental changes in temperature and humidity.

- The Tritocerebrum: the third pair of ganglia are involved in taste perception and the sensory and motor control of mouthparts.
  The tritocerebrum connects the brain with the ventral nervous cord and also with the stomodaeal nervous system that functions separately to control internal organs (see below).
- The Sub-oesophageal Ganglion: below the brain a set of fused ganglia form the sub-oesophageal ganglia. The sub-oesophageal ganglia control mouthparts including the proboscis, neck muscles and any information from sensory neurons in this area is relayed and integrated in these ganglia (Figs 30 and 34).

Fig. 34
The brain and ventral
nerve cord (dorsal
view)

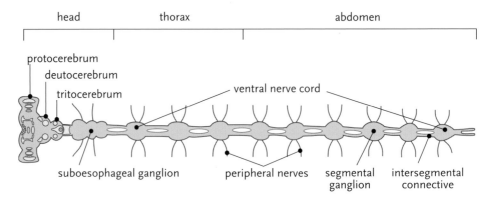

The Ventral Nerve Cord

The ventral nerve cord consists of paired segmental ganglia running along the ventral midline of the thorax and abdomen. The paired ganglia are connected to each other by short nerve called a commissure and are connected to adjacent ganglia by intersegmental connectives. The pair of cords lie so close together they essentially fuse into a single nerve cord (Figs 30 and 34).

- Signals from the cell bodies of neurons in the brain pass to the ganglia of the ventral nerve cord by way of their descending axons and signals return to the brain via ascending axons.
  In the ventral ganglia these axons make synaptic connections with sensory and motor neurons of the peripheral nervous system.
- Peripheral motor neurons from the three thoracic ganglia innervate (supply nerves to) the wings, legs and the muscles of locomotion. Sensory information from setae on thorax, wings and legs is transmitted to these ganglia via the peripheral sensory neurons.
- Peripheral motor neurons from the six abdominal ganglia innervate the muscles of the abdomen, the reproductive organs and the anus and receive input from numerous sensory receptors located at the posterior end of the insect.
- Insect behaviour is mostly integrated and controlled by these segmental ganglia although the brain may stimulate or inhibit their activity.

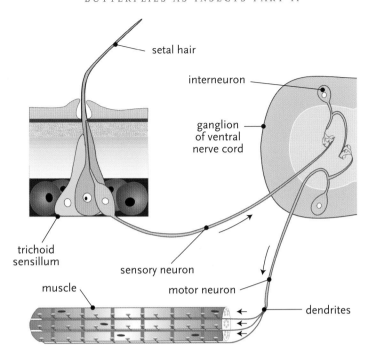

Fig. 35
Ganglion and peripheral sensory and motor nerve supply of seta and muscle fibres

The Peripheral Nervous System

The Peripheral Nervous System consists of:

- Motor neurons whose axons branch out from their cell body in the segmental ganglia of the brain or ventral nerve cord and innervate the muscles and glands of the body.
- Sensory neurons from cuticular and sub-cuticular sense organs such as the trichoid sensilla and chordodontal organs or from photoreceptor cells of the insect's compound eyes.

Cell bodies of sensory neurons lie largely at the periphery of the insect's body just below the cuticle or in and around joints. Their axons run inwards and connect to the neurons of their segmental ganglion (Fig. 35).

Stomodaeal Nervous System

A separate but connected nervous system called the Stomodaeal Nervous System innervates most of the body's vital organs. The stomodaeal nervous system is part of the Autonomic Nervous System which produces involuntary nerve discharge in preparation for what is called "flight or fight" in vertebrates.

The tritocerebrum connects the brain to the stomodaeal nervous system which is formed by:

- A frontal ganglion that is situated on the anterior wall of the oesophagus in the head. A single frontal nerve arises from the anterior part of the frontal ganglion and innervates the contractor (compressor) and dilator

Fig. 36
Stomodaeal nervous
system

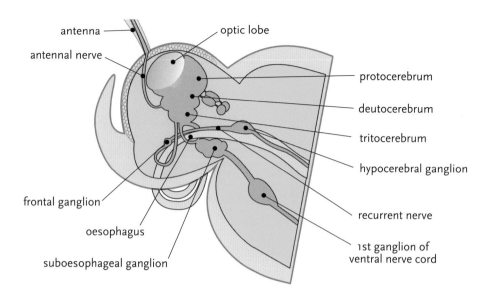

muscles of the cibarium (sucking pump of proboscis) and sub-
oesophageal ganglia respectively (Figs 46 and 36).

The frontal ganglion in the adult Lepidoptera is necessary for the activity of
the cibarial pump which controls movement of liquids through the proboscis
and the swallowing of air and moulting fluid during eclosion.

- A single median recurrent nerve on the dorsal surface of the foregut
  which innervates the heart, corpora cardiaca and parts of the musculature of the gut and salivary glands.
- The midgut of Lepidoptera is probably innervated by an elaborate
  network of nerves, termed the enteric plexus, that extend long axons to
  innervate much of the musculature of the midgut.
- The stomodaeal nervous system also includes ganglia whose neurons
  innervate some endocrine organs, spiracles, reproductive organs and the
  remainder of the gut.

The Coelopulse Nervous System

The Coelopulse Nervous System controls many important physiological
functions in the insect and is also part of the autonomic nervous system. It
has its centre located in the thoracic ganglion of the ventral nerve cord (Fig. 34).
From the thoracic ganglia nerve impulses are sent into the abdominal intersegmental and dorsoventral muscles (Fig. 37). The rhythmic contractions of these
muscles produce special extra-cardiac pulsations in haemocoelic pressure
(blood pressure), which are actively involved in the internal equilibrium
(homeostasis) of some vital physiological functions such as:

- Respiratory gas exchange through individual spiracles (see The Tracheal
  System).

- Water balance by control over respiratory water loss (see The Tracheal System).
- Control of mechanical pressure within the haemocoele (see The Circulatory System).
- In addition it regulates circulatory pumps known as accessory pulsatile organs (APOs) which enhance circulation of haemolymph through the appendages and body regions that are too far to be reached by the heartbeat (see The Circulatory System).

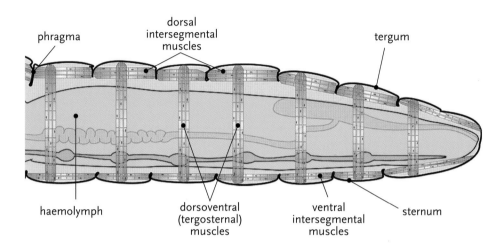

Fig. 37
Abdominal intersegmental and dorsoventral muscles of insect (simplified)

phragma

dorsal intersegmental muscles

tergum

haemolymph

dorsoventral (tergosternal) muscles

ventral intersegmental muscles

sternum

Small Blues mating

(vii) CIRCULATORY SYSTEM

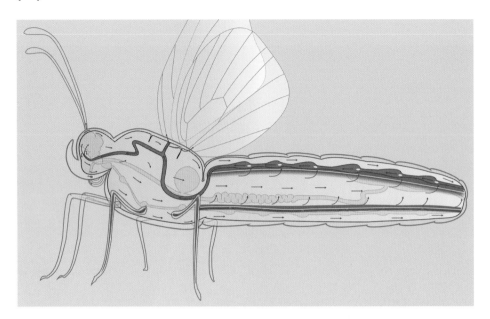

Butterflies like all insects have an open circulatory system in which the heart drives the haemolymph flow within the body cavity or haemocoele where it bathes and maintains all internal organs and tissues.

The dorsal vessel is the main structural component of the insect's circulatory system. It runs longitudinally through the thorax and abdomen, mainly along the inside of the dorsal body wall.

In the abdomen the dorsal vessel is called the heart which is divided into distinct chambers separated by small valve-like openings called ostia through which blood enters the heart. Each chamber has a pair of alary muscles that assist the flow of haemolymph through the heart and control the opening and closing of the ostial valves (Figs 38 and 39).

The section of the dorsal vessel in front of the heart is a simple tube that facilitates transport of haemolymph to the head and is called the aorta.

The dorsal vessel contracts and beats rhythmically, propelling haemolymph (blood) mainly forward from the abdomen towards the head from where it flows back through the body in the open haemocoele. It re-enters the heart through the ostial valves and the cycle begins again.

Well regulated and constant perfusion of vital organs and tissues is ensured by the pumping of the dorsal vessel which is aided by dorsal and ventral diaphragms and abdominal muscles. In addition, circulation in the appendages is assisted by accessory pulsatile organs (APOs) (Fig. 38).

Although the circulatory system is under the control of the central nervous system it is now accepted that it is the Coelopulse Nervous System that is responsible for coordinating and controlling both circulation and respiration in insects (see The Nervous System).

Oxygen is supplied to tissues and carbon dioxide is removed by ventilation through the insect's tracheal system and not the circulatory system.

The Circulatory System

The dorsal vessel forms a hollow tube which extends along the midline, on the inside of the dorsal body wall, from the posterior end of the abdomen to the head.

The Heart

In the abdomen the heart is divided into distinct segmental dilatations which form heart chambers.

The heart muscle contracts spontaneously (systole) due to the presence of specialised pacemaker tissue that can initiate repetitive contractions. Each contraction is followed by a period of rest (diastole). Neural and hormonal factors may influence or modulate this pacemaker activity.

The Aorta

The aorta is a slender, poorly contractile vessel which usually begins in the first abdominal segment. It continues forward from the first heart chamber, under a phragma, which is a cuticular ingrowth of the body wall that partially separates thorax and abdomen and to which muscles are attached.

In Lepidoptera, after passing under the phragma, the aorta makes a large loop upwards (dorsally) in the mesothorax and gives off a small branch called the dorsal diverticulum. This is the region of the accessory pulsatile organ which aids pumping of haemolymph and directs it to and from the wings into the head via the aorta (Fig. 38).

The aorta dilates after passage through the brain and divides in each side of the head forming open-ended arteries. The posterior end of the dorsal vessel is closed.

Heartbeat Reversal

The heart is generally regarded as the pulsating part of the dorsal vessel and, in most insects, contraction of the vessel is in one direction beginning at the posterior end and moving forward as a peristaltic wave propels the haemolymph through the aorta into the head and from where it circulates around the body.

However, in resting Lepidoptera and other high performing fliers, there is shown to be a very regular heartbeat reversal that becomes apparent at the end of the larval period and continues through the pupal and adult periods.

Contraction waves of the dorsal vessel towards the head alternate with waves towards the rear of the body and in between there are short periods of rest. This results in haemolymph being transported back and forth between thorax and abdomen during these alternating phases.

Haemolymph transport to the head leads to compression of the tracheal air sacs in the head and thorax increasing ventilation to the tissues. When the heart reverses flow direction, the net haemolymph flow is out of the thorax and the air sacs reinflate.

Heartbeat reversal may be essential for the complete perfusion at both extremities of insects bodies and may also play a role in the release of carbon dioxide from diapausing pupae and adults as spiracular opening periods are influenced by episodes of heartbeat reversal.

Because the dorsal vessel is a relatively weak organ the circulation of haemolymph is assisted by other extra-cardiac muscular organs:

- The dorsal and ventral diaphragms
- Accessory pulsatile organs (APOs)
- Extracardiac pulsations

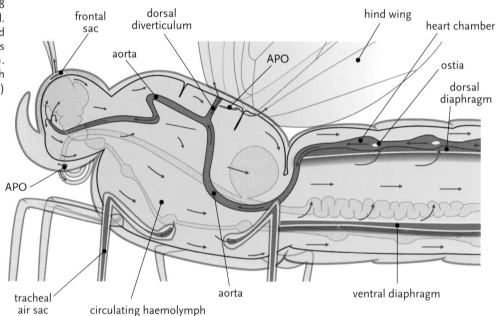

Fig. 38
The dorsal vessel. APOs, Dorsal and Ventral diaphragms (green). Haemolymph circulation (arrows)

Dorsal and Ventral Diaphragms

The dorsal diaphragm (DD) consists of two delicate connective tissue membranes enclosing between them alary muscles, so called because in many insects they resemble wings, although in Lepidoptera they are arranged in a loose meshwork. Alary muscles have their origins on the body wall and are inserted on the ventral wall (underside) of the heart (Fig. 39).

The heart contracts spontaneously at a constant and relatively rapid rate whereas the alary muscles perform infrequent and slow contractions and do not play any role in the heartbeat but are capable of assisting and directing haemolymph circulation.

The ventral diaphragm (VD) in most Lepidoptera consists of muscle fibres originating on the abdominal wall and are inserted onto the top of the abdominal ventral nerve cord (VNC). Contraction of the muscle of the ventral diaphragm can cause not just movement of the VD but also lateral oscillations of the VNC. These contractions have been shown to specifically circulate

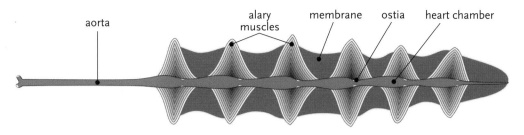

Fig. 39
The dorsal vessel and the dorsal diaphragm showing membrane and alary muscles

haemolymph from the anterior to the posterior part of the abdomen.

The ventral diaphragm plays an important role in perfusing the ventral nerve cord of insects. Also, it assists thermoregulation during flight by the removal of warm haemolymph from the heated thoracic muscles and circulating it through the abdomen for cooling.

Accessory Pulsatile Organs (APOs)

Although the dorsal vessel and both diaphragms are partially responsible for the circulation of haemolymph through the body cavity, they are not capable of achieving circulation through the body appendages such as wings, antennae and legs.

Instead insects depend on special circulatory pumps known as accessory pulsatile organs. Many of these pumps are muscular diaphragms, independent of the dorsal vessel and function autonomously. They are generally located at the base of appendages and are connected to special diaphragms or vessels which direct the flow through the appendages (Fig. 38).

- The wing circulatory organ forms a pulsating membrane stretched across the anterior half of the mesothorax above a tracheal air sac in Lepidoptera. Flow in and out of the wings is correlated with periodic heartbeat reversal, activity of the wing's APO and fluctuations of the wing tracheal air volume.
- There are no pulsatile organs in the legs of Lepidoptera. Instead, a large tracheal air sac partitions the leg, to a point just short of the tip, into two compartments with counter current flow. Increased thoracic haemolymph during heartbeat reversal causes fluctuations in the volume of the tracheal air sac in the leg which propels the haemolymph through the counter current compartments.
- Non-pulsatile organs at the base of antennal vessels in Lepidoptera form ampullae or frontal sacs. They are indirectly compressed by movements of the pharynx, directing haemolymph through the antennal vessels.
- The lepidopteran proboscis has a haemolymph pumping organ located near its base which is involved in its hydraulic extension. This circulatory organ consists of compressible cuticular tubes with attached muscles. Contraction of the muscles presses the tubes together forcing haemolymph into the proboscis and thus extending it.
- Although the APOs function autonomously there is a superimposed neuronal influence from the Coelopulse Nervous System (See the Nervous System).

Extra Cardiac Pulsations

Extra cardiac pulsations are simultaneous contractions of intersegmental muscles, mainly of the abdomen which cause a sharp rise in haemocoele pressure in the insect body (Fig. 40). The pressure produced by each pulsation can be much greater than pressure produced by contraction of the dorsal vessel and these pulsations are transmitted by the haemolymph throughout the insect's body and to areas not easily reached by the dorsal vessel and APO structures.

Extra cardiac pulsations in coordination with the opening of certain spiracles assist ventilation, or if in coordination with tightly closed spiracles, assist haemolymph perfusion.

Extra cardiac pulsations are controlled by the Coelopulse Nervous System.

Fig. 40
Intersegmental muscles
and dorsoventral
muscles of abdomen

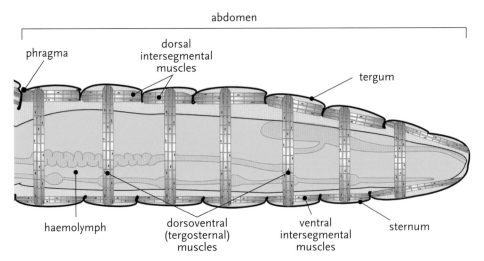

The Haemolymph

Haemolymph is usually clear or slightly green in Lepidoptera (especially larvae).

Composition

- Haemocytes (cells such as phagocytes that engulf harmful organisms or foreign particles).
- Water 84-92%.
- Inorganic ions, Na, K, Ca, Mg, Cl, P, carbonate.
- Nitrogenous waste, (usually uric acid, the main end product of nitrogen metabolism in terrestrial insects).
- Carbohydrates (mainly trehalose), lipids, amino acids, proteins and enzymes.
- Antifreeze.
- Pigments.
- Hormones.

Haemolymph circulation ensures

- Delivery of nutrients, salts and hormones to all tissue cells.
- Removal of waste metabolites.
- Sealing-off of wounds by haemocytes through a coagulation reaction.
- Encapsulation and destruction of internal parasites or other invaders by phagocytes.
- Provision of immunity against harmful organisms.
- Provision of a pathway for the transport of hormones to coordinate biological functions and development.
- Maintenance of homeostasis by a feedback mechanism ensuring the insect's body maintains normal biological function and stability. Any change in the haemolymph quickly affects all tissues.
- Hydrostatic pressure of the haemolymph, generated by muscle contraction, facilitates
  - Hatching
  - Moulting
  - Nectaring
  - Wing expansion after eclosion
  - Reproduction (e.g. insemination and oviposition)
  - Thermoregulation.
- Cooling by conducting excess heat away from active flight muscles.
- Heating by collecting and circulating absorbed heat while basking.

(viii) TRACHEAL SYSTEM

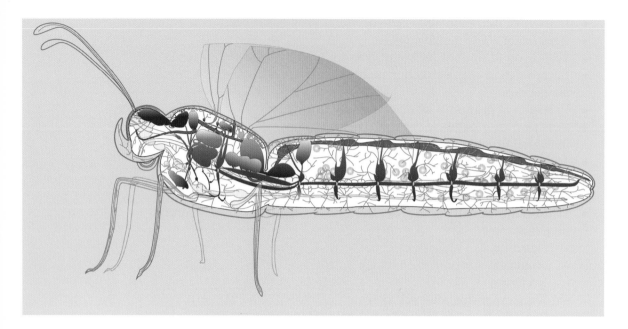

Similar to most terrestrial insects, butterflies ventilate through an extensive interconnecting and branching network of air-filled tubes formed from the cuticle, called tracheae. Tracheae ramify throughout all parts of the body, providing a pathway for the rapid movement of oxygen and carbon dioxide directly between the insect's tissues and the surrounding environment. As gas exchange occurs directly between the air in the tracheoles and the tissue cells, the efficiency of gases exchange in insects is high.

Spiracles and Tracheae

The tracheal system opens to the environment through spiracles which are small pores in the external cuticle located along the lateral margins of the insect's body (Fig. 43).

Each spiracle opens into a chamber called an atrium. In the atrium the spiracular trachea divides to form the dorsal, ventral and visceral tracheal trunks in each body segment. The anterior branches of the spiracular trachea join to form a long lateral longitudinal tracheal trunk which extends throughout the thorax and abdomen. The tracheal trunks form branching networks of tracheal tubes of decreasing diameter that extend throughout the body. Cuticle continuous with that of the outer body lines these tracheal trunks and tubes.

In some areas of the trachea densely coiled ridges called taenidia reinforce the wall, hold it open and resist pressure changes during movement of the integument and peristalsis of the intestine which is important during the larval stage. In adults, certain parts of the trachea have no taenidia and the tracheal tube enlarges to form thin-walled air sacs capable of storing air.

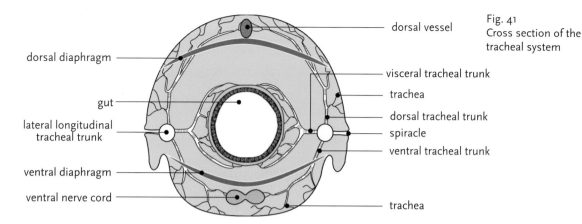

Fig. 41
Cross section of the
tracheal system

Tracheoles

Tracheae branch into increasingly narrower air tubes called tracheoles. Tracheoles are small blind-ending cuticular canals whose lumen is continuous with the lumen of the trachea. They form the terminal endings of the tracheal system and are non-taenidiated. They are formed from cells known as tracheolar end-cells, which are derived from the epidermal cells lining the trachea, and have many branching processes (Fig. 42).

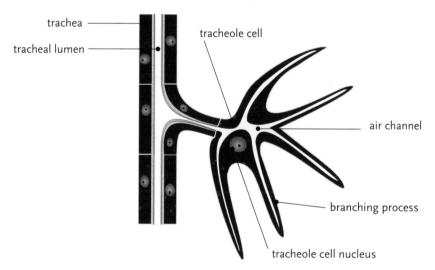

Fig. 42
Tracheole cell

These special tracheolear end-cells provide a thin, moist interface for the exchange of gases between the atmosphere and every living cell of the insect's body. Each cell lies adjacent to or is penetrated by a tracheolar process. They are particularly numerous in metabolically active tissues such as flight muscles and eyes. At rest, the distal end of the tracheolar lumen is fluid filled. This fluid is absorbed into the tissues during flight.

Air Sacs

Portions of the tracheal system enlarge to form thin-walled air sacs that may store a reserve of air and, because they lack taenidia, they can collapse and expand with variation, in haemolymph pressure. They act like a bellows by producing strong movements of air through the tracheal system. Air sacs are common in active, high performing flying insects, especially those with a rigid cuticle like Lepidoptera (Fig. 43).

During the late pupal stage air sacs are highly folded but, after wing inflation, they become expanded due to haemolymph reduction by post-ecdysial diuresis. Much of the volume occupied by the haemocoele becomes replaced by distended air sacs. The haemocoele is reduced to vessel-like sinuses which pass through the air sacs in the head, thorax and anterior abdomen. This reduction of haemolymph volume is essential in order to achieve a light weight for the ability to fly (Wasserthal 2003).

Flight muscles, especially of the mesothorax are surrounded by air sacs which not only supply the flight muscles with oxygen but also allow the antago-nistic systems of intersegmental muscles and dorsoventral muscles to function without friction.

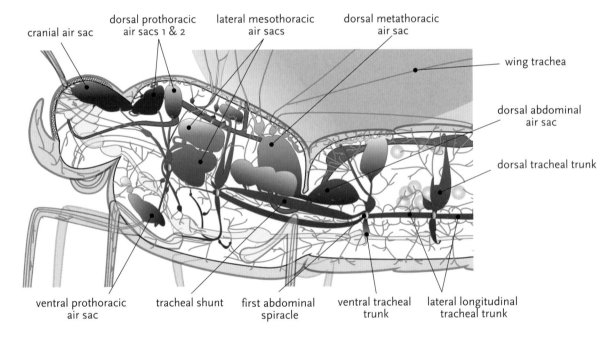

Fig. 43
Tracheal airsacs and tracheal trunks (blue), tracheae (green), heart and aorta (red) (after Srivastava 1975).

Spiracles
Spiracles are small pores in the external cuticle located along the lateral margins of the insect's body. They are protected by valves that are controlled by muscles and hairs that filter out dust as the air enters the spiracles.

Lepidopteran caterpillars have one pair of thoracic spiracles in the protho-racic region and eight pairs of abdominal spiracles. Pupae have one large thoracic spiracle in the prothoracic region and eight abdominal spiracles. The first abdominal spiracle is hidden under the wing sheath and the last is non-functional. Butterflies have two pairs of thoracic spiracles located in the thoracic region, one each in the prothoracic and metathoracic regions and seven pairs of spiracles located in the abdomen.

Spiracles in adult Lepidoptera mainly serve to

- Control the intratracheal pressure gradient.
- Maintain efficient air flow.
- Minimise water loss.

During the various stages of metamorphosis not all spiracles open and close simultaneously. Observations of some pupae of various lepidopteran species has revealed active regulation of inspiration and expiration through one or two spiracles while the majority remained hermetically closed for prolonged periods.

Gas Exchange Mechanisms

The purpose of the tracheal system is for oxygen to gain access to the insect's tissue cells for cellular respiration and eventual production of energy which is required especially for flight, sight and reproduction.

Oxygen enters through the spiracles and proceeds through the tracheal trunks and the numerous branches of the trachea and tracheoles by diffusion or convection. It dissolves in the fluid-filled lumen of the tracheolar cells from where it diffuses into the cytoplasm of all living cells of the body.

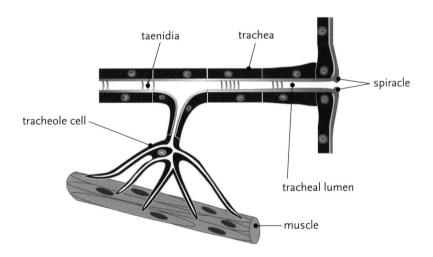

Fig. 44
Trachea and
tracheole cell

Diffusion and Convection

Diffusion is the basis of all gas exchange systems in organisms and is the passive movement of molecules down their concentration gradient. However, this mechanism is not always sufficient to transport the oxygen required especially during insect flight. Additional mechanisms that drive air by convection are employed by well coordinated actions of muscles and spiracles.

Mechanisms that drive convection

- Autoventilation, a form of thoracic pumping during which movements of the wings and legs change the volume of tracheal air sacs creating air flow.
- During heartbeat reversal, haemolymph is transferred from one region of the body to another, increasing or decreasing pressure in different compartments. As haemolymph accumulates, it compresses air sacs in that compartment causing convective air flow through tracheae and spiracles.
- Abdominal pumping producing contraction and expansion of the abdomen due to the coordinated rhythmic contractions of intersegmental (dorso-ventral in certain species) muscles. These contractions form the rhythmic abdominal pumping movements (telescoping) that drive convective ventilation and have been described in various developmental stages in a number of insect species including Lepidoptera.

  Contraction of these muscles reduce body volume and increased pressure on haemolymph and surrounding tissues compressing the air sacs and driving convective air flow through tracheae and spiracles. When the muscles relax, the abdomen springs back into shape, the tracheae expand and draw in air.
- Muscles that have the primary role of driving haemolymph circulation, such as heart and ventral diaphragm, also play an important role in producing convective ventilation.
- Recently, researchers have discovered the presence of active tracheal compression of parts of the tracheal system in many orders of insects. Further research should reveal if rhythmical compression cycles are a major factor of insect's ventilation (Socha *et al.* 2008).

The insects need for oxygen alters greatly as the metabolic rate varies with transition from various states such as rest, flight, basking or migration. If required, increased gas exchange can be accomplished by:

- Opening a larger number of spiracles or by increasing the length or frequency of opening.
- Increasing convective ventilation by rhythmic abdominal pumping.
- Reducing fluid levels in the tracheoles.

Control of tracheal gas exchange capacity in turn depends mainly on neuroendocrine control of muscles that drive convection and control spiracular opening.

The Discontinuous Gas Exchange Cycle (DGC)

An insect utilizes muscular contraction of the abdomen along with coordinated spiracle contraction and relaxation to generate gas exchange and to reduce water loss into the atmosphere.

For many insects, especially those that are highly active, the spiracles close for only brief periods if at all, and oxygen and carbon dioxide are exchanged relatively continuously. However, Lepidoptera and some insects exhibit discontinuous gas exchange.

The discontinuous gas exchange cycle divides into three distinct phases which differ in the behaviour of the spiracles. Periods of spiracular closure in which no or reduced gas exchange occurs are followed by a flutter phase, characterised by continued rapid spiracle openings that still restricts external gas exchange. The final phase includes a period of spiracular opening and greatly increased gas exchange lasting several minutes. During this phase, all accumulated CO_2 is released in bursts from the tracheal system and the haemolymph.

Regardless of the insect's gas exchange pattern oxygen metabolism at a cellular level continues at a constant rate but discontinuous gas exchange permits the insect to store carbon dioxide and just release it intermittently, thus avoiding continuous water loss.

Of all these gas exchange patterns characteristic of insects, the discontinuous gas exchange cycle is perhaps the best known yet it is a pattern that is known to occur among only a few insect orders, which include the Lepidoptera, and then only when at rest or during pupal diapause. When the insect becomes active the pattern disappears and is replaced by continuous gas exchange to meet metabolic needs.

The discontinuous gas-exchange cycles have engendered much debate and many hypotheses have emerged. That discontinuous gas-exchange cycles reduce respiratory water loss appears to be the most plausible.

(ix) FAT BODY

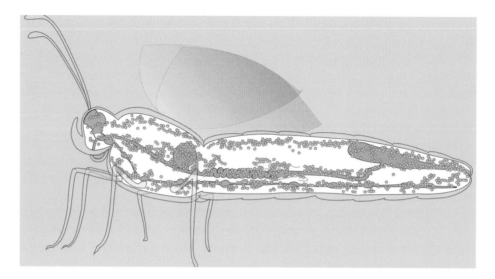

Insects share with other invertebrates the common metabolic pathways of carbohydrate, protein and lipid. Synthesis and storage of these metabolic compounds takes place in the fat body. Being a major biosynthetic and storage organ and the main site of intermediate metabolism in insects, the fat body is analogous to the vertebrate adipose tissue and liver.

In insects the fat body consists of loose aggregates or compact masses of cells suspended in the haemocoele where it and all other internal organs and tissues of the insect's body are bathed in haemolymph.

Two major regions can be distinguished. The peripheral cuticular fat body positioned near the insect's integument and musculature which functions largely as storage. And the second, mainly peri-visceral fat body where it is metabolically most active and around the brain, heart and aorta, tracheal system and reproductive organs.

Functions of Fat Body
- Absorption from the haemolymph and subsequent fat body build-up of storage nutrients mainly during the larval stage. The main purpose is the accumulation of reserves for later stages and principally to serve adult activities.
- It contains the enzymes responsible for the metabolism of glucose. Especially the metabolism and utilisation of trehalose which is the principal haemolymph sugar of insects.

  Trehalose is unique to insects and some other invertebrates and serves as a storage carbohydrate used as fuel for flight and as antifreeze (cryoprotectant).

  But nectar-only feeding butterflies and moths are unable to use sugar directly. They must first convert it into fat before it can be burned.

- The fat body contains detoxifying enzymes.
- It synthesises most of the major haemolymph proteins required by the insect, in particular vitellogenins (yolk proteins) at the adult stage required by the maturing oocytes and also diapause proteins.
- It has the homeostatic function of responding to nutritional and hormonal cues that regulate haemolymph levels of carbohydrates, proteins and lipids.

Role of Fats

- Used as substrate for
  - Reproduction
  - Embryogenesis
  - Metamorphosis
  - Energy for flight.
- Constituents of
  - Pheromones for communication
  - Hormones for physiological processes
  - Cell membranes
  - Cuticle for protection.

The fat body is largely under the control of the endocrine system. Neuroendocrine hormones from the brain and ganglia, moulting hormones, juvenile hormones and adipokinetic hormone, all affect the metabolic state of the fat body cells.

(x) PROBOSCIS AND DIGESTIVE SYSTEM

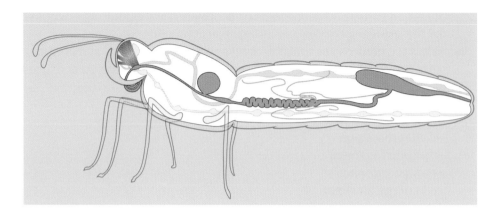

The feeding mechanism of Lepidoptera is a simple device for extracting nutrient fluids from deep inside flower corollas.

Essentially, the feeding mechanism consists of:

- A long tube called the proboscis whose lumen opens into the mouth
- A pumping organ (sucking pump) formed by the anterior wall of the foregut.

The proboscis is the external part of the insect's sucking apparatus. It is formed by the greatly elongated lobes of the maxillae called galeae (Fig. 45). These lobes are hollow flexible tubes containing muscles and trachea and are held

Fig. 45
Lepidopteran
proboscis (cross
section)

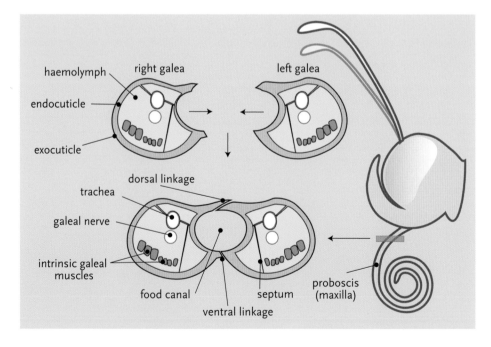

together by rows of interlocking cuticular processes. The opposed walls are thickened and concave and enclose between them a fluid-tight canal through which liquid feed is drawn into the mouth by the sucking pump. The outer walls of the galeae have alternate sclerotised and membranous rows which facilitate coiling.

The sucking pump is highly developed in adult Lepidoptera and includes the mouth and pharyngeal regions of the foregut. The cibarium (preoral food cavity) forms the anterior portion of the pump (Fig. 46).

The sucking pump is composed of three structures, the oral valve in the cibarium, the expandable lumen and the oesophageal valve that controls movement of fluid into the oesophagus.

Dilator muscles of the sucking pump expand the lumen which in turn opens the oral valve and fluid can be drawn into the lumen from the food canal of the proboscis. Circular compressor muscles attached to the sides of the sucking pump reduce the size of the lumen.

Liquid food is forced along the oesophagus into a crop-like enlargement of the foregut known as the "food reservoir". The stomach is tublar and beyond it lies the intestine, where nutrients are mainly absorbed, and into which open three pairs of excretory (malpighian) tubules.

In the resting position the proboscis is tightly coiled leaving no space between the coils. It lies against the labium and between the labial palps.

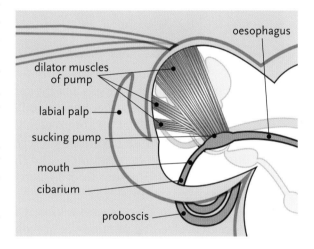

Fig. 46
The sucking pump

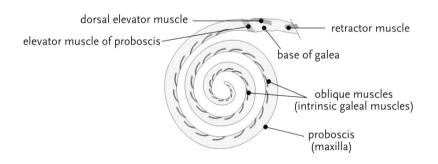

Fig. 47
Muscles of the proboscis

The proboscis (maxillary) muscles of adult Lepidoptera are composed of two groups called the galeal and stipes muscles. Uncoiling of the proboscis relies on an hydraulic mechanism. Repeated contractions of the stipes muscles force haemolymph into the galeae and the proboscis uncoils when pressure inside the galeae increases.

Proboscis coiling is achieved by the elasticity of the cuticle which loosely

Fig.48
Painted Lady feeding and showing the 'knee' bend of the proboscis

recoils the spiral into one or two coils and the contraction of the intrinsic galeal muscles are responsible for tightening the coil (Fig. 47).

Numerous mechanoreceptors are present on the external surface of the proboscis. They may provide information on the width and depth of tubular flowers during probing, the position of the tip of the proboscis inside the flower and on the nectar. The sensilla of the food canal provide information on the sugar content of flowers.

Butterflies approach flowers with a loosely coiled proboscis and uncoil it after landing. In the feeding position the proboscis shows a distinct bend after approximately one third of its length, enabling the proboscis to adjust to various floral positions and depths.

Fig. 49
The digestive tract and cibarial pump

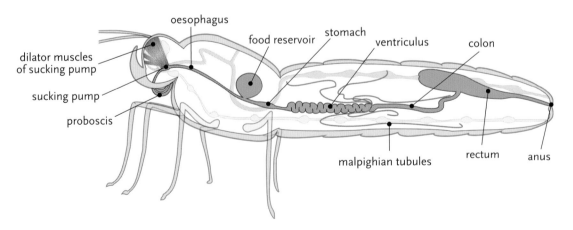

oesophagus
food reservoir
stomach
ventriculus
colon
dilator muscles of sucking pump
sucking pump
proboscis
malpighian tubules
rectum
anus

(xi) DIAPAUSE AND COLD-HARDINESS

Diapause

Many insect species, including Lepidoptera, adapt to regular seasonal changes and to variations in environmental conditions by manifesting various forms of dormancy which enable them to circumvent adverse conditions. Migration is another strategy employed by insects as a way of escaping climatic extremes.

Dormancy can best be described as a generic term for 'a rest period' and, when undertaken by Lepidoptera and other insects with a seasonal life cycle, dormancy is manifest by quiescence and diapause.

Quiescence is an immediate survival response to adverse seasonal conditions and is directly induced and terminated by extrinsic factors in the surrounding environment. This dormancy state involves a reduction in the insect's basal metabolic rate resulting in a slowing down of direct development (morphogenesis) and, unlike diapause, is under the control of the central nervous system. It enables insects to cope with unpredictable and inclement environmental periods such as high or low temperature or food shortage. This explains why one may observe Small Tortoiseshell butterflies and a great deal of other insect activity on warm sunny days in the middle of winter.

By contrast, diapause serves to synchronise the insect's complete life cycle to seasonal changes in the environment, thus ensuring that further growth and development, and eventual reproduction, happen at a time when it will have the most favourable outcome.

Often referred to as the Diapause Syndrome, because it is not a single physiological event but a dynamic series of recognisable phases, diapause occurs at any metamorphic stage in response to token (indirect) stimuli from the environment during a sensitive period in the life cycle.

All phases of diapause are genetically determined for each species and under the control of the neuro-endocrine system, consequently diapause, once initiated, is not influenced by surrounding climate fluctuations according to Tauber *et al.* (1986):

> Diapause is a neurohormonally mediated, dynamic state of low metabolic activity. Associated with this is reduced morphogenesis, increased resistance to environmental extremes, and altered or reduced behavioural activity.
> Diapause occurs during a genetically determined stage of metamorphosis and its full expression develops in a species-specific manner, usually in response to a number of environmental stimuli that precede unfavourable conditions. Once diapause has begun, metabolic activity is suppressed even if conditions favourable for development prevail.

All metamorphic stages in the life cycle of Lepidoptera can participate in diapause.

- Embryonic diapause can occur at any stage of embryogenesis.

- Larval diapause is most frequent in the final instar but can also occur in earlier instars.
- Pupal diapause usually occurs in the true pupal state but is known to occur after completion of adult differentiation (pharate adult).
- Adult diapause entails a halt in reproduction and is referred to as reproductive diapause.
  It involves a significant delay in sexual maturity. Male and female genitalia may remain small, accessory glands inactive and there is strongly suppressed mating behaviour.

Cold-hardiness

In temperate latitudes and polar regions, insects are subject to freezing conditions for a greater or lesser period of each year.

Physiologically, many insects prepare for winter by biosynthesising "antifreeze" compounds such as glycerol, sorbitol or trehalose. Raising levels of one or more of these compounds in the haemolymph and body tissues of Lepidoptera can increase cold-tolerance by decreasing freezing point thus protecting tissues and cells from damage due to the formation of ice crystals.

Glycerol is a common cellular metabolite in insects. At various stages of their metamorphosis the haemolymph concentration of glycerol increases and decreases in a seasonal pattern. Besides playing a major role in energy metabolism it also has important supercooling properties. The sorbitol mode of action appears to be similar to glycerol.

Glycerol confers cold-hardiness on insects by:

- Depressing the freezing point of body fluids by increasing its osmolality. This alone is not sufficient to maintain cold-hardiness as the insect will strive to correct this osmotic imbalance.
- Supercooling.
  Increased haemolymph concentration of glycerol permits lowering of body temperature well below freezing point without the formation of ice crystals.
  Many insects can be supercooled to 20°-30°C below their freezing point (cold-hardened) without formation of damaging ice crystals.
- Supercooling point protection.
  A point arrives when supercooling capacity is exceeded and ice crystals form in the insect's tissues.
  The presence of increased haemolymph glycerol concentration confers protection to tissues and cells from the damage that these ice crystals can potentially cause. However, a further super cooling point can be reached when the temperature dependent enzyme metabolism is slowed down or ceases resulting in glycerol synthesis shut down and the death of the insect.

Holly Blue

Small Copper

Butterflies in the Garden

6

BUTTERFLIES are increasingly under threat through loss of habitat and gardens can play a significant role as refuges by providing flowering plants as nectar dispensing 'filling stations'. They can also provide breeding opportunities through the provision of lightly managed 'natural' areas with suitable larval food plants including native grasses. Many butterflies are habitat specialists and will never visit your garden. But, in general, bright coloured flowers, especially red, orange and purple are particularly attractive to butterflies whose vision extends into the ultraviolet spectrum. Smell also has a role in the location of flowers. Butterflies do appear to give little in return to plants as they are (with some exceptions) relatively poor pollinators having little physical contact with the reproductive parts of flowers. Nor have they any adaptations designed for collecting pollen while probing nectaries. But butterflies are decorative and a delight to view as they flit around from plant to plant, and only the "cabbage whites" (Large White and Small White) with their predilection for brassicas, could be described as anything but an asset to a garden. But if you are growing brassicas why not sacrifice one or two for the whites? There are two categories of plants which may be grown to encourage butterflies and moths to not only visit, but to make their homes in your garden, namely nectar-rich flowering plants and larval food plants.

Nectar-rich flowering plants

The butterfly mouth has evolved into a proboscis, so the adult cannot chew and must rely for nourishment on the liquid nectar or sap which they imbibe from flowers. In nature, butterflies would find only wild flowers and a recommended list of 30 of the best is shown in Table 1. Of course, not every garden has space for a large number of wild flowers but you can choose plants from the list below which will fit in with your style of gardening and integrate them into your facility.

While many flowers in horticultural use are devoid of suitable or accessible nectar sources, others are particularly attractive to butterflies and gardeners may feel that this is where they can most usefully contribute to encouraging butterflies. From the vast number of nectar plants available, the following in Table 2 have been selected to provide sources through the season when butter-flies are normally active, that is from March to October. Flowering seasons are indicated by Sp (Spring), Su (Summer) and A (Autumn).

Table 1: Nectar-rich Wild Flowering Plants

Biting Stonecrop *Sedum acre*	Marjoram *Origanum vulgare* *
Bluebell *Hyacinthoides non-scripta*	Lesser Celandine *Ficaria verna (Ranunculus ficaria)*
Bramble *Rubus fruticosus*	Marsh Thistle *Cirsium palustre*
Bugle *Ajuga reptans*	Mayweed *Tripleurospermum maritimum*
Buttercup *Ranunculus* species	Orchid, Common-spotted, Heath-spotted, Marsh *Dactylorhiza* species
Common Fleabane *Pulicaria dysenterica*	
Cowslip *Primula veris*	Ox-eye Daisy *Leucanthemum vulgare*
Creeping Thistle *Cirsium arvense*	Primrose *Primula vulgaris*
Cuckooflower *Cardamine pratensis*	Purple Loosestrife *Lythrum salicaria*
Dandelion *Taraxacum officinale*	Ragwort *Senecio jacobaea*
Devil's-bit Scabious *Succisa pratensis*	Red Campion *Silene dioica*
Early-purple Orchid *Orchis mascula*	Saxifrage *Saxifrage* species
English Stonecrop *Sedum anglicum*	Sea Pink (Thrift) *Armeria maritima*
Field Scabious *Knautia arvensis*	Self-heal *Prunella vulgaris*
Fragrant Orchid *Gymnadenia conopsea*	Spear Thistle *Cirsium vulgare*
Hemp Agrimony *Eupatorium cannabinum*	*Wild* Teasel *Dipsacus fullonum*
Knapweed *Centaurea nigra*	Wild Thyme *Thymus polytrichus*
Lady's Smock *Cardamine pratensis*	Yarrow *Achillea millefolium*
Lesser Burdock *Arctium minus*	Yellow Toadflax *Linaria vulgaris*

Table 2: Nectar-rich Garden Flowering Plants

Ageratum *Ageratum houstonianum* Su	Leopard's-bane *Doronicum pardalianches* Sp
Aubretia *Aubretia deltoides* Sp*	Ling (Heather) *Calluna vulgaris* Su, A
Butterfly Stonecrop *Sedum spectabile* A*	Marigold *Calendula officinalis* Su, A
Canadian Goldenrod *Solidago canadensis* Su, A	Michaelmas Daisy *Aster novi-belgii* A*
Candytuft *Iberis umbellata* Su*	Phlox *Phlox paniculata* Su
Caucasian Scabious *Scabiosa caucasica* Su	Poached Egg-plant *Limnanthes douglasii* Su
Chrysanthemum *Chrysanthemum* species A	Polyanthus *Primula polyantha* Sp
Dahlia *Dahlia* spp. Su, A	Red Valerian *Centranthus ruber* Su*
Dame's-violet *Hesperis matronalis* Sp	Soldiers & Sailors (Lungwort) *Pulmonaria saccharata* Sp
Elephant's-ears *Bergenia cordifolia* Sp	
French Marigold *Tagetes patula* Su*	Squill *Scilla* species Sp
Globe Thistle *Echinops ritro* Su	Sweet Alyssum *Lobularia maritima* Su
Goldenrod *Astilbe x arendsii* Su	Sweet William *Dianthus barbatus* Su
Hoary Stock *Matthiola incana* Su	Verbena (Vervain) *Verbena bonariensis* Su, A
Honesty *Lunaria biennis* Sp	Wallflower *Cheiranthus cheiri* Sp
Heathers/Heaths *Erica* species Sp, Su, A	White Arabis *Arabis albida* Sp
Hyacinth *Hyacinthus orientalis* Sp	Yellow Alyssum *Alyssum saxatile* Sp
Iceplant *Sedum spectabile* A*	

There are also quite a number of flowering shrubs, including the outstanding and aptly named Butterfly-bush *Buddleja,* which are very attractive to butterflies, bees and other insects. Sunny, sheltered locations are suitable for most of them, and this enables butterflies to both bask and take nectar.

Table 3: Nectar-rich Shrubs

Butterfly-bush *Buddleja davidii* *	Potentilla *Potentilla* species
Californian Lilac *Ceanothus* species	Privet *Ligustrum* species
Escallonia *Escallonia* species	Pussy (Goat) Willow *Salix caprea*
Hebe *Hebe* (Veronica) *	Rosemary *Rosmarinus officinalis*
Lavender *Lavendula* species *	Senecio *Senecio (greyii) laxifolia*
Lilac *Syringa vulgaris*	Viburnum *Viburnum* species
Strawberry-tree *Arbutus unedo 'rubra'*	Yellow Buddleja *B. x weyeriana*

* = top ten favourite nectar plants from *Gardening for Butterflies* (Margaret Vickery 1998)

Larval food plants

In most instances the essential larval food plants which the caterpillars require are wild grasses, shrubs or 'weeds'. Many of them would be considered unsuitable for a small well-kept suburban garden, but the larger urban and country gardens ought to have a wildlife area in which at least some of them are to be found. Indeed it may be difficult to exclude them. Below is a list of some of the larval food plants used by the butterflies found in Ireland. The list should not be considered as exhaustive. You will notice that some foodplants are common to a number of butterflies.

Essex Skipper	Likely to be Meadow Foxtail *Alopecurus pratensis*, Marsh Foxtail *A. geniculatus*, Cock's-foot *Dactylis glomerata* and Common Couch (Scutch) *Elytrigia repens*.
Dingy Skipper	Common Bird's-foot-trefoil *Lotus corniculatus*, Greater Bird's-foot-trefoil *L. pedunculatus*.
Wood White* and **Cryptic Wood White**	Meadow Vetchling *Lathyrus pratensis*, Common Bird's-foot-trefoil *L. corniculatus*, Greater Bird's-foot-trefoil *L. pedunculatus*.
Clouded Yellow**	Common Bird's-foot-trefoil *L. corniculatus*, Greater Bird's-foot-trefoil *L. pedunculatus*, Black Medick *Medicago lupulina*, Red Clover *Trifolium pratense*, White Clover *T. repens*, Lesser Trefoil *T. dubium*.
Brimstone*	Alder Buckthorn *Frangula alnus*, Buckthorn *Rhamnus cathartica*.
Large White	Cabbage *Brassica oleracea*, Nasturtium *Tropaeolum majus*, Wild Turnip *Brassica rapa*.
Small White	Cabbage *B. oleracea*, Nasturtium *T. majus*, Charlock *Sinapis arvensis*, Garlic Mustard *Alliaria petiolata*, Wild Turnip *B. rapa*, Radish *Raphanus raphanistrum*.
Green-veined White	Garlic Mustard *A. petiolata*, Cuckooflower *Cardamine pratensis*, Dame's-violet *Hesperis matronalis*, Hedge Mustard *Sisymbrium officinale*, Cabbage *B. oleracea*, Hairy Bitter-cress *C. hirsuta*, Water-cress *Rorippa nasturtium-aquaticum* agg., Charlock *S. arvensis*.
Orange Tip	Garlic Mustard *A. petiolata*, Cuckooflower *C. pratensis*, Bitter-cresses *C. hirsuta* and

	C. flexuosa, Dame's-violet *H. matronalis*, Honesty *Lunaria biennis*, Hedge Mustard *Sisymbrium officinale*, Water Cress *R. nasturtium-aquaticum* agg.
Green Hairstreak*	Common Bird's-foot-trefoil *L. corniculatus*, Greater Bird's-foot-trefoil *L. pedunculatus*, Bilberry *Vaccinium myrtillus*, Gorse *Ulex europaeus*, Broom *Cytisus scoparius*.
Brown Hairstreak*	Blackthorn *Prunus spinosa*.
Purple Hairstreak*	Oak *Quercus* species.
Small Copper:	Common Sorrel *Rumex acetosa*, Sheep's Sorrel *R. acetosella*, Broad-leaved Dock *R. obtusifolius*.
Small Blue*	Kidney Vetch *Anthyllis vulneraria*.
Common Blue	Common Bird's-foot-trefoil *L. corniculatus*, Greater Bird's-foot-trefoil *L. pedunculatus*, Black Medick *M. lupulina*, Lesser Trefoil *T. dubium*.
Holly Blue:	Holly *Ilex aquifolium*, Ivy *Hedera helix*, Firethorn *Pyracantha species*.
Red Admiral** **Small Tortoiseshell Peacock, Comma***:	Common Nettle *Urtica dioica*.
Painted Lady**	Thistles *Cirsium* species, occasionally Common Nettle, Burdock and Mallow.
Dark Green Silver-washed Pearl-bordered Fritillary*	Dog-violets and other *Viola* species.
Marsh Fritillary*	Devil's-bit Scabious *Succisa pratensis*.
Speckled Wood Wall Brown Grayling, Gatekeeper Meadow Brown, Ringlet Small Heath	Various native grasses *Poaceae*.
Large Heath*	Hare's-tail Cotton-grass *Eriophorum vaginatum*.

* = rare or local, ** = non-resident summer visitor

Do's and Don'ts

Do allow wild flowering plants and grasses to flourish in uncultivated areas and on hedgerows and roadside verges.

Don't use pesticides or weed killers.

Don't allow too much shade. Ideally butterflies need full sunshine from 11:00 to 15:00 hours.

Do encourage a 'natural' or wild garden with a minimum of management, but not a total wilderness.

Do try and replicate meadow management with one autumn cut per annum, removing all the severed vegetation.

Don't introduce any butterflies to your garden. *Do* let them find you.

Don't be fooled into thinking that "wild flower mixes" are really from your locality. They are usually imported and hence the species are non-native even if they look similar in some respects.

7

Species Accounts

THE ACCOUNTS for an individual butterfly species generally follow the format of an introduction followed by paragraphs on its distribution and descriptions of the four stages of the species' life cycle – adult, egg, larva and pupa. There are 34 full species accounts for all Ireland's resident or frequent migrants.

The photographs of the adults are chosen to assist in identification especially where there are significant differences in appearance between the male and female or where confusion between different species is possible. For many organisms, there is considerable variation in detail between individuals. Butterfly scales are easily lost and colour and appearance do substantially change through wear and tear throughout their lives, especially in inclement weather. The symbols ♂ and ♀ are for male and female respectively.

Eggs change in appearance as the embryo develops within and since a variety of moths and other insects lay their eggs on the same food plants, caution must be exercised in identifying eggs. Similarly, larvae vary considerably in appearance from instar to instar and the accounts here refer to the late or final ones. Some larvae and pupae have different colour forms related to background colour (for camouflage) or to diet or other environmental factors.

The distribution maps use the Irish National Grid and have a 10 km resolution. Mapping is mainly for the fifteen year period 1995-2009 but some additional records have been added for 2010 and a small number for 2011 for RoI. Records have been received from 1008 squares. The maps shown in the text were generated using Levana and DMAP software. Further information on the Irish National Grid and the Vice-County system is to be found in the Appendices.

Time of Flight Charts are constructed from the database using information on the adult numbers reported. The charts are designed to provide an indication of when a species may be seen. Earliest and latest dates of appearance can vary very much from year to year and usually relate to reports of a very small number of insects. The charts have not been normalised to taken account of the length of recorder visits and the weather which are generally unknown. One recorder, paying a brief visit to a site, might report a single sighting of a species while another might linger for a much longer period and carry out a more systematic survey. So some of the 'false peaks', especially for the scarcer

Distribution Map for All
Butterfly Species in
Ireland

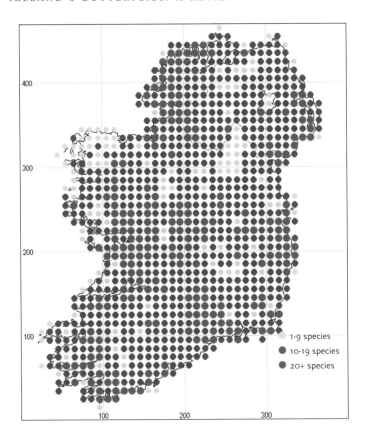

400

300

200

100

1-9 species
10-19 species
20+ species

100   200   300

species, are due to recorder rather than butterfly behaviour. The plotted interval is the week and the mid-point of the first week is taken as 4th January. The period used for the charts is the fifteen years 1995-2009.

The dots indicated the number of reports of the species in each 10 km square and the code use for sightings is ● *1 sighting,* ● *2-9 max seen* and ● *10+ max seen.* In the particular instance of the *overall distribution map* only, the colour code refers to the number of species recorded. The mapping symbol "+" normally refers to an older record outside the main period of this work. Stages, other than adult, are simply recorded as present (= 1 sighting). Based on current knowledge, the 10 km square has been chosen as a reasonable resolution to display the data on the distribution of the species. A small number of scarce species are mapped by tetrad (2x2 km square). Brief accounts are also given for the rarer migrants and vagrants to Ireland. The Monarch and the Camberwell Beauty are both mapped as single insect sightings because of the existence of some duplication within reports. Due to their infrequency some species may well go unnoticed, unrecognised or unreported. Good close-up photographic evidence, or ideally a specimen that can be released unharmed after confirmation of its identity, is required for most of these "rarities".

The habitat classification used in the text is based on Fossitt (2000) and should be viewed as a qualitative categorisation, with which the insect may not entirely concur. A key to the Fossitt classification may be found in the Appendices.

HESPERIIDAE

Essex Skipper *Thymelicus lineola* Léimneoir Essex

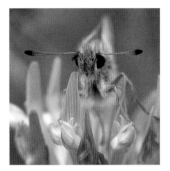

Black-tipped undersides of antennae

General

The Essex Skipper is believed to be a very recent newcomer to Ireland having been first reported from Co Wexford in 2006. Its origin and year of arrival are unknown but it is considered that it may have been transported to Ireland either in hay used as fodder or bedding for livestock or in imported grass seed, rather than being carried by favourable winds from Britain. Alternatively, it might be a deliberate introduction. Its present known habitat includes rough grassland inland or near the sea, grassy forestry rides and dry waste ground [Habitat: GS1, GS2, GS4]. First recognised in Essex in 1889, it is univoltine, with its flight season from July to mid-August. The similar looking Small Skipper has been reported from Kildare some years ago but confirmatory details are still awaited.

Distribution

Six squares. By the end of 2011 it had been recorded from at least twelve sites in six 10 km squares in south-east Wexford. In Britain in 1999 (*Millennium Atlas*) it was widespread south of a line between the Severn and the Humber but it has since spread into Wales and Scotland. This species is easily misidentified as the Small Skipper and in Britain they are sympatric (fly together). Its distribution is throughout Europe and through North Africa to Eastern Asia and it was an unintentional introduction to North America in 1910.

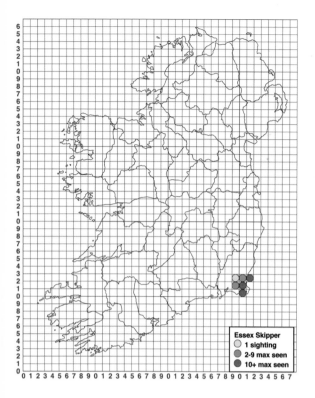

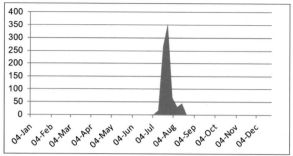

Egg

Fully formed larvae within eggs (pharate).

Adult

Wingspan 26-30 mm. Its antennae are orange-brown and, unlike the Small Skipper, the undersurface of the tips of the antennae are glossy black, as if dipped in ink, rather than brown. The genitalia of the two species are distinctly different under the microscope. The forewing is bright fulvous orange with a dark terminal border and white cilia. The male has a fairly prominent androconial brand on its forewings. The adult is not a strong flier.

Egg

The egg is oval in shape with flattened sides, 0.8 mm wide x 0.3 mm high, with very fine reticulation. Initially pale yellow, it becomes a deeper colour after a few days. The larva develops and its head becomes visible but it does not hatch for about 8 months and is termed a pharate larva. The food plants in Ireland have not been confirmed but may include grasses such as Meadow Foxtail, Marsh Foxtail, Cock's-foot, Timothy and Common Couch (Scutch) with eggs being laid in batches lengthwise within the sheaths of the chosen grass.

Larva

20-25 mm in length. Its head is pale green with brown and white bands and covered with white hairs. The body, which narrows towards the anal segment,

Essex Skipper

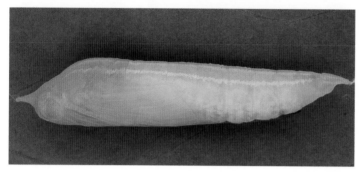

has a green ground colour, a darker medial dorsal and pale lateral stripe. Five instars are reported from Britain.

Pupa

15-17 mm in length. It has a white conical beak on its head and a tapering abdomen; the ground colour is light yellowish green; the white cremastral area has a cluster of small hooks. Pupation takes place in a silken cocoon within leaf blades at the base of plants. Duration is about 20 days.

Additional information

Its introduction to North America was through the importation of Timothy grass seed containing eggs. The eggs have an ability to survive both the 'cleaning' of seed and transport in bales of hay. As a consequence, this skipper has spread with major populations occurring in the north-east United States and Canada and more isolated colonies in Saskatchewan, Alberta and British Columbia (Layberry *et al.* 1998). It is often the most plentiful butterfly in these areas and has no known major parasites. It is likely to spread widely in Ireland.

Essex Skipper

Dingy Skipper *Erynnis tages tages* and *E. tages baynesi* Donnán

General

Until recently, this was the only skipper occurring in Ireland. Both sub-species, *tages* and *baynesi*, occur here. Its flight is fast and has a skipping-like motion. It sometimes flies with and is mistaken for either the day-flying Mother Shipton (*Callistege mi*) or the Burnet Companion (*Euclidia glyphica*) moths which bear a superficial resemblance but lack 'clubs' on their antennae. In the evening, or in overcast weather, the Dingy Skipper may be found resting on tall grasses with its wings folded over its back, unlike the other butterflies which hold their wings upright over their body.

Distribution

128 squares. The Dingy Skipper is entirely absent from the north-eastern part of Ireland and from Cork and Kerry. Its headquarters is the Burren area of Clare and south Galway (including the Aran Islands). It is found locally in the rest of Galway, scattered through the Midlands and Roscommon, Mayo and Sligo to south Donegal, Cavan and Fermanagh. Its favoured habitats are quarries, eskers, dunes, woodland clearings, rocky outcrops and limestone grassland including canal sides [Habitat: GS1, ER2, CD3,]. The sub-species *baynesi* occurs in the Burren and part of Galway and perhaps elsewhere, but the extent of its distribution is not at all clear. Abroad, the skipper's range covers all of Europe except northern Scandinavia, and continues eastwards into Asia.

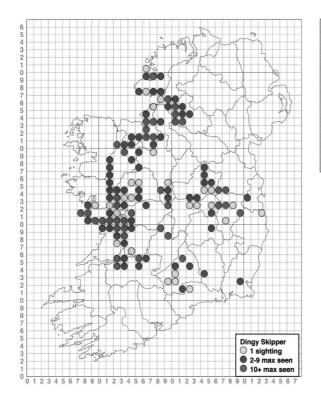

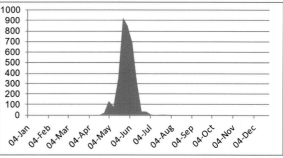

Dingy Skipper
○ 1 sighting
● 2-9 max seen
● 10+ max seen

Adult

Wingspan 27-34 mm. The upperside forewing of sub-species *tages* has a greyish brown ground colour and is darker towards the base, with a series of poorly defined greyish white transverse bands. It has a terminal dark brown line edged white spots on the inside and in greyish cilia. The hindwing has a similar ground colour and has long basal hair scales. The underwing is a pale golden brown with similar distribution of white. Sub-species *baynesi* has a brownish-black ground colour on the upper side of the forewing with pale grey to white markings. The main flight period is late-April into June, but a few individuals have been noted in July and August, suggesting a partial second brood.

Egg

The egg is spherical; 0.6 mm wide x 0.6 mm high, flattened at the base, with a sunken micropyle and has c.12 longitudinal ribs. Initially pale yellow when laid, it deepens to orange and finally to grey prior to hatching. Eggs are laid singly near the base of the upper surface of Common Bird's-foot-trefoil leaflets. Hatching takes 4-10 days.

Larva

16-20 mm in length. The stout body is yellow-green, narrowed towards either end, with a darker dorsal and a lighter lateral stripe, covered with white setae.

Hibernaculum with larva

It has a purple-black head. The freshly hatched larva does not eat its shell but wraps silk around a few leaflets of its food plant to form a tent for shelter and grazes the leaf surface from within. New tents are formed as the larva grows through its five instars. In August, when fully grown, it builds a more elaborate hibernaculum spinning together several leaves low down on the food plant and remains there until the following April. The larval stage lasts for ten months.

Pupa
14 mm in length. The pupa has a round head and a noticeably inflated thorax and abdomen. The abdomen is reddish brown with tiny setae; head and thorax are dark green; wings are lighter and more transparent with a tuft of black setae at the thoracic spiracle. Pupation in a hibernaculum takes 30-36 days.

Additional Information
Baynes and Huggins (Huggins 1956) simultaneously recognise that sub-species *baynesi* merited differentiation in Ireland. This rather sedentary species is very vulnerable to changes in land management and its last known site in Dublin was extinguished by insensitive dumping of spoil from the Royal Canal. This butterfly is a Priority Species in Northern Ireland (UK) where it is confined to Fermanagh. Its Red List status is *near threatened*.

Dingy Skipper

PIERIDAE

The Wood Whites   *Leptidea juvernica* and *Leptidea sinapis*

General

The Wood Whites, the smallest of the Pieridae, are fragile looking often with a weak fluttering flight, especially in breezy conditions. Females are frequently seen flying slowly and close to the vegetation as they search for egg laying sites. One other characteristic is that their wings are always closed at rest. They are often overlooked or dismissed as "small whites". Nelson *et al.* (2001) showed that there are two species of Wood White in Ireland that cannot be reliably distinguished in the field. The names were then considered to be *L. reali* and *L. sinapis.* However, recent work by Dincă and colleagues (2011) has shown that *L. reali* is in fact made up of two species and that the one which occurs in Ireland should now be named as *L. juvernica* (Cryptic Wood White). The evidence from Ireland, to date, is that *L. sinapis* and *L. juvernica* have somewhat differing ecological requirements and are not sympatric, although both have been found in a small number of 10 km squares where the geology and soils change quite abruptly (See second distribution map below). The two species are both known to use a number of legumes as larval food plants. There is one main generation extending from April to the end of June and sometimes a partial second brood in July/early August.

The courtship behaviour of the two species is interesting and has been described by Wiklund (1977), Lorkivić (1993) and others. In both species the male and female face one another and the male initially moves his head from side to side and waves his proboscis, alternately touching each hindwing of the female. After a short interval the male Wood White briefly flicks his wings open and repeats this ritual frequently over a period of some minutes (Barkham 2010). In contrast, the male Cryptic Wood White does not open his wings during the ritual. If this behavioural difference is substantiated, then it would be possible, in appropriate circumstances, to distinguish the two species in the field. However, it remains to be seen if this behavioural differentiation is universal. Experimentation has shown that males will woo females of either species, whereas females reject any male which is not of the same species.

Cryptic Wood White   *Leptidea juvernica*   Bánóg choille dhuaithne

Distribution

446 squares. *Leptidea juvernica* formerly called *L. reali* is widespread except in the Burren region and on the limestone pavements of Clare and Galway where it is apparently totally absent. It is scarce in northern and south-western Ireland. The butterfly is considered to be colonial and flies on unimproved grassland, bog edges, disused railway lines, some coastal areas including the Great Saltee Island, roadside verges, quarries and scrub [Habitat: WS1, GS2, CD4, WN7], but it is generally not a woodland butterfly despite its name. Abroad, *L. juvernica* occurs eastwards across Europe from Spain to the Ukraine, but not in Britain. Its exact European distribution is not currently known.

Adult

Wingspan is 42 mm. The upperside ground colour of the forewing of the *male* is white, covered with grey near the base; the apex has a rectangular grey-black patch and the tips of veins below are black. The hindwing has a similar ground colour with underside markings penetrating through as light grey. The underside of the forewing is yellowish with greyish scales giving an overall light greenish appearance; the hindwings have a yellowish ground colour with veins outlined in grey and greyish blotches, giving an overall grey-green appearance. The forewing of the *female* is more rounded with the apical dark patch on the upper surface reduced in intensity. There is one main generation

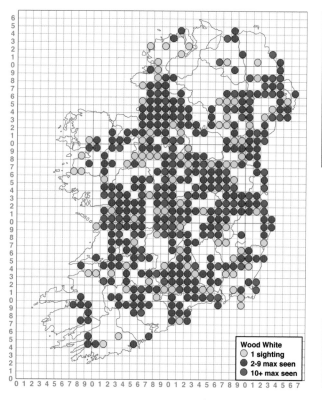

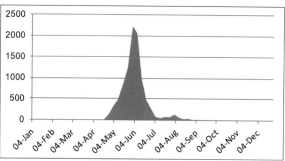

Both Wood White Species

from late April to early July but the time of flight varies from place to place and is not fully understood. In southern half of the island there is a small second brood from mid-July until late August. The adult lifespan of this butterfly may be only 5-10 days.

Egg

The egg is spindle shaped, 0.4 mm wide x 1.3 mm high with 11 longitudinal and many linking transverse ribs. It is pale cream to yellow, darkening before hatching in 11-20 days. Eggs are laid singly on the undersides of leaves of the food plants, often on taller plants, but preferences are not fully known or understood. One factor may be the relative maturity or freshness of the available food plants. Both Wood White species are believed to oviposit mainly on Meadow Vetchling and Common Bird's-foot-trefoil.

Larva

18-20 mm in length. The newly-hatched dull green larva eats its eggshell and then spins a silken web which is discarded in later instars as the foodplant is eaten. Its body is bright green, cylindrical, tapering towards the rear with the last segment overhanging the anal segment; the mid-dorsal line is darker, the spiracles are white with a bright pale yellow stripe edged with dark green; the

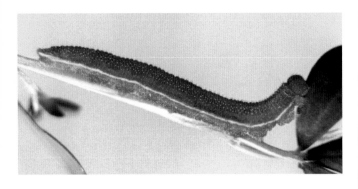

surface is rough with many very small tubercules and early instars are covered with tiny pale setae. There are four or five instars and when full-grown the larva is bright green with yellow lateral stripes. This stage lasts for 5-8 weeks until pupation.

Pupa
16 mm in length. Its head terminates in a slender beak, the thorax is swollen, wing cases are keeled and triangular and the abdomen is slender. The body is light green to pale yellow with a white-bordered lilac-pink stripe extending down either side from the beak to the anal segment. The head and thorax have a black centre line. The pupa is suspended by a silk girdle and a cremaster attached to a silk pad and can be found on a variety of plants. This stage takes up to 9 months.

Additional Information
Williams (1946) recognised that the Wood White in Ireland was different to that in Britain. He examined 57 specimens of Wood White from Ireland, many of which were collected by M.S. Dudley Westropp (Keeper of Art in the National Museum of Ireland) from Cos Kildare and Dublin. Six specimens from unstated locations in Cos Galway and Clare were included in the study. Williams concluded that the Irish butterfly was much more strongly marked, on both wing surfaces in both sexes, than its English counterpart. He also stated that it had some resemblance to the continental *L. duponcheli*. He proposed that the Wood White in Ireland be given the status of a sub-species which he described and named as *L. sinapis* sub-species *juvernica*. Type specimens from the Williams investigation are held by the Natural History Museum, London, and the University Museum, Oxford.

Work done by Henry Heal in the 1960s casts some doubt on the precise identity of the Wood White species in Ireland but he never pursued this line of inquiry. He postulated that the spread of the 'species' into and through Northern Ireland was along recently abandoned railway lines. *L. reali* Réal's Wood White was first recognised as a species separate from *L. sinapis* by Réal in 1988 from specimens taken in the French Pyrenees (Lorković 1993). However, the correct name for the species in Ireland is now considered to be *L. juvernica* recognising the Williams nomenclature. This butterfly is a Priority Species in Northern Ireland (UK).

Wood White   *Leptidea sinapis*   Bánóg choille

Distribution

23 squares. It occurs throughout the scrubby and wooded areas and roadsides of the Burren and other similar areas of Clare and Galway. It extends westwards from near Athenry and is in the limestone pavement areas around Lough Corrib. To date it does not appear to be in the vicinity of Lough Carra or in the Aran Islands where it might reasonably be expected to occur [ER2, GS1, WS1]. In Britain it is considered as a rare and declining woodland species. Abroad it is found throughout Europe and into Asia. The species could be endangered by indiscriminate removal of hazel scrub which provides shelter. The map shows the distribution of the two species in Cos Clare and Galway as determined by the dissection of museum and contemporary samples collected for scientific purposes. Its Red List status is *near threatened.*

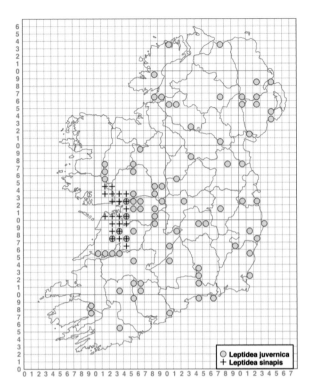

Legend:
○ Leptidea juvernica
+ Leptidea sinapis

Adult, Egg, Larva and Pupa

The adults can only be reliably differentiated from *L. juvernica* by dissection of their genitalia. There is currently no information available to suggest that any of characters of the other stages of the two species can be readily used to separate the species. Eggs have also been discovered on Bitter-vetch in the Burren (S. Jeffcoate pers. com.) and Tufted Vetch (J Harding pers. com.). Thomas and Lewington (2010) state that the pink line along the antenna in pupae is less well defined in the Cryptic Wood White. However, pupae are rarely seen in the wild.

Note: There are now known to be seven species of Wood White in Europe, *L. sinapis. L. reali, L. juvernica, L. amurensis, L. morsei, L. lactea* and *L. duponcheli*. The latter four are quite localised in Eastern Europe. Dincǎ and colleagues (2011) investigated '*reali*' using techniques which included chromosome counts and DNA profiling. *Juvernica* has a much larger number of chromosomes than either of the other two species. They discovered that '*reali*' was in fact two cryptic species which are now given the scientific names of *L. reali* and *L. juvernica*. The DNA and chromosome work indicates that a single common ancestor of *sinapis, reali* and *juvernica* split into two about 270,000 years ago. One of these lines eventually evolved into *juvernica*. The other division split about 120,000 years ago and developed into what we currently know as *sinapis* and *reali*. 27,000 years ago, *sinapis* expanded into the territory of *juvernica*. Is *L. sinapis* in Ireland an interloper that arrived late but failed to colonise the whole island, or has it more recently contracted its range and retreated to the "Burren"? The current state of understanding of the European distributions is that *reali* is a south-western European species, *juvernica* is a more northerly species stretching into Asia and *sinapis* is perhaps the most widespread of all. But these are preliminary distributions from data currently published.

Wood White

Clouded Yellow *Colias croceus* Buíóg cróch

General

The Clouded Yellow is not commonly seen in Ireland because it is a rather erratic migrant originating in southern Europe and northern Africa. While reported fairly regularly from the south and south-east coasts in small numbers, in some years it is more widespread and numerous throughout the country. The ground colour is normally orange-yellow, very different from the primrose coloured Brimstone, and the upper side of of its wings are edged with a broad black border. Arrival time is typically, but not always, early summer with the resultant Irish progeny emerging in August and September.

Distribution

405 squares. Being a migrant and not an all-year resident breeding species, the Clouded Yellow is not restricted to any particular locations. It can, in favourable years, be encountered almost anywhere, although there are relatively few records from the north-west and midlands of Ireland. It is resident in the Mediterranean area, North Africa and eastwards through Turkey to Iran.

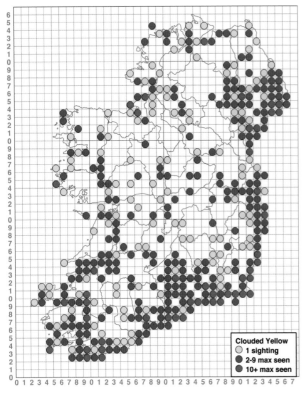

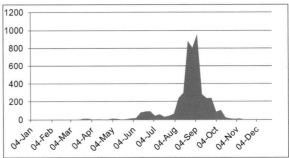

Adult

The wingspan is 52-62 mm, with the female being slightly larger than the male. The orange-yellow colour of the wings combined with the lighter yellow underside give an overall impression of a yellow butterfly, especially when at rest with wings closed. There is a black discal spot on the forewing and under the hindwing is a dark edged white spot, usually double as in the figure '8'. The cilia is pinkish. The black border, which extends from the apex towards the termen, is solid in the male but contains yellow spots in the female. 5-15% of females are of the form *helice* where the ground colour is replaced by light primrose yellow or off-white, thus resembling the very scarce Pale Clouded Yellow (*C. hyale*). In fine migratory years its Irish progeny may be seen in October and very occasionally in November. There is evidence from Wexford that the species is able to survive milder Irish winters in the larval state.

Egg

The egg is spindle-shaped, 0.4 mm wide x 1.1 mm high with many longitudinal and horizontal ribs and is laid singly on the upperside of legumes such as Common Bird's-foot-trefoil and on Clover species.

Larva

32-35 mm in length. The larva is cylindrical with a green head and body, the spiracles are ringed with white and the yellow spiracular stripe is spotted with

Clouded Yellow

orange. The body is covered with black pinacula each containing a white seta. The length of the larval stage is temperature dependent but in a suitable summer the larva will be completely fed in 5-6 weeks.

Pupa

20 mm in length. Ground colour is light yellow-green. The wing cases are a darker green with black spots across the outer margin and in the centre. Black spots are found under the anal segments and dark blotches under the abdomen. The yellow cremaster is attached to a silken pad and there is a silk girdle. Pupation takes about 18 days.

Additional Information

An old name for this species was *Colias edusa*. An early 19th century report of Clouded Yellow by Williams (1871) mentions a sighting c.1820 between Wicklow and Arklow Head. Good years for this species include 1892, 1913, 1928, 1937, 1955, 1959, 1983, 1998 and 2006. The years 1877, 1947, 1992 and 2000 were exceptional or 'edusa' years when the Clouded Yellow was seen in great numbers. In 2000 it was seen in exceptional numbers in the north-west where it bred on Tory Island, and in 2010 a small influx occurred in West Cork in October.

Brimstone   *Gonepteryx rhamni gravesi*   Buíóg ruibheach

General

Where this conspicuous bright yellow butterfly occurs, it is one of the first signs of spring as it emerges from hibernation in February or March. The brightly coloured male appears before the greenish-white female. Once referred to as the "butter-coloured fly", it is probably the origin of the word 'butterfly'. The Brimstone's breeding range is restricted to areas where either or both of the two species of its food plants, Buckthorn and Alder Buckthorn, grows. It is a noted vagrant and individuals are reported outside its food plant range. This butterfly is generally on the wing from February to June or early July and then again from July to September before entering hibernation. It is found in calcareous grassland, limestone pavement, hedgerows, and damp or scrub woodland [Habitat: GS1, ER2, WL1, WS1] where its food plants grow.

Distribution

225 squares. The Brimstone breeds from Kildare westwards to the Shannon estuary and Galway. In the limestone pavement areas of the Burren and around Lough Corrib it can be quite abundant. Some reports a long way from its known breeding areas may well be misidentifications of rather yellow Large Whites. The Brimstone is believed to be no longer resident in Northern Ireland. The last evidence of it breeding there was a report about 1985 from the

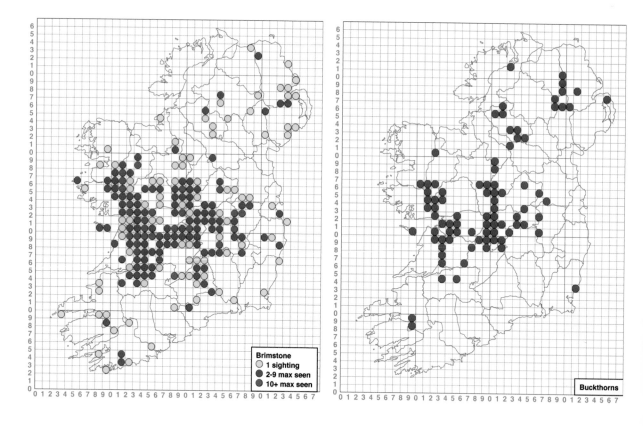

Brimstone
○ 1 sighting
● 2-9 max seen
● 10+ max seen

Buckthorns

Erne basin of Fermanagh. Buckthorn still grows there and Alder Buckthorn is established in the Lough Neagh area. The map shows the occurrence of the Buckthorns in Ireland. The Brimstone is a Palaearctic species, its western range extending from northern Africa through Europe to 67°N.

Adult
Wingspan 60-74 mm. The upperside ground colour of the male is sulphur-yellow and the hindwing has a greenish hue. The female is white tinged with yellow-green. The forewing has some black scales at the base, small orange discal spots and a brown costal margin with spots and the hindwing has a larger discal spot. The undersides of wings are paler than upperside with larger brown discal spots. The costa of the foewing tapers to a point near V7, and the hindwing is sharply angled at V3. When the wings are closed they resemble pale green leaves.

Egg
The egg is skittle-shaped, 0.4 mm wide x 1.3 mm high, with about 10 longitudinal and 45 horizontal ribs. It is initially pale green, becoming yellow and finally grey before hatching in 4-10 days. Eggs are usually laid singly on the underside of the leaves of Buckthorn or Alder Buckthorn from April to about July.

Brimstone

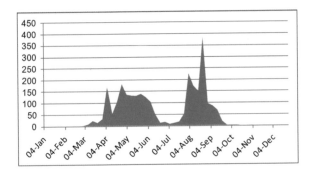

Larva

32-36 mm in length. Its head is green, and its body cylindrical in shape, glaucous-green above, yellowish green below, with a darker mid-dorsal stripe and a white stripe below the white spiracles which are yellow-tinged. The whole body is covered in tiny black bristles. The legs are yellow-green. The larva may be found on the mid-rib or petiole of a leaf of the food plant. It is well camouflaged but can be detected by careful examination of leaves which have been partially eaten, or by the presence of frass. The larval stage lasts for a month with a total of five instars.

Pupa

22-24 mm in length. Its head has a pointed beak, the abdomen is also tapered and the wings are strongly rounded. The body colour is bright green above and paler underneath, with a purple blotch at the base of the mottled wing cases and dull spots on the body. The pupa is leaf-like in appearance, attached by its cremaster to a silken pad and wrapped with a silken girdle. This stage lasts about two weeks. Before the emergence of an adult male, the pupa turns bright yellow with vermilion marginal spots.

Additional Information

Andrews (1860) reported to the Dublin Natural History Society of the occurrence of the Brimstone in some numbers at Killarney. In the early 20th Century, the British Brimstone sub-species *rhamni* and the related Cleopatra *G. cleopatra*, together with a range of Buckthorn food plants, were introduced at Greenfield, Co. Tipperary by Captain Purefoy (1902) who, apparently, was blissfully unaware of the Brimstone's existence in Ireland. Happily, this well-meant venture failed. The Sea Buckthorn, which is rampant on some sand dune systems, belongs to a different family and is not a larval food plant.

Brimstone

Large White *Pieris brassicae* Bánóg mhór

General

The largest of the whites it can often be recognised by its size and the prominent black markings on its wing apex. But there is an overlap in size with the Small White. It may be quite yellow in appearance and, in flight, may be mistaken for the Brimstone. This bivoltine species flies mainly from April to June and July to September. Numbers are often boosted by immigrants which may be accompanied by other butterflies. Extra large specimens seen may be migratory in origin. The larvae are a pest on brassicas and will be very familiar to vegetable gardeners.

Distribution

811 squares. This butterfly may be found anywhere in Ireland, sometimes in considerable numbers, but is most frequent in or near centres of population where cultivation occurs or on waste ground. Large numbers (with more numerous Small Whites) are seen in fields of Oilseed Rape which have not been treated with insecticide. The Large White is much less common in remote rural areas, mountains and wetlands.

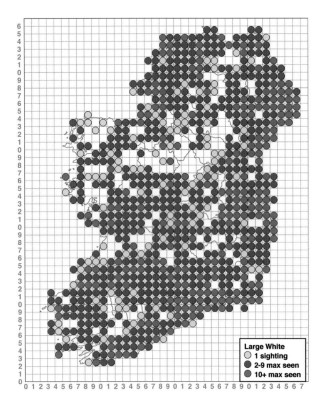

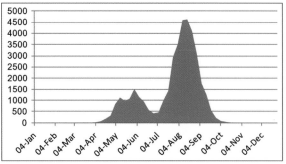

Large White
○ 1 sighting
● 2-9 max seen
● 10+ max seen

Adult

Wingspan from 58 to 70 mm. The upperside of the forewing of the *male* of the spring generation is white and speckled blackish-grey in the basal and costal areas. The apical area to approximately S2 is pigmented black and speckled with white; the hindwing has a grey-black spot on the costa in space S8. The underside of the forewing is scattered with grey. The apical area is broadly yellow and there are two black patches in spaces S2 and S4. The hindwing is yellow with grey veins and has an orange-yellow costal margin. The upperside of the *female* forewing has a blacker apical area, two black patches in spaces S2 and S4 and a black bar on the inner margin (space S1a). The hindwing is yellowish. The summer generation for both sexes has more intense and extensive dark markings and the underside is a paler yellow.

Egg

The egg is skittle shaped, 0.5 mm wide x 1.2 mm high, with 12-18 longitudinal ribs and many fine lateral ribs. The pale yellow eggs are laid in batches of 40-100 on the upper or lower surfaces of the leaves of crucifers that include culinary Cabbage, Brussels Sprout, Wild Turnip, and the garden Nasturtium. Hatching takes place in 4-10 days.

Large White

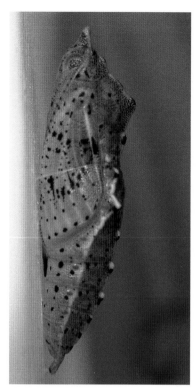

Larva

40-45 mm in length. The head is mottled grey black and the body is greyish-green, heavily marked and spotted with black. The body has raised tubercules with grey hairs, orange spiracles and conspicuous yellow dorsal and lateral stripes with a shiny black anal segment. There are five instars and larvae may be found from May to December. The larvae are gregarious, feed in the open and are distasteful to birds. When fully fed they leave their foodplant to find a niche to pupate on buildings, tree trunks, fence posts etc. The Large White's braconid parasitoid *Cotesia glomerata* is common and plays a major role in its population regulation and is used in horticulture for biological control.

Pupa

20-23 mm in length. It may be either green or brown depending on the background. Its body is peppered with black spots and tubercules with yellow marking underneath on the ventral ridge. The pupa attaches itself by cremastral hooks and a silk girdle to a substrate where it overwinters. It is known to move when predators are present in order to unsettle them.

Small White *Pieris rapae* Bánóg bheag

Summer generation

General

The Small White, or Small Cabbage White, is a common pest on cultivated brassicas all over Ireland, especially in and near urban areas. It is resident, but migrants from Britain and further afield boost local populations. It has probably been under recorded in some areas because of the difficulty of distinguishing this species from the Green-veined White in flight. There are two broods, the first from April to June and the second, always larger, from July into September. Habitat is very varied, from embryonic sand dunes with Sea Rocket to fields of Oilseed Rape.

Distribution

765 squares. The Small White is widespread and common except, perhaps, in Cos Mayo and Monaghan, but this is attributable to insufficient attention being paid to these counties, or a lack of brassica crops. It is common in gardens and on waste or disturbed ground, but much less so in bogs, wetland habitats and upland areas. Its world range is across Europe, Asia and North America since its introduction there in 1860. Its introduction to Australia and New Zealand dates from the late 1930s.

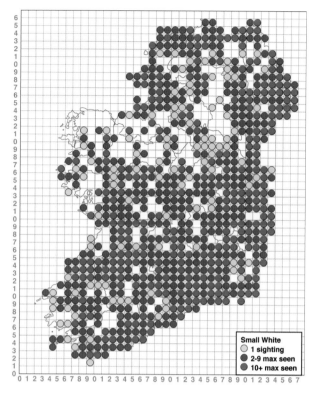

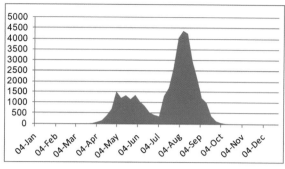

Small White
○ 1 sighting
◐ 2-9 max seen
● 10+ max seen

Adult

Wingspan is 38-57 mm, usually about 50 mm for both sexes. Spring generation: on the upperside the *male*'s white forewing has a black post-discal spot with the basal area and the costa is speckled black. A grey apical patch extends from the apex into the costa and beyond the termen and a black post-cliscal spot is present in S3. The hindwing is of similar colour with a speckled black basal area and a black spot on costa in spaces S7 and S8. The underside of the forewing is white with some dark scales along the costal area, a pale yellow apical patch and black post-discal spots in spaces S1b and S3. The hindwing is pale yellow and speckled with black dots. The *female* differs from the male in that the ground colour is pale yellowish-cream and there are more widespread black scales in the basal and costal areas. The underside of the forewing has a darker post-discal spot. Summer generation: the black markings on the upperwing are more extensive and intensive and the hindwing is more sparsely speckled.

Egg

The egg is bottle-shaped, 0.5 mm wide x 1.0 mm high, with 12 longitudinal ribs radiating from the apex. It is initially pale yellow, later becoming primrose yellow and then brownish-grey before hatching in 3-7 days. Eggs are laid singly

on the underside of a leaf of young food plants in fairly sheltered locations.

Food plants include many brassicas/crucifers such as cultivated Cabbage, Charlock, Garlic Mustard, Wild Turnip, Radish and garden Nasturtium.

Larva

25-28 mm in length. Its head is green speckled with black. The body is cylindrical and bluish-green in colour, finely speckled with small black pinacula each containing a single bristle. The dorsal line is narrow and yellow and the incomplete spiracular line is identical in hue. There are five instars and pupation takes place after about five weeks. On cultivated Cabbages, the later instars bore into the heart of the plant depositing a trail of frass and unpleasant smelling mustard oil. The braconid wasps *Cotesia rubecula* and *C. glomerata* are considered to be its main parasites. (See Figs. 12 and 13)

Pupa

19 mm in length and pointed at either end. Overall colour is very variable from light green to pale brown in an apparent response to its background in order to improve camouflage. The spring generation has a higher percentage of the green form than subsequent generations. Its body is speckled with black and larger black spots are present on each segment. The pupa over-winters attached to a silken pad by the cremaster and is held in position by a silk girdle. The substrate, like the Large White, may include fencing posts, garden buildings etc.

Additional Information

Small Whites obtain nectar from a variety of wild and cultivated flowering plants and are often seen along sea shores where crucifers are present. Adults are occasionally reported as early as February, but these almost certainly have emerged from pupae which have over-wintered in a greenhouse or outhouse.

Small White

Green-veined White *Pieris napi britannica* Bánóg uaine

General

The Green-veined White is virtually indistinguishable from the Small White in flight and great care must be taken when reporting these species. They are often lumped together as 'small whites' by inexperienced observers, leading to anomalies in counts and distribution patterns. The Green-veined White is without doubt the most numerous and widespread butterfly species in Ireland. It is bivoltine, breeds on a range of wild crucifers and is not normally a pest of cabbage crops [Habitat: GS4, FW4, GM1, PB4].

Distribution

983 squares. The Green-veined White is common throughout Ireland, especially in damper situations and in remote countryside away from human habitation, from Rathlin Island in the north to Cape Clear Island in the south. Its world wide distribution is Holarctic.

Adult

Wingspan 40-52 mm. The ground colour is white, often tinged with yellow. Very yellow forms occur in Ireland. The species and its marking are very variable within and between the two generations. In the spring generation the

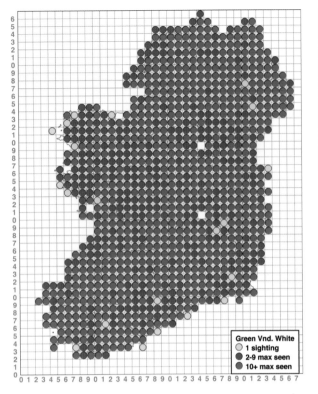

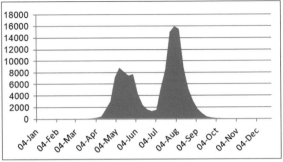

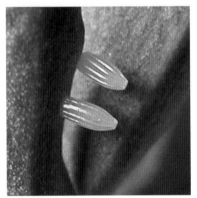

Green Vnd. White
○ 1 sighting
● 2-9 max seen
● 10+ max seen

veins and costal margins of the upperside of forewing of the *male* are speckled grey, with grey-black markings at both apex and base. The hindwing has a black post-discal spot on the costa and the underside veins are yellow with black scales giving them an overall green appearance. In the summer brood, the veins may be more prominent on the upperside with an additional post-discal black spot.

The *female* has a more creamy-white ground colour. Her forewing has more extensive black markings in the basal area and the veins and apical patch are darker than for the male. Post-discal spots are present in cells S1a and S3, with a third spot bordering the apex. Her hindwing has a more prominent costal spot than the male. The underside ground colour is lemon yellow and the outer veins are less prominent.

Egg

0.5 mm wide x 1.0 mm high with 10 longitudinal ribs. The eggs are yellowish-green but sometimes rust-coloured, and turn white before hatching in 4-10 days. They are laid singly on the leaves of crucifers such as Cuckooflower, Hairy Bitter-cress, Water-cress, Garlic Mustard and Charlock. Eggs have been found on garden Aubretia and Arabis species and very occasionally on cultivated brassicas including Turnip.

Green-veined White

Larva

24-27 mm in length. Its head is green and its body, which tapers slightly at either end, is bluish-green and covered in tiny black pinacula with black and white setae. When fully grown after four moults, the dorsal line is darker than the ground colour and the black spiracles are ringed with bright yellow. The ventral surface and legs are paler than upper body. The larvae of the first generation eat the leaves of the same crucifers as the Orange Tip. This is a good example of similar species having their separate niches.

Pupa

19-21 mm in length. The pupa is frequently a light green, but colour and markings range from green to pale brown, possibly an adaptation for camouflage. Its head is beaked and the thorax has a dorsal keel with a single crest and there is an additional keel on either side of the anal angle of the wing cases. The pupa is attached by its cremaster and a silken girdle and generally well hidden in vegetation. Pupation is complete in 10-12 days for 'summer generations' and 7-11 months for the over-wintering generation.

Additional Information

There is no agreement as to whether this very variable species is a group of sub-species or 'forms'. Müller & Kautz (1939) described the Irish butterfly as *britannica*. Warren (1984) recognised the Scottish form as *thomsoni* and the bulk of the mainland British population is referred to as *sabellicae*. Distinctions are made on the basis of general appearance and differences in the quantity and appearance of androconial scent scales. Nash (1997) has stated that specimens exhibiting the appearance of all forms, British or worldwide, are to be found in local populations in Ireland. The 'Donegal' variations of the Green-veined White include "bright yellow", "sulphur" and "citron" coloured specimens (Donovan 1936) and were collectively described as belonging to the aberration *sulphurea*. Colours were often enhanced by selective breeding and false accusations were made in one instance that colours had been enhanced by the use of solutions of picric acid, saffron or turmeric.

Orange Tip   *Anthocharis cardamines hibernica*   Barr buí

General

This butterfly is named on account of the bright orange coloration of the submargin of the forewing of the male, but the female is white and may be confused with the smaller "whites". The orange colour is a warning to birds that this butterfly is distasteful and is not to be consumed. The Orange Tip is one of the first species to emerge in spring, and as for other species, the males appear several days before the female. It is univoltine, with the main flight season from April to June.

Distribution

949 squares. This butterfly is common all over Ireland, especially so in the north and throughout wet pastures, roadsides and gardens [Habitat: GS4, BC4, PB4, GS2]. The Irish sub-species *hibernica* is also resident in the Isle of Man. The Orange Tip is a Palaearctic species, occurring from Western Europe to China, but not in North Africa.

Adult

Wingspan is 37-49 mm. The *male* has a white forewing with the submarginal and postdiscal areas of the wing covered with orange scales, tipped with lunate

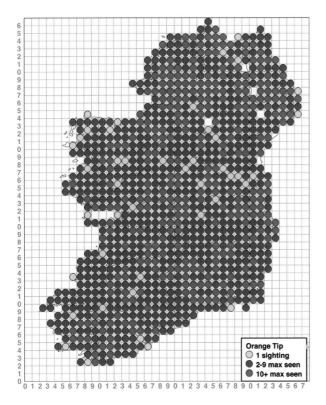

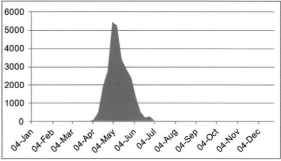

black markings at the apex. There is a discal black spot and both basal and subcostal area to the end of the cell are speckled black. The hindwing is also speckled black at its base and a mottled greenish grey colour shows through from underneath. The underside of the forewing has a discal spot and orange marking as above and is bordered on the apex and termen by green mottling due to a mixture of black and yellow scales. The hindwing of both sexes is heavily mottled with black and yellow scales giving the semblance of green. The *female* forewing ground colour is as for the male, but she lacks the orange tips and instead has a larger apical black patch. At rest with wings closed and the forewings retracted, the mottling provides excellent camouflage, for example, when resting on an umbel of Cow Parsley.

Egg

The egg is bottle shaped, 0.5 mm wide x 1.2 mm high, with c.18 prominent longitudinal and many transverse ribs. Greenish-white when first laid, the egg becomes orange and, finally, rusty-brown before hatching in 4-10 days. Eggs are deposited on the pedicels of the food plant, immediately below the flower, and are visible at a distance of a metre. The main food plants are Cuckooflower, Water-cress and Garlic Mustard. Many other crucifers such as Hairy Bitter-cress and Dame's-violet are used.

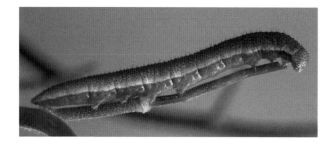

Larva

29-32 mm in length. It has a green bristle-covered head and a slender and slightly tapered body. The dorsal area ranges from green to a bright blue-green and the spiracular surround is white. Underneath, the body is dark green. Tiny pinacula bear black setae. The well-camouflaged larva starts by eating its own eggshell and then moves on to ripening seedpods whereas the Green-veined White feeds on leaves. After a month's feeding the final instar pupates and over-winters in dense cover.

Pupa

20 mm in length. It is crescent-shaped, pointed at either end, with wing cases projecting on the ventral surface. The pupal colour can vary depending on the background. Typically the initial colour is green with white markings and after a couple of weeks it changes to a light brown. The dorsal surface becomes pink to dark red, a white stripe extends from the apex to the anal area, the wing veins are prominent and the spiracular area is yellowish. The pupa hangs vertically, held by a silken girdle until emergence in April or May in the following year.

Additional Information

A few individuals may not emerge until late the following summer having spent at least 15 months in the pupal stage. This is thought to be a strategy to avoid wipe-out in a cold spring. Greer (1922 & 1923) made a study in Tyrone of the Orange Tip and its aberrations. He noted amongst other things the occurrence of gynandromorphs with intermediate male-female characteristics, *e.g.* a butterfly with only one wing orange-tipped. Late flying females, particularly in southern coastal areas, should be carefully examined to eliminate the possibility of a migrant Bath White.

LYCAENIDAE

Green Hairstreak *Callophrys rubi* Stiallach uaine

Egg laying in sunshine – metallic green wings   In shade – bluish wing hue

General

This is an attractive 'green' spring butterfly found most frequently in upland hillsides and near the edges of lowland bogs. Like many of the Lycaenids, its colour is due in part to the interference of light within its complex wing structure. At rest, its perceived colour may be green or blue depending on the circumstances and lighting. It is univoltine with its main flying period from late April to mid-June, but a limited number of sightings in the period from mid-July to early September suggest a partial second brood. Winter is passed in the pupal stage.

Distribution

364 squares. It is a colonial butterfly which is often found with a local population numbering up to a couple of dozen. This hairstreak is typically found where there is either Gorse (Whin) or Bilberry (Fraughan) on moorland, bogs and hillsides [Habitat: PB1, PB2, PB3, PB4, HH1, HH3]. In sheltered sunny positions on the edges of raised bogs, Green Hairstreak may congregate on Birch or Bramble. It is a widely distributed species, especially in the west and north, but is scarce in the south-east and much of Cork. However, it is considered that this species is often overlooked and under-recorded.

Adult

Wingspan is 27-34 mm. There is little obvious difference between the sexes.

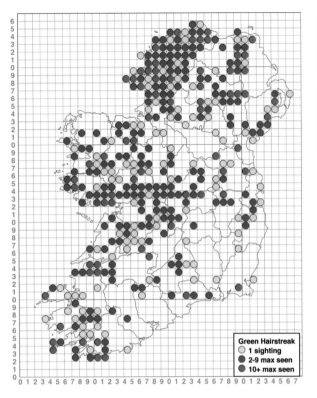

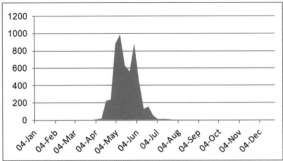

The upperside of the forewing is a bronzy-brown with a small patch of androconial scales at the upper end of the discal cell in the male. The cilia is pale grey delineated with brown. The hindwing is similar but has a dentate termen and small prominent tornus. On the underside, the forewing is metallic green with a narrow grey-brown edge near the margin. The hindwing is similar. A variable line of white spots traverses the underwings. In flight, the brown upperside colour renders it hard to see, and when it settles with closed wings on young leaves of Birch, Gorse or Hawthorn, its green underside gives excellent camouflage. Males are found perching in sunny dominant positions on gorse.

Egg
The egg is 0.7 mm wide x 0.7 mm high, a flattened reticulated sphere with many small pits, especially near the micropyle. Initially it is glassy and plain green, becoming grey-green before hatching. Eggs are laid singly on fresh shoots or buds of its food plants Bilberry and Gorse, hatching after 4-10 days. In Donegal this hairstreak occurs on heathy hillsides and sheltered sea cliffs often distant from either of the food plants mentioned above.

Larva
16-19 mm in length. The first instar larva feeds by boring into tender buds. The body is woodlouse shaped, bright yellow-green with oblique yellow stripes

Green Hairstreak

and smaller yellow spiracular spots. The shiny brown head, which is usually hidden under the prothorax, has a white band above the mandibles when fully grown. The larvae are said to be cannibalistic. Pupation takes place in late July.

Pupa
9 mm in length. The brown dumpy-shaped pupa is mottled with black and the whole cuticle is densely covered with fine hairs and small glands. Pupation takes place unsecured among the litter at the base of the food plant, with only a few silk strands loosely binding bits of moss and debris for cover. The pupal stage lasts until April/May.

Additional Information
The males are territorial and aggressive towards other insects, but the females are less often seen as they travel in search of nectar and suitable plants for egg-laying. In Ireland this hairstreak is rarely found in limestone areas even where Gorse is plentiful. There is good circumstantial evidence to suggest that Common Bird's-foot-trefoil and perhaps Bramble are larval food plants. Bilberry, Bog Rosemary and Bird's-foot-trefoil are favoured nectar sources. Broom, a food plant in Britain, has not yet been associated with it in Ireland. As with other Lycaenids, the pupa audibly squeaks when it is disturbed, although a stethoscope may be useful to hear the sound.

Brown Hairstreak   *Thecla betulae*   Stiallach donn

General

The very local and restricted range of this butterfly makes it one of the rarest on the island. There are old records from several southern counties from the late 19th and early 20th century. It is single-brooded and is often the last species to emerge, flying from about mid-July into September. Males and females may be seen on warm sunny days imbibing nectar on bramble flowers.

Distribution

21 squares; 60 tetrads. The Irish stronghold of this butterfly is the limestone pavement areas of the Burren, adjacent Co Galway and to the west of Lough Corrib. Isolated outliers occur east of Lough Derg in Co Tipperary. There is a specimen in the National Museum collected by Phillips near Portumna, Co Galway. In Co Clare, it is perhaps most abundant at Tulla, Boston and Dromore Wood where it may be seen feeding mainly on Bramble associated with blackthorn scrub and hedgerows [Habitat: WS1, WS2, ER2, WL1]. Its range abroad extends from southern Britain over middle Europe to the Black Sea and southern Finland between 40° and 60° N. Unsuccessful searches have been made in localities in Cos Kerry, Cork, Waterford and Wexford where there were old records by Kane, Mathew, Sabine and Moffat (Baynes 1964).

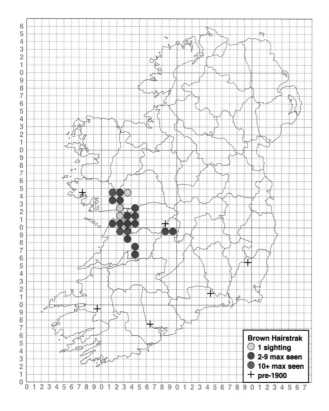

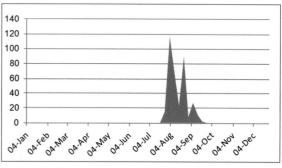

Brown Hairstrak
○ 1 sighting
● 2-9 max seen
● 10+ max seen
+ pre-1900

Adult

Wingspan 36-42 mm. The female tends to be somewhat larger than the male. The ground colour is dark brown and the main difference between the sexes is the presence in the female of bright orange bands on the upperside of the forewing, replaced in the male by a small area of pale yellow-brown androconial scales. There are up to three small orange marks on the scalloped outer edge of the hindwing, the largest being at the base of the 'tail'. The undersides are an attractive light reddish-brown with black bands edged in white across both wings. Emergence is in late July or early August, depending on ambient temperature.

Egg

The white eggs, 0.8 mm in diameter, wider than high, are laid singly near a dormant bud or at the base of a spine of the only known larval food plant in the wild, Blackthorn. The eggs overwinter before hatching the following April or May and systematic and patient searching (when the food plant has lost its leaves) will locate them in the axils of the previous year's growth. They are thus very vulnerable to winter hedge trimming or injudicious scrub clearance.

Larva

16-19 mm in length. The larva eats it way out of the shell and enters a

Blackthorn bud, feeding on the tender shoots. It is triangular in cross-section, hairy and pale grey after hatching. In its fourth instar, after 6-9 weeks, it is green and slug-shaped with pale yellow dorsal stripes, two oblique lines on each segment and white underneath. Feeding takes place at night. The fully-fed larva will leave its food plant a few days before pupation, turn mottled purple for camouflage and pupate in a crevice or in leaf litter.

Pupa

The pupa is stout and dumpy, about 12 mm long, smooth and glossy, speckled and blotched with light and darker brown. It is attractive to ants which may possibly transport and bury it. The pupal stage lasts 3-6 weeks, during which time many fall prey to predators. It is reported to be able to make a low pitch rattle-like sound, but whether this is to communicate with ants or warn off predators is not known.

Additional Information

Relatively little is known about the extent of Irish populations. It may indeed be scarcer than the Pearl-bordered Fritillary and a substantial number of records relate to eggs rather than adults. In Britain, populations have been much reduced by inappropriate and indiscriminate flailing of Blackthorn hedgerows and scrub clearance. This is the most likely cause of the contraction of its range in Ireland and disappearance from former sites in Wexford and Waterford.

Brown Hairstreak

Purple Hairstreak   *Favonius quercus*   Stiallach corcra

General

This handsome butterfly resides mainly in oak canopy and is seldom seen close up. A sighting is often a glint of silver or purple from a male flying high in the late evening sun. Binoculars are generally a prerequisite for success in viewing it. It is to be found in 'native' oak woodlands and also in groves with several oak trees. The Phoenix Park is the only known example of an urban park in Ireland where the Purple Hairstreak is present. [Habitat: WN1, WN2, WD5].

Former names are *Neozephyrus quercus* and *Quercusia quercus*, recognising its association with the oak genus *Quercus*.

Distribution

69 squares. An apparently scarce and local butterfly throughout Ireland except for the north-east and Donegal, it is found in southerly counties such as Wicklow and Kerry and sparingly in some woods in Fermanagh, Sligo and Londonderry. In the Burren, the Purple Hairstreak occurs on low Oak in scrubby woodland. Due to its normal tree-topping habitat it is probably very much under-recorded. Outside Ireland, it is apparently much more common in southern Britain and extends from North Africa to southern Scandinavia and across Central Europe into Asia.

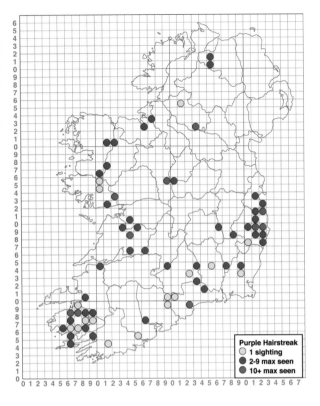

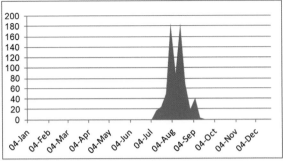

Purple Hairstreak
○ 1 sighting
◔ 2-9 max seen
● 10+ max seen

Adult

Wingspan 31-40 mm (the male is the larger). The upperside of the fore-wing is a deep purple to indigo blue in the male, while the female has an iridescent purple patch on each forewing, resulting in a metallic glint in direct sunlight. Both sexes have short white-tipped projections on the hindwing. The undersides are light grey, with a black-edged diagonal white stripe running across both the fore and hindwings, and black-centred orange spots at the base of the tail. The adults feed mainly on honeydew secreted by aphids in the crowns of large oak and ash trees and are thus not easily visible from the ground. This arboreal life-style renders it impossible to determine population sizes. However, some individuals do descend close to the ground, in the morning or afternoon, to feed on dew or nectar and females lay a portion of their eggs at a low level. Purple Hairstreaks may be seen throughout the day. Late on balmy evenings when the sun is low they can perhaps best be observed, darting around the crown of oak trees.

Egg

The egg is 0.8 wide x 0.5 mm high, a compressed sphere with a network of veins and prominent spikes. Under a hand lens or microscope, with a magnification of 15-20, it is reminiscent of a sea urchin. The egg is pale bluish-white when laid and becomes grey-white, but sometimes a greenish algal growth develops on the surface over the winter. Eggs are laid in ones or twos at the base of oak buds

on the tips of a twig in July/August, and at various heights above ground level in sunny sheltered positions. The larva develops soon after laying but immediately hibernates and does not hatch until eight months later in April.

Larva
15-18 mm in length. In April, the newly hatched green larva bores into a developing bud and feeds. The body is woodlouse-like in appearance and, when fully grown, is a warm reddish-brown colour with a deep brown dorsal stripe and oblique brown markings on its sides and a creamy white sub-spiracular line. There are short and toothed spines on the body. The later instars are well camouflaged and, being nocturnal feeders, spend the day in a silk web. There are four instars over a 6-7 week period. Prior to pupation, the body becomes a dull yellowish-green.

Pupa
Length 10 mm. It is stout and rounded without cremastral hooks and the overall colour is reddish brown with purple-brown streaks. Most of its body, except wings, is reticulate and covered with tiny spines. Pupation takes place at ground level and pupae have been observed in ant nests under oak (Thomas & Lewington 2010) and occasionally adults are seen on the ground around emergence time. This stage takes about 30 days.

Additional Information
Recent field work, by Ian Rippey (unpublished) in particular, has shown that the Purple Hairstreak is more widespread than had previously been thought. Steep wooded oak slopes or scrubby trees (in the Burren) may sometimes allow an unaided view of the adult. Some woods, for example in Co Wicklow, support very large numbers of this insect. It is likely that more colonies will be found and perhaps some will be in 'semi-mature" plantations. In Ireland, only deciduous oaks have been reported as food plants. Adults have been noted on Ash trees in Britain, presumably feeding on honey dew.

Small Copper   *Lycaena phlaeas hibernica*   Copróg bheag

aberration *caeruleopunctata*

General

This butterfly is small, copper-coloured, and often solitary. The Irish sub-species *hibernica* differs a little from its British or continental relatives in being brighter and more orange in colour. Riley (2007) believes that this sub-species may also occur on the Isle of Man, whereas *eleus* occurs elsewhere in Britain. It is bivoltine.

Distribution

668 squares. The Small Copper is to be found in suitable habitat everywhere and blank squares on the distribution map are attributable to a lack of observations rather than its absence. Favoured habitats include rough wet meadows, grazed grassland, woodland edges, heaths, bog margins, sand dunes, wasteland, old pits and quarries, and road verges. [Habitat: CD3, PB4, GS1, GS2, GS4, WS1]. The Small Copper has a Holarctic range from North Africa, through Europe and Asia to Japan and in North America, as a variety of sub-species.

Adult

Wingspan 30-36 mm. The uppersides of the forewing are mainly a bright iridescent copper, with black spots and the edges are black. The hindwing is largely grey-black except for the coppery sub-terminal bands. The underside of the forewing is paler orange and that of the hindwing is a light greyish-brown.

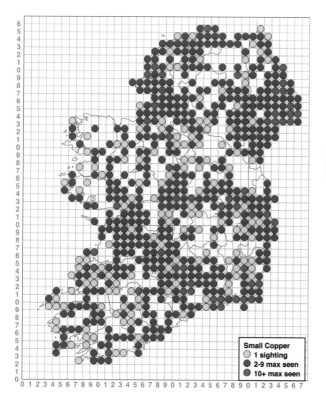

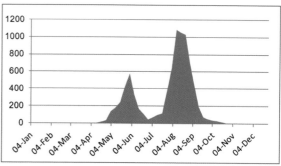

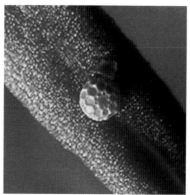

Small Copper
○ 1 sighting
● 2-9 max seen
● 10+ max seen

The male is slightly smaller with narrower more pointed forewings. A fairly common variation is the aberration *caeruleopunctata* which has a series of blue interneural spots on the hindwing. First appearances are in April and there are at least two broods in the year centred on May-June and July-August, and, occasionally, a partial third in late September and October.

Egg

The egg is an oblate spheroid, 0.6 mm wide x 0.3 mm high, with an irregular honeycomb structure. It is pale green-white when laid, becoming grey before hatching in 4-10 days. The eggs are laid singly on the mid-rib of the leaves of food plants Common Sorrel and Sheep's Sorrel and occasionally on Broad-leaved Dock. The newly-hatched larva does not eat its eggshell but feeds on the underside of its food plant leaving only the thin epidermis.

Larva

15-18 mm in length. Its retractable head is small, green-brown with black markings. The body is light to dark green and woodlouse shaped, often with a crimson stripe along the dorsal ridge and the lower edge of the sides, and may be pink underneath. It is totally covered with small white pinacula bearing short brown setae. Eggs laid by the spring brood result in adults in July and August, but those laid by the summer brood produce larvae which overwinter in any

instar up to the third. In winter it rests on silk pads attached to the food plant and feeds in mild weather. Pupation commences in April at the 4th or 5th instar.

Pupa
10-11 mm in length. Stout and rounded shape, the ground colour of the pupa is light brown, speckled with dark spots along its length. The dark dorsal line has a black spot on each abdominal segment and the wing cases are dark brown with off-white spiracles. The rest of the body is sprinkled with tiny glassy white spots which resemble the stalk and calyx of a flower. The pupa is formed among leaf litter and is attached to a silk pad using a cremaster and silk threads. This stage has a duration of up to 30 days.

Small Copper

Small Blue   *Cupido minimus*   Gormán bheag

General

This tiny butterfly, Ireland's smallest, is not really blue at all. Its colour ranges from smoky blue-black to dark bronze-brown. It is very local and inconspicuous and probably overlooked by many observers. The sole larval food plant is Kidney Vetch. In sand dunes, the male is often found perching on tall grasses which dominate the habitat and will roost there overnight. The Chimney Sweeper moth and small dark forms of the female Common Blue are sometimes misreported as this species. Its Red List status is *endangered*.

Distribution

102 squares. Its distribution is mainly on coastal sand dune systems and on limestone pavement, but it may still be found on some eskers/moraines and quarries in the Midlands [Habitat: ED1, CD4, CD6, GS1, ER2]. The Small Blue is now absent along the coast from Sheephaven Bay, Donegal, to north Co Dublin. It appears to have died out at its last known remaining site in Northern Ireland (Monawilkin in Co Fermanagh) in the past decade, following its disappearance from the north shore of Belfast Lough early in the last century. There are few recent records on the south coast of Ireland from Dingle Bay to Carnsore Point. However, on the Co Donegal coast from Bundoran to Ards Forest Park many new colonies have been found as a result of intensive searching. Inland colonies still exist on eskers in Cos Carlow, Galway, Offaly and Roscommon, but its Irish headquarters must be considered to be on the limestone pavements of the Burren in Co Clare where it is widespread and

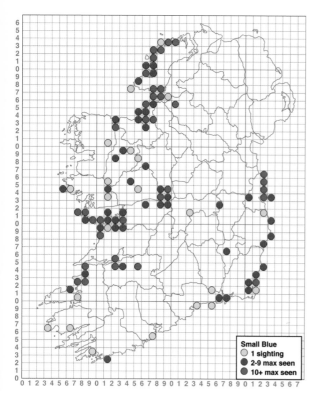

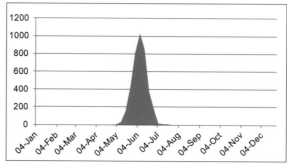

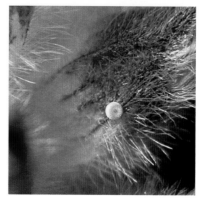

Egg on Kidney Vetch

abundant. Co Dublin's contracting sites are found in Portrane-Donabate, Portmarnock, Rush, Skerries and smaller areas in the Howth region. Abroad, it is found in Britain and from central Spain eastwards into Asia.

Adult

Wingspan is 18-27 mm. The upper side of the wings of the male is smoky-black with the basal half speckled with silvery blue scales. The outer fringe is white. The ground colour of the underside is shiny grey with up to nine black spots on the forewing and eleven on the hind wing. The upperside of the female wing is dark brown-bronze. The underside ground colour is similar to the male. An occasional male without any dark pigmentation (aberration *pallida*) is seen.

Egg

The egg is a flattened sphere, 0.4 mm wide x 0.2 mm high, with a surface network of ridges and depressions and a sunken micropyle. The female usually lays the pale blue-white eggs singly, low down, between the florets of an immature Kidney Vetch inflorescence. Egg hunting, helped by the persistence of the egg case, is often the best way to confirm the presence of a colony. Hatching takes place after 4-10 days.

Larva

9-12 mm in length. The body of the fully grown woodlouse-shaped larva is pale

Camouflaged larvae on Kidney Vetch   Small Blue cocoon on moss

ochreous with pinkish markings and a brown dorsal line. The small black head is retractable. The newly emerged larva tunnels its way through the perianth of the Kidney Vetch to feed on the developing seeds. The larvae are cannibalistic. When they outgrow the flower in size they may be seen feeding with their anterior bodies deep inside a floret. After three months the larvae enters hibernation on the ground in a crevice, loose soil or moss, emerging in the following year from mid-April onwards when they pupate without further feeding.

Pupa
8 mm in length. The head and thorax are rounded with the abdomen curved down to the anal segment. The ground colour of the abdomen is cream-buff the head and thorax are ochreous-grey, with brown stripes, spots, and white bristle-like hairs. The pupa is attached by a cremaster to a silk pad and may be found low down in vegetation. Pupation takes 6-18 days.

Additional information
The *Millennium Atlas* (2001) attributes the Small Blue decline in Britain and Ireland to the loss of semi-natural habitat and reduction in grazing. Intensive farming results in habitat loss and, conversely, the abandonment of grazing may cause the food plant to be squeezed-out by succession. In some areas rabbit grazing can be crucial in keeping the habitat open. Many coastal and inland sites have been damaged or lost through intensive grazing, large scale quarrying and manicuring of roadside verges. Coastal sites have been damaged by excessive and inappropriate recreational use. The butterfly's presence in some midland quarries has been attributed to the accidental transfer of Kidney Vetch with larvae during gravel extraction (Hillis 1975). Thomas and Lewington (2010) refer to a possible association between pupae and ants perhaps similar to that known to occur for the Large Blue. Small Blue is on the 'Priority List' for Northern Ireland (UK), but is considered likely to be extinct.

Common Blue
Polyommatus icarus mariscolore and *P. icarus icarus* Gormán coiteann

Subspecies *mariscolore*

General

The Common Blue is Ireland's most plentiful blue. The male is an unmistakeable bright shining blue colour while the normal female is less bright with her wings bordered with a series of orange crescents.

Distribution

690 squares. While the species is frequent all around our coasts, it is much scarcer in inland locations, especially in the north, where it tends to occur in more isolated colonies. Favoured habitats are unimproved and rough dry grassy areas, sand dunes, machair, eskers and roadside verges where Common

Common Blue

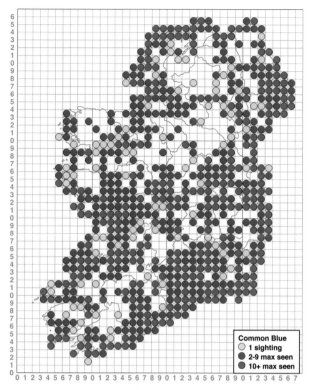

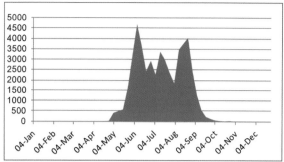

Common Blue
○ 1 sighting
◑ 2-9 max seen
● 10+ max seen

Bird's-foot-trefoil grows [Habitat: GS1, GS2, ER2, CD3]. It is a Palaearctic species, its western distribution covering North Africa, the Canary Islands and the whole of Europe.

Adult

Wingspan 30-38 mm. The Irish sub-species (*mariscolore* Kane) is slightly larger and more brightly coloured than the sub-species *icarus* found in Britain and on the continent, especially in the case of the female. By no means are all Irish females distinctly blue and many are brown with a variable amount of blue. The wings are bounded by a thin black line inside a white fringe. The basal areas of the pre and hindwings are distinctly blue. The undersides of both sexes are grey (brown-grey in the female) with a pattern of white-ringed black spots, and the female has a series of orange crescents mirroring those on her upperside. The male has less prominent orange markings on his underwings. The number of broods varies, with the general position being a main brood from late May through June and a second one in August/September. In the northern part of the country there is evidence for a *partial* second brood and in southern coastal areas at least three broods centred around April, July and September.

Egg

The egg is a flattened sphere, 0.6 mm wide x 0.3 mm high, with a deep micropyle

and a surface network of ridges and depressions. The egg is initially pale green grey becoming white and hatches in about nine days. In Ireland, eggs are found singly on the surface of young leaves of Common Bird's-foot-trefoil and Lesser Trefoil. It is possible that other legumes such as Black Medick and Greater Bird's-foot-trefoil are also used as food plants.

Larva
12-15 mm in length. The body is arched dorsally and tapers towards either end and has a glossy black retractable head. Overall, it is usually bright green with darker dorsal and white lateral stripes. The spiracles are white and the setae are short and coloured brown and white. A Newcomer's gland, which provides amino acid food for ants, is found on the 7th abdominal segment. Larvae, which do not give rise to a second generation, grow slowly and hibernate low down in vegetation as a third instar. Feeding recommences in spring and continues to the end of May with four moults.

Pupa
10 mm in length. The pupa is green and brown and lies free on or near the ground among decaying grass stems. The cuticle is finely reticulated, covered with small white setae. The head is brownish-buff, the thorax green, the wings pale brown and the abdomen green. Pupation takes place on the ground or attached by silk to a plant stem.This stage lasts for about two weeks. It is attractive to ants which may bury it and Thomas (1986) has found pupae in ant nests under stones.

Additional Information
Kane (1885) in his *European Butterflies* drew attention to the "brilliant female" form of the species in Ireland. The fact that there is an overlap of characteristics in Britain and Ireland has led some such as Higgins and Riley (1970) to the conclusion that the Common Blue in Ireland is a variety rather than a subspecies. Small specimens are sometimes misreported as being the Small Blue.

Common Blue

Holly Blue   *Celastrina argiolus britanna*   Gormán cuilinn

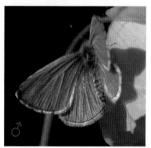

General

The Holly Blue is the first of the three blues to emerge. The first generation is typically on the wing in April and May, but has been recorded as early as the end of February flying around shrubs and trees, often above head height. It can be distinguished from the Common Blue by the presence of black dots and the absence of orange spots, on the underside of its wings. A second generation may occur in the period July to September and, recently, a partial third has been found late in autumn in Dublin and Cork cities. The main food plants are hollies and ivies.

Distribution

366 squares. In Ireland is widespread but scattered in sheltered areas especially where Holly and Common Ivy grow in the remnants of deciduous (oak) woodland, in hedgerows, urban parks and gardens [Habitat: WN1, WL1, BC4, WD5,]. It is quite a mobile species in warm weather. The Holly Blue is widespread in England and Wales. There is recent evidence that it is expanding into the south of Scotland and in Denmark. It is a Holarctic species found in Europe, Asia and North America.

Adult

The adult wing span is 26-34 mm. The male and female are similar in size. The ground colour of the upperside of the forewings of the male is silvery-blue tinged with lilac and the hindwing has a similar ground colour. The upperside of the forewing of the female is darker than the male and is readily distinguishable by

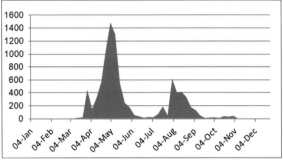

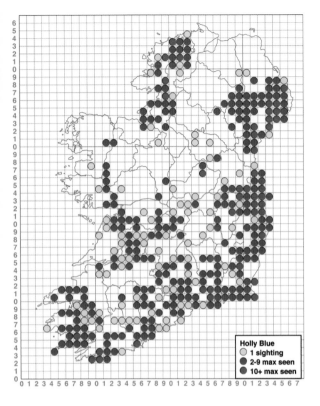

Holly Blue
○ 1 sighting
◑ 2-9 max seen
● 10+ max seen

its 3 mm wide black marginal band and the hindwing which has a row of six black spots near the margin. The underside of the wings of both sexes is pale bluish white with small black spots. The second generation female has a deeper blue-white colour and a broader black margin on the forewing.

Egg

The egg is a pale blue-white small flattened sphere, 0.6 mm wide x 0 .3 mm high, with a surface network of ridges and depressions. The first generation female usually lays her eggs singly at the base of unopened flower buds of the female Holly. Occasionally, eggs have been found in the corresponding position on male Holly bushes (Pollard 1985). The second and third generation eggs are found on Common Ivy. Hatching takes 4-10 days.

Larva

14-17 mm in length. The larva is yellowish-green with the body shaped like a woodlouse and covered by short white setae. The head is shiny black and retractable. It is well camouflaged. The larva exists in various colour forms which do not have any obvious ecological explanation and Frohawk (1924) described three different forms. The larva initially feeds on the flowers and then on the developing fruits of the food plant. Pupation takes place after about four weeks of feeding. There is little evidence of a strong association between the Holly Blue and ants despite the Newcomer's gland which secretes amino

(LEFT) *Listrodromus nycthemerus*

(BELOW LEFT) *Listrodromus* pupa in cocoon

(BELOW) Holly Blue larva on Ivy

acids that are attractive to ants (Emmet & Heath 1990). Numerous other food plants including Gorse have been reported from Britain and Europe. Eggs and larvae have been observed on Firethorn species (F. Smyth pers. com.) in a north Dublin garden.

Pupa

The pupa is stout and round, about 9 mm long, with a brown ground colour and is covered with short hairs and black speckles. A black line extends from the head to the end of the abdomen and the wings are dark brown. Little is known directly about the location of pupae in the wild. Where there is a second brood the spring generation pupa hatches within a few weeks. The pupa is the over-wintering stage.

Additional Information

The Holly Blue is listed by Greene (1854) and Boyd & More (1858) as being fairly widespread. Birchall (1866) expressed a view that a second brood would be found in the south but not until 1940 was it reported at Timoleague, Co Cork (Lucas 1940). Currently, a second brood occurs as far north as Cos Armagh and Down and a third (autumn) brood has been reported in Greater Dublin and Cork City (Aldwell & Nash 2005). It has become very much a species of urban gardens in Dublin and Belfast.

The increased frequency of reports of the Holly Blue, with additional broods, is attributable to both climate change and more intensive field work by lepidopterists. In Donegal, the warm sunny spring of 2011 has resulted in the discovery of many additional sites. In the *Millennium Atlas* (2001), cyclic fluctuations in Holly Blue numbers in Britain have been attributed to the larval-pupal ichneumonid parasitoid *Listrodromus nycthemerus*. This parasitoid together with *Enytus apostatus* and the braconid *Cotesia inducata* have recently been reported from Dublin (Bob Aldwell pers. com.). The species name *argiolus* derives from the Latin (via Greek) 'argilla', meaning white potter's clay.

NYMPHALIDAE

Red Admiral *Vanessa atalanta* Aimiréal dearg

General

The vibrant coloured Red Admiral is one of our largest butterflies and the most regular of our migrants, originating in the Mediterranean area. Small influxes occur at various times of the year and successful breeding results in a substantial Irish generation which may be found in autumn feeding on nectar from a variety of flowering plants such as Thistle, Knapweed, Butterfly-bush and Michaelmas Daisy and on fermenting apples and tree resin. Common Nettle is the sole larval food plant known to be used in Ireland.

Distribution

815 squares. The Red Admiral is usually first reported on the southern and eastern coasts but may occur in the north-west depending on meteorological conditions. It is the most consistent migrant to arrive on our shores and it disperses very widely. Numbers fluctuate very substantially from year to year. It is widespread in Britain and its world range encompasses North America, Africa north of the Sahara and across Europe and Asia to Iran.

Adult

Wingspan is 64-80 mm. The ground colour of the upperside is velvety black. A scarlet band traverses the forewing from the costa almost to the anal angle. A short white band extends from costa at two-thirds and in the sub-apical area there are five white spots, faint lilac spots near the apex and two more lower

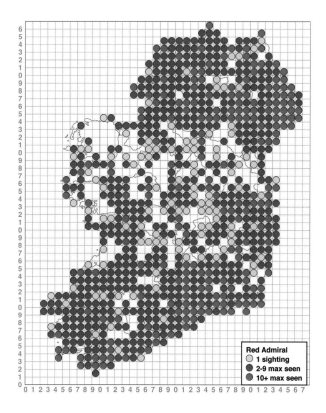

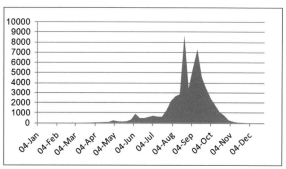

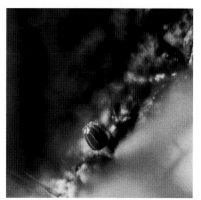

Red Admiral
○ 1 sighting
● 2-9 max seen
● 10+ max seen

down. The hindwing has similar ground colour and a terminal scarlet band from space S1b to S6 with black spots sometimes speckled with blue between veins. On the underside the forewing is blackish brown with more blue than above, and a scarlet band which is less intense near the tornus. The hindwing is a multicoloured collage with an orange-brown band near the outer margin and a sub-terminal series of five variously coloured ocelli.

Egg
The egg is barrel-shaped, 0.7 mm wide x 0.8 high, with 8-10 longitudinal ribs disappearing into the micropylar depression. Initially the eggs are pale green becoming darker and finally greyish green before hatching within 10 days. The eggs are laid singly on the upper surface of leaves of the Common Nettle.

Larva
32-36 mm in length. The stout body and head are usually black but may range to olive-green. A row of pale yellow sub-spiracular markings occur on the abdominal segments near the spiracles and each segment has seven pinacula with variously coloured branched spines. The solitary larva forms a tent from a nettle leaf which is folded over and hangs down. It eats the leaf from within and then forms a fresh tent. When resting it curls into the shape of a number 6. This stage takes up to a month depending on the weather. Winter tents are more elaborate.

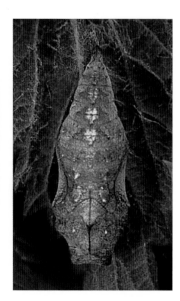

(ABOVE) Larval nettle tent
(RIGHT) Pupa in nettle tent

Pupa

22-24 mm in length. Its head is quite blunt, thorax angled and the cremaster is attached to abdomen and suspended from a silken pad in the final larval tent made from nettle leaves. The pupa's body colour is variable and dependent on lighting, often brown or greyish brown. Black-pointed projections are often found on the abdomen. Spots of gold are present along the dorsum of the abdomen and above each wing case.

Additional Information

Kane (1901) noted that the Red Admiral was common and widespread, but commented that its appearance in Ulster was "capricious" depending on climatic conditions. Baynes (1964) noted its abundance in several years in the 1950s and believed that it was capable of surviving mild winters especially in the 'deep south'. Early spring appearances on the south coast may well be due to over wintering rather than migration. The butterfly has been recorded in the northern islands of Tory and Inishtrahull. Recent investigation (Smyth and Nash 2008) has shown that the Red Admiral has successfully overwintered at Howth, Co Dublin, with the adult and larvae present throughout the winter, and egg laying can occur in both November and February. The braconid parasitoid *Microgaster subcompletus* was been confirmed in winter larvae.

There is some evidence of reverse migration in autumn, and in Britain the use of vertical-looking radar by the Rothamsted Centre has confirmed the profiles of moving insects which correspond to the Red Admiral and the Painted Lady travelling with the prevailing wind, several hundred metres above ground. The radar evidence for Red Admiral supports the concept of reverse migration. Insects flying high are able to avail of stronger winds during migration but will simultaneously have to endure lower temperatures.

Painted Lady *Vanessa cardui* Áilleán

One of our largest butterflies, it is migratory and originates in North Africa and Southern Europe. The numbers arriving in Ireland are very dependent on successful breeding in Morocco and favourable timely winds and in some years numbers are extremely small. The Painted Lady is a fast and erratic flier. Thistles are the main larval food plants. It has been unable to survive the Irish winter in any of its stages.

Distribution

785 squares. In good migratory years, the Painted Lady is reported in May or June from all over Ireland, especially on the south and east coastlines. Smaller influxes may occur both earlier and later in the year. When the summer weather is favourable a substantial Irish generation emerges in early autumn. It is a worldwide species except for South America and possibly Australia where there is disagreement as to its precise identity.

Adult

Wingspan is 58-74 mm. The female is larger than the male. The upperside of the forewing is orange-buff in the basal and discal areas but may be pinkish at emergence. Three angular black patches cross from one-third costa to the mid inner margin. The outer margin is slightly scalloped and there is a sub-marginal black band and white cilia. The outer portion of the forewing to the apex is black with white spots at the apex. A short white band is present from two-thirds costa to the inner margin, with one lower white spot. The slightly scalloped hindwing

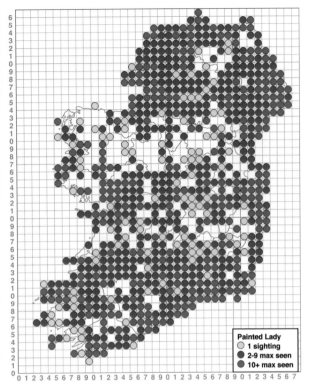

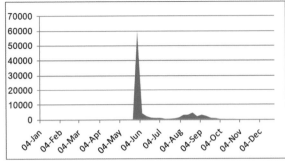

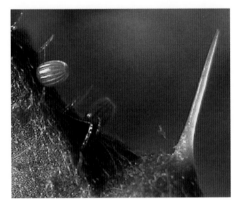

Painted Lady
○ 1 sighting
◑ 2-9 max seen
● 10+ max seen

is also orange-buff with rows of black spots in the marginal and sub-marginal areas and a blue lunule at the anal angle. Close to the body, along the inner margin, are long, silky hair scales. The undersides of the wings are similarly marked. The hindwing is mottled with black brown, green-brown and white areas and has a series of four ocelli and a sub-terminal series of blue lunules.

Egg
The egg is ellipsoidal, truncated at either end, 0.7 mm wide x 0.8 mm high, with 16 conspicuous longitudinal ribs. Initially a glassy green, it becomes darker green and then greyer near hatching in 7-10 days. Eggs are laid singly on the leaves of the Creeping and Spear Thistles.

Larva
28-36 mm in length. The larva's head is black with black and white setae. The body is velvety black, covered in rows of short branched yellow and black spines. It has yellow crescent-shaped markings on the abdominal segments in the spiracular region, twin dorsal stripes composed of off-white coloured speckles, a copper colour underneath and yellow-brown legs. The larva lives in a silk web on the underside of a leaf until the final instar. In warm sunny summers, when there has been a significant earlier migration, larvae will successfully enter pupation after about four weeks of feeding.

Painted Lady

Pupa

25 mm in length. The head is blunt and thorax wide with prominent wing margins and curved abdomen. Prominances are present in place of old dorsal spines. The ground colour is variable but frequently grey-brown with a metallic lustre. Emergence of the imago usually occurs within a fortnight in suitable weather, but in prolonged wet and cold weather the pupa dies.

Additional Information

Next to the Red Admiral this is the most regular and frequent of our migratory species and often arrives accompanied and outnumbered by it. While immigration is usually first noticed in coastal areas of the south and east, D.J. O'Sullivan, the keeper on Inishtrahull Island lighthouse Co Donegal, observed two or three per hour arriving from the south-west on three consecutive days in July 1960 (Baynes 1961) which was a "poor year". The large numbers observed in August/September are usually the offspring of earlier migrants. Recent exceptionally good migrant years were 1995 and 2009. In 2009 there was a very large influx and food plants used included Common Nettle, Burdock, Mallow species and the three commonest Thistle species, but a wet summer resulted in a relatively small Irish generation. Its relative, the American Painted Lady, has been very rarely reported from Ireland.

Small Tortoiseshell   *Aglais urticae*   Ruán beag

General

The Small Tortoiseshell will be familiar to many as a frequent garden visitor feeding on nectar-rich plants such as Michaelmas Daisy and Butterfly-bush. In the wild, it uses a wide range of plants including Dandelion and Thistles. In autumn, it hibernates in available locations such as tree hollows and out-buildings and some may enter houses through open windows and roost in secluded corners or behind curtains. In warm years, two broods occur widely in late June to July and August. In the north, depending on the weather, there may be only one emergence in August. A (partial) third brood was widely noted in 2010. The adult butterfly has been observed in every month of the year.

Distribution

894 squares. The Small Tortoiseshell is found in a wide variety of habitats from urban areas to coastal islands. It is apparently very scarce in north-west Mayo but this is most likely to be an artefact related to the absence of resident lepidopterists. It is also a part-migratory species but there is little knowledge of the magnitude of its immigration to Ireland. The butterfly is widely distributed in the northern hemisphere from the Western European Atlantic to the Asian Pacific.

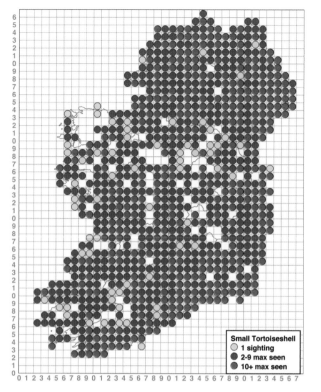

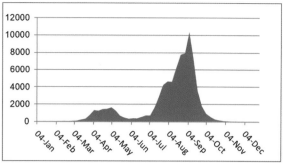

Small Tortoiseshell
○ 1 sighting
◐ 2-9 max seen
● 10+ max seen

Adult

Wingspan 45-62 mm. Both sexes are very similar in appearance. The ground colour of the upper side of the wings is bright orange-red and the basal area is blackish. The forewings have a series of alternating black and creamy-yellow markings just below the costal margins ending with a white patch near the apex. There is a series of interneural blue spots along the sub-termenal borders of fore and hindwings. The forewing has a prominence or 'tail' on the termen at space 5 and the hindwing has a similar prominence on termen at space 3. The cilia is brown.

Egg

The eggs are globular, narrowing towards the top, 0.7 mm wide x 0.8 mm high, with 8-9 prominent ribs running into the micropylar depression. Initially, they are a glassy pale green becoming a duller green before hatching in 7-10 days. Eggs are laid in clumps of up to 100 on the underside of terminal leaves of young Common Nettle plants in stands having an open and sunny aspect. The eggs can readily be mistaken for those of the Peacock.

Larva

27-32 mm. The larva's head is shiny black with yellow tubercules each bearing a hair. Its body is cylindrical, narrowing toward the head. The ground colour

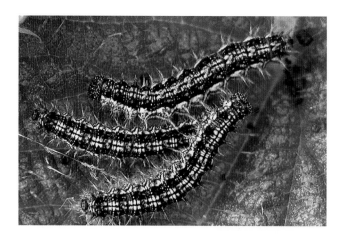

varies from yellow to black with a blackish dorsal line and markings on either side and may have a yellowish line above the black spiracles which are encircled with yellow. The body is covered in short hairs and, as in other nymphalids, there are seven rows of tubercles with short yellow spines. The larvae are gregarious and, on hatching, form a silk web wherever they are eating on the upper surface of nettles. By the fifth and final instar they have become solitary and, when fully fed, will travel some distance to pupate. Early instars are very similar to those of the Peacock. The removal of large numbers of larvae by worker wasps has been observed resulting in the depletion of a colony (Bob Aldwell pers. com.)

Pupa

The pupa is 20-22 mm in length, smaller and slimmer than the Peacock and Red Admiral. Its head ends in two pointed projections and the thorax is raised to a point, and there is a series of projections along the dorsum, which may be golden in appearance. Overall colour is variable from grey to brown mottled with black, and splashed with metallic lustres which can extend to the thorax and wing cases. It is believed that the reflective gilding bewilders predators. The pupa may be found hanging from a silk pad on its foodplant or on neighbouring vegetation. In prolific years large numbers of pupae can be found hanging from nettle patches which have been denuded of leaves by the larvae. The stage length is 12-28 days depending on ambient conditions.

Additional Information

The Small Tortoiseshell is a species that appears to be benefiting from climate change with a tendency towards an extra brood. Substantial stands of nettles, usually found around nutrient-rich cultivated areas, are required as the larval food plants, so the use of herbicides and excessive "tidying" are detrimental to this butterfly. There are reports from Britain of a 'new' parasitoid *Sturmia bella* which has had a significant affect on population size there, but the numbers in Ireland are holding up.

Peacock *Inachis io* Péacóg

General

Perhaps the most recognisable of our native butterflies, its name arises from the prominent false eyes on its wings which are strongly evocative of its avian namesake. It may be seen flying on mild days in winter and spring and occasional tattered specimens are seen as late as July. A very territorial butterfly, it is not unduly intimidated by human visitors and is commonly found taking nectar in gardens from plants such as Butterfly-bush. Normally there is one generation which flies from mid-July until autumn, before hibernating in cracks and crevices in trees and walls, in outhouses, wood piles and in unheated domestic buildings. On mild spring days it re-emerges seeking nectar sources.

Distribution

908 squares. Widely distributed, and in recent years common in the more northerly counties where populations have strongly fluctuated during the past century. The butterfly is a strong flier and disperses widely on emergence. In Britain it is spreading northwards and produces a partial second generation (SOBBI). In Ireland, second generation larvae have been seen, but there has been no confirmation of their successful completion of metamorphosis. It is a Palaearctic species extending from Western Europe to Japan and from the Mediterranean to 60° north in Scandinavia.

Adult

Wingspan 63-75 mm. The outer margins of the wings are crenulate and the

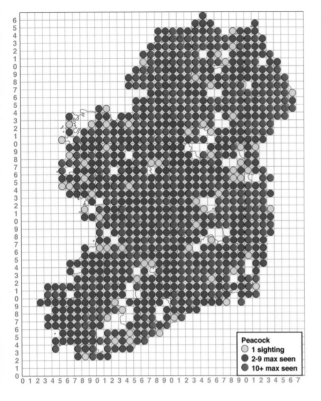

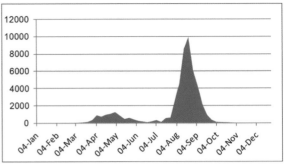

Peacock
○ 1 sighting
◉ 2-9 max seen
● 10+ max seen

forewing has a rounded projection in space 5. The ground colour is mahogany-red with a blacker basal area. The medial half of the costa is black with numerous fine yellow lines. Distally to the apex are two unequal black spots separated by a creamy-white one. The forewing ocellus is composite with a dark orange-red pupil encircled by yellow on one side and lilac on the other, traversed vertically by white spots – the 'peacock eyes'. The hindwing ground colour is similar to forewing, but darker, and the ocellus is black, spotted with blue, surrounded by an off-white disk. The undersides of the wings are brown to black with the hindwing darker than the forewing. With wings closed, the insect is well camouflaged when perched on bare ground.

Egg

The egg is relatively small, barrel shaped, 0.6 mm wide x 0.8 high, with 7-8 prominent longitudinal ribs disappearing into the micropylar depression. The eggs are laid in large numbers, in batches of up to several hundred on top of one another, on the underside of the Common Nettle. They are yellow-green when laid becoming olive-green before hatching in about 21 days. Usually the eggs are laid in more sheltered positions than the Small Tortoiseshell, with which they can be readily confused, but both may be found together.

Peacock

Larva

38-42 mm in length. The head is shiny black and covered with hairs.
Its cylindrical body is velvety black covered with short hairs and shiny black
spines and the abdomen is sprinkled with tiny white spots. When young, the
larvae are greenish and are very difficult to differentiate from those of the Small
Tortoiseshell, but the later of the five instars are readily distinguishable.

Pupa

The pupa appears elongated with the head having two pointed projections.
The thorax, on the dorsal surface, has a keel that that rises to a central projection and the wing bases are prominent. The abdomen has a series of paired
spines. The body ground colour varies from grey-pink to green-yellow and is
dappled with black outlining the wings and antennae. Gilding is often present
on the head, wings and thorax. For a period of 2-4 weeks, pupae may be found
suspended on Common Nettle or other vegetation.

Additional Information

Kane (1901) reported it as "common in many parts of the south.... occasional
in Co Wicklow, rarely in Co Dublin, with occasional specimens in Ulster" and
in the *Guide to Belfast etc* (BNFC 1874) for the British Association Meeting it is
stated: "The Peacock is very rare; one specimen was taken by Rev. J. Bristow at
Knockbreda". Donovan (1936) noted it as common and distributed over the
south, but more restricted in its range and numbers in the north. Occasional
aberrations with one or more of its ocelli absent have been reported ('blind
Peacock'), for example from Co Donegal (R. McCafferty pers. com. 2006). This
species does not seem to be under threat but 'excessive tidiness' and weed
killing of its food plant, especially in urban areas, are detrimental to its success.
Climatic warming may result in a second generation becoming viable.

Comma *Polygonia c-album* Camóg

General

The Comma resembles a rather ragged Small Tortoiseshell in appearance and is found in similar habitat. It has been confirmed as being present in Ireland in recent years on more than seventy occasions. It has presumably arrived on favourable winds from Britain, or else was initially introduced as larvae or pupae attached to imported food plants such as Elm and Currant species.

Distribution

32 squares. Small numbers, generally one or two, have been reported from Cos Antrim, Carlow, Donegal, Down, Dublin, Kilkenny, Meath, Waterford, Wicklow and Wexford since 1998 and it appears to be successfully over-wintering. The Comma is widespread in England and Wales and is spreading northwards into Scotland and is now regularly reported from the Isle of Man. It is Palaearctic in extent from North Africa through Europe and Asia to Japan.

Adult

Wingspan is 44-48 mm, but size does vary. The upperside ground colour is a brownish-yellow and the wings are spotted with various shapes varying in colour from black to brown. The outer margin of the forewing is deeply indented with projections at veins 2 and 6. The hindwing has a prominence at space 2 forming a distinct 'tail'. The underside is a deeper brownish-yellow covered with brown setae, with sub-termenal spots black surrounded by dull metallic green. The cilia

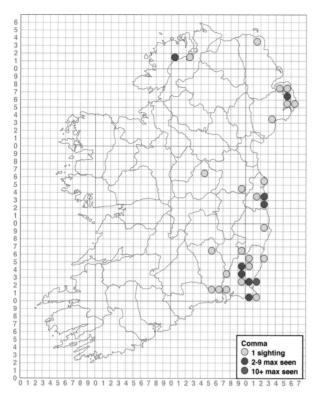

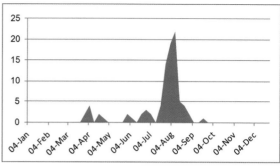

Comma
○ 1 sighting
● 2-9 max seen
● 10+ max seen

is short and mainly white. The bright white comma-like mark in the cell space gives the species its common name. The form *hutchinsoni* is a paler brownish-yellow in appearance, has a less scalloped margin, and occurs in the summer generation.

Egg

The egg is a flattened sphere, 0.7 mm wide x 0.8 mm tall, with about ten longitudinal ribs. It is initially pale green becoming more yellow and final grey-green before hatching in 11-20 days. In Britain, the eggs are laid on several plants which include Common Nettle, Elm and Currant species but there are no reported observations of egg-laying activity in the wild in Ireland.

Larva

30-34 mm in length. The head is black, flattened and square with branched orange spines bearing fine, white setae. Its legs are white in late instars. The body is cylindrical, black with a greyish network. Areas between segments are yellow to white and there are dark orange and pale stripes respectively above and below the spiracles. The abdomen is covered with rows of spiny projections. The larva, which has the appearance of a bird dropping due to white dorsum from segments 3 to 7 of its abdomen, initially feeds on the top of a leaf. In Britain, 4-5 instars are reported.

Pupa

21 mm in length. Head beaked, thorax keeled and rising to a central projection. Body waisted and abdomen elongated. The body has a pinkish-buff ground colour with black reticulation. The body has a series of ochreous, black and metallic silver points, coppery-gold patches are present on the dorsum of the 1st and 3rd abdominal segments.

Additional information

There have been a small number of historic reports of the Comma in Ireland. Birchall (1873) refers to a sighting at Powerscourt, Wicklow. However, Kane (1894) states that the observer's companion, A.G. More, was of the view that it was at too great a distance to differentiate it from a tattered Small Tortoiseshell. Rev. C.L. Garnett (Johnson 1901) reported a sighting from Malahide, Dublin. This is a butterfly that can be easily overlooked because of its superficial resemblance to a ragged Small Tortoiseshell, so it may be more widespread and plentiful than recent reports indicate. Its spread would appear to be favoured by climate change.

Pearl-bordered Fritillary *Boloria euphrosyne* Fritileán péarlach

General

The Pearl-bordered Fritillary is Ireland's rarest butterfly and it remained unknown until discovered by Phillips and Fogarty in 1922 at Clooncoose in the Burren area of Co Clare. A report *via* Graves (1924) of a sighting on limestone pavement in the Askeaton area of Co Limerick was never subsequently confirmed. It has one annual brood with a flight period from late-April to mid-June. Since the larval food plants are mainly Dog-violets, common plants of deciduous woodland and shaded hedgerows, this should not be a limiting factor in the distribution of the species. This colourful butterfly, with an overall reddish-brown appearance, flies fast over limestone pavement. [Habitat: ER2, GS1, WS1]. Red List status is *endangered*.

Distribution

12 squares; 35 tetrads. It is known from the 'Burren' area of Co Clare and from the adjacent area in south Co Galway with their thin soils over limestone pavement. Colonies are located in open areas of scrub/woodland where Hazel and Bracken grow. It has been recently reported for the first time from Inis Meáin (P. Strickland 2006 pers. com.) and Inis Mór in the Aran Islands. These are believed to be previously overlooked colonies rather than recent arrivals. There are pre-1980 sightings (Ní Lamhna 1980), which have not been since confirmed, from four 10 km squares and a more recent observation from an area to the north-east of Moycullen near Lough Corrib in 1984 (B. Leonard pers. com.). It is a Palaearctic species found in Western Europe as far south as Sicily and across to Asia. Once widespread in Britain, its main remaining

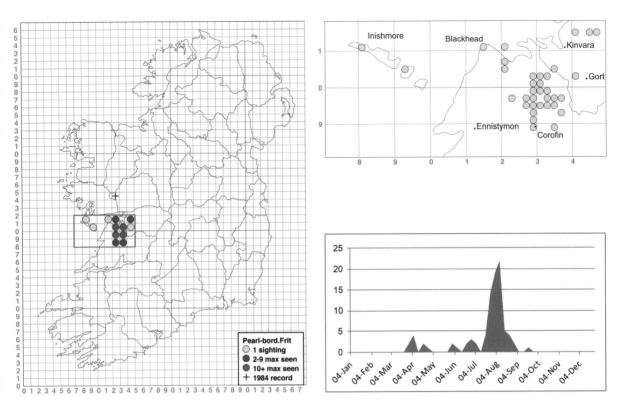

'strongholds' are now western and highland Scotland and some very southerly areas in England. The severe decline in Britain has been attributed to the cessation of coppicing and to blanket afforestation.

Adult
The wingspan is 38-47 mm. The upperside of the butterfly's wings are brownish yellow interrupted by black veins, crossbars and spots. The larger female is somewhat darker in colour than the male. The underside of the forewing is paler than the upperside with the apical area blotched red-brown. Underneath, the hindwing has mixed ground colours of brown and yellow with seven silvery lunules near the outer border [hence its name] and two more nearer the body.

Egg
The egg is conical in shape, 0.6 mm wide x 0.8 mm high with approximately 27 vertical ribs. It is cream when first laid, becoming pale yellow and then eventually grey prior to hatching. Eggs are laid singly or in pairs on Dog-violet or other violet leaves or more frequently on nearby moss or plant detritus. Hatching takes place in 11-20 days.

Larva
22-25 mm in length. The larva is tapered, being widest at its black head. The

Pearl-bordered Fritillary

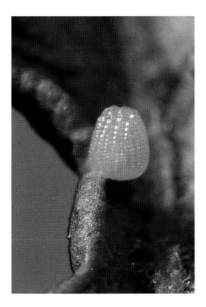

body is a velvety-black with a twin row of yellowish spines along the sub-dorsal area, and inconspicuous white lateral and dorsal stripes. Along the spiracles the body is mottled with grey. The larva feeds and basks from June to September and the half-grown fourth instar hibernates in litter. In spring it resumes feeding and then pupates.

Pupa
The pupa is 14 mm long. Its head has two large and two small projections. The body ground colour is grey with dark markings below and on wings. The angular body has a depression between the third segment of thorax and abdomen. The abdominal segments have a twin series of dorsal conical projections of differing size, and the dorsal surfaces of the wings protrude. The pupa is suspended in a loose silk 'cocoon' low down in vegetation for up to 19 days.

Further Information
Its comparatively recent discovery in Ireland is attributable to its restricted distribution, despite the fact that the Burren area had long been a favoured territory for entomologists. The Clooncoose specimen, captured using Fogarty's hat, was added to the National Museum collection. The fritillary's survival in the Burren has been assisted by the low agricultural value of its habitat and grazing by feral goats which has contributed to vegetation management. Continued 'development' and land reclamation in the area has resulted in habitat loss and there is a hypothesis that in other areas it may be under threat from encroachment by Hazel. Further investigation and monitoring is required to gather information on the current status of this species, its population levels, ecological requirements and threats to survival. This species has been under-investigated in Ireland.

Dark Green Fritillary   *Argynnis aglaja aglaja*   Fritileán dúghlas

General

This large butterfly is a species of open countryside and is a fast and powerful flier. It can be difficult to identify except when it is feeding or roosting when it may be easily distinguished from the Silver-washed Fritillary by the convex/scalloped shape of the outer margin of the forewing and the discrete nature of the silver spots on the underside of the hindwing. The Dark Green Fritillary is single brooded and may be seen on the wing from June to early September. Donovan (1936) and others have remarked on the rich reddish colour of the Irish male compared with typical specimens from Britain. Its Red List status is *endangered*.

Distribution

192 squares. The Dark Green Fritillary is generally found in areas where there is good herb rich open habitat and range of flowering plants, such as sand dune systems, coastal cliffs, hillsides and limestone grassland [Habitat: ER2, CD3, CD5, CD6, GS1]. Its Irish distribution is predominately coastal or sub-coastal. It is plentiful in the Burren and some sand dunes systems such as Doagh Isle (Donegal) and Ballyteigue (Wexford). There are relatively few known inland sites but this species may be under-recorded. Sometimes it overlaps with the Silver-washed Fritillary, for example, at the Umbra (London-derry), Murvagh (Donegal), Slieve Gullion (Armagh), Termon (Clare) and the Raven (Wexford). A Palaearctic species, it stretches from Western Europe to Japan and from the Arctic Circle to Morocco and is widespread in Britain.

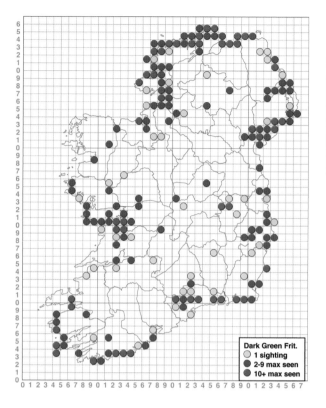

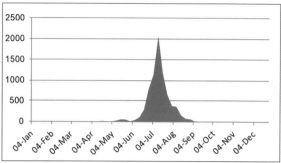

Dark Green Frit.
○ 1 sighting
◉ 2-9 max seen
● 10+ max seen

Adult

Wingspan 58-68 mm. The termen of the male forewing is almost straight and the upperside ground colour is bright fulvous-orange. Veins are black with medial areas displaying androconial scales. The *female* has a paler ground colour, larger black spots and the termen of the forewing is more rounded. The underside of the forewing is pale fulvous. The basal half of the costa is green and there are green apical markings.

The underside of the hindwing is yellow-ochreous with about 20 silver spots and the basal half is a dull green. The series of seven submarginal white spots are surrounded by green lunules. Both margins are crenulate. The cilia is white and the veins are chequered black.

Egg

The egg is conical in shape 0.8 mm wide x 1.0 mm high with about 20 irregular vertical ribs. Initial colour is pale cream, becoming purple-cream and finally brown-grey prior to hatching in 11-20 days. The female locates its food plant and then oviposits on moss or other nearby vegetation. The larval food plants are likely to include the Dog-violets, Hairy Violet, Marsh Violet and Heartsease.

Dark Green Fritillary

Larva

38-42 mm in length. Its head is black and the body is velvety black with a branched dorsal and lateral spines. The larva has a row of brick-red square sub-spiracular spots and a scattering of white dots on each segment. On hatching, the larva eats the outer shell of its own egg and goes into hibernation in the plant litter for nine months. On warm spring days the larva commences feeding on fresh violet leaves. The distinctive larva is sometimes spotted basking or on the move in search of fresh food plants or a niche for hibernation. Pupation commences in May.

Pupa

The pupa is red-brown about 19 mm long. Its abdomen is strongly curved and has black wings, head, thorax and spiracles. Pupation takes place low in vegetation within a case formed from dried leaves bound together with silk. The pupa hangs by its cremaster attached to a silk pad. This stage lasts for 3-4 weeks.

Additional Information

Greene (1854) considered that the Dark Green Fritillary was generally distributed in Ireland. Kane (1901) stated that it was widespread and mentions locations near Derry, Portballintrae, Greystones, Kenmare and inland in Cos Cork and Galway. Birchall (1873) attributed part of its distribution pattern to the scarcity of woods and the frequency of stone walls rather than hedges in Ireland! Recent careful checking in Donegal has confirmed it at a number of inland locations including Glenties and a wooded area near Lough Eske.

The main threat to this species is the continued loss of coastal sand dune habitat. Much of its inland habitat has been victim to agricultural development and coniferous monocultures. Riley (2007) classifies the Irish, Scottish and Isle of Man forms as sub-species *scotica* but it is not clear why he rejects sub-species *aglaja*. W.M. Crawford's specimen of the abnormal black streaked form *aberrans*, which he found at Portballintrae, Co Antrim, in 1919, is in the Cockayne collection in the British Natural History Museum.

Dark Green Fritillary

Silver-washed Fritillary   *Argynnis paphia*   Fritileán geal

General

This is the largest of Ireland's native butterflies and the season's last fritillary to emerge. The flight period extends from late June to early September. The spectacular orange-coloured male may be observed patrolling along woodland borders and rides. Both sexes feed on bramble, thistle flowers and honey dew and visit gardens for other nectar sources. It is distinguishable from the Dark Green Fritillary by the slightly concave shape of the outer forewing margin and the 'silver washes' under the hindwing. The female is larger and much darker than the male. The main food plants are the Dog-violets.

Distribution

377 squares. This species is widespread in Ireland. It frequents deciduous and mixed woodland and copses where violets are plentiful and is seen along the margins, in glades and roadways that receive direct sunlight [Habitat: WN1, WN2, WD1, WD2, WD5]. Its flight is strong and undulating as it soars and swoops from almost ground level to the tops of trees. Unlike the Dark Green Fritillary it is not found in treeless landscapes. Good sites include Glenarm, Upper Lough Erne, The Raven Wood, Cleengort and Cratloe. In England and Wales it is has a south (westerly) distribution and it is absent from Scotland. It is a Palaearctic species, extending from the Mediterranean to Sweden, to Indochina and to North Africa and Turkey.

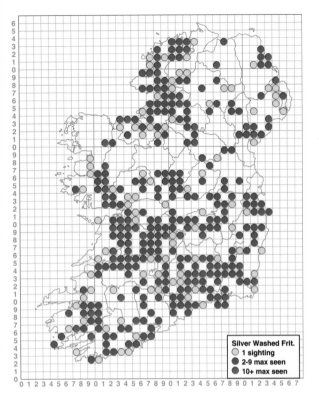

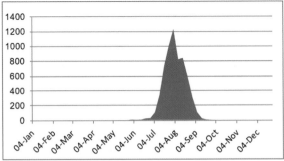

Silver Washed Frit.
○ 1 sighting
● 2-9 max seen
● 10+ max seen

Adult

The wingspan is 69-80 mm. The upperside of the forewing of the *male* has a strongly arched costa and a slightly scalloped outer margin. The ground colour is bright fulvous and the veins, costa, outer margins and distal part of the inner margins are black. Veins 1-4 are surrounded by black androconial scales in the median area. The hindwing is more scalloped than the forewing. The underside forewing ground colour is fulvous orange but the hindwing is silver-green. Three silver bands (washes) extend from vein 8. The distal part of the wing is tinged with copper. The *female* upperside is a paler tawny colour and the underside is darker green.

Egg

The egg is conical, 0.8 mm wide x 1.0 mm high, with 25 vertical ribs, linked by transverse ridges, alternately reaching the apex. Initially, it is pale-yellow becoming off-white and finally a translucent grey before hatching. When egg-laying, the female flies close to the ground in search of its foodplant, Dog-violet, which she first touches to confirm its identity before ovipositing on moss or lichen on the north side of a nearby tree trunk. Eggs hatch in 11-20 days.

Silver-washed Fritillary

Larva

38-44 mm in length. The head is black and body ground colour is dark purplish brown. Two yellow mid-dorsal stripes and four lighter sub-dorsal lines run the length of the body. There are many light brown branched spines on the abdomen and thorax. On emergence from the egg in August, the larva moves into fissures in the bark of a tree and immediately hibernates. In March/April the larva seeks out a nearby patch of violets and feeds on fresh leaves until ready for pupation.

Pupa

The pupa is 22 mm long. The ground colour is buff-brown speckled with a network of darker brown lines. Its head has two diverging horns. The thorax and abdominal segments have two rows of conical projections, the first five pairs of which are lustrous silver-gold. The developing wings have an angled dark brown stripe. The cremaster is pointed with hooks attached to a silk pad from which it is suspended. The pupa is very effectively camouflaged resembling a discarded leaf. Hatching occurs within 18 days.

Marsh Fritillary *Euphydryas aurinia hibernica* Fritileán réisc

Subspecies *hibernica*

General

This species, the smallest and most colourful of the fritillaries, is in apparent decline due to loss of damp meadows, marsh and boggy habitats through drainage, agricultural improvement, afforestation and unsuitable grazing regimes (including abandonment). Habitat fragmentation is believed to be an important factor in its decline. The larval food plant is Devil's-bit Scabious but hungry larvae have been known to eat Honeysuckle and Plantain. All 'good sites' contain a very substantial amount of Devil's-bit Scabious.

The habitat for this butterfly is very variable and includes coastal machair and heath, dune slacks, heathy grassland, margins of raised and blanket bog, fens, lake margins and thin and sometimes heathy soils over limestone [Habitat: GS4, CD3, CD5, CD6, PB4, GS4, GS3/HH1-PB2/3, HH2, PF1]. Some sites are quite sheltered, others are windswept. Contrary to some beliefs, it is by no means exclusively an insect of wet fields. In some sites, webs may be found in the shelter of tussocks of Purple Moor-grass. The species is generally quite sedentary but in warm weather has been known to travel several kilometres. The flight season is from mid-May to the end of June. Its Irish Red List status is *vulnerable*.

Distribution

248 squares. The Marsh Fritillary has become very much a western species although there are some significant colonies in the Midlands as far east as Cos

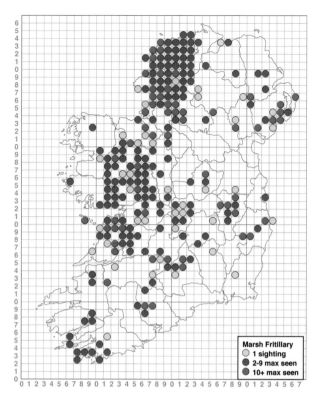

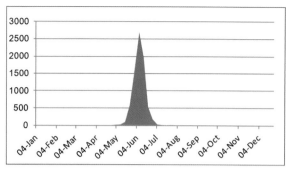

Marsh Fritillary
○ 1 sighting
◐ 2-9 max seen
● 10+ max seen

Kildare and Down. It has been refound in Wicklow in small numbers and at one site in Co Dublin The latter, the North Bull Island, may be a recent introduction. Recent work has shown that there are substantial and widespread populations in both Co Donegal (B. Aldwell pers. com.), where it has been located in more than fifty 10 km squares, and in Co Fermanagh where previously it had been largely unknown. There have been a number of contemporary reports in neighbouring Co Leitrim. Much of the country has yet to be explored for this species. In Britain, the Marsh Fritillary is now largely confined to the south-west and is suffering a major decline in western European countries. Beyond Europe it extends eastwards in Asia as far as Korea. In the IUCN European Red List it is now considered of *least concern*.

Adult

Wingspan is 30-50 mm. Both sexes are very similar in appearance. The upper surface of the forewing has a dark brown costa speckled with buff scales. The surface is divided by veins into rectangular cells outlined by brown scales. The ground colour is deep orange-red with a dark basal area. The discal cell has two orange-red and two straw-coloured patches. There is a sub-marginal series of orange-red cells with straw-coloured centres and a marginal series consists of alternate dark brown and straw-coloured patches. The cilia is buff, chequered by dark vein tips. The hindwing has a sub-marginal series of deep orange-red cells with black spots in spaces 2-7. The underside of the fore and hindwings have similar patterns to the above but are much paler in colour.

Marsh Fritillary

Egg

The egg is 0.7 mm wide x 0.8 mm high, sub-spherical in shape, flattened above and below with 20 longitudinal ribs extending two-thirds of the way to the base. It is pale cream when laid, darkening to reddish-brown and becoming greyish before eclosion in up to 35 days. The eggs are laid on the underside of a large leaf of Devil's-bit Scabious in batches of upwards of a hundred. The female emerges with mature eggs according to Porter (1992), and the first batch of eggs may be laid within a day of mating and then, if weather permits, additional much smaller batches are laid.

Larva

25-30 mm in length. The body and head are shiny black, cylindrical in shape with white spots and patches, each segment having seven groups of black bristles. The prolegs are brown-black and the spiracles encircled in white. The gregarious first instar larvae spin a silk web around a couple of leaves of food plant and eat only the lower epidermis from within their shelter. The resultant browning of the leaf surface betrays them to the careful observer. Further instars develop more extensive webs, and bask on the surface in suitable weather. The absorption of solar radiation is clearly a very important process for the larvae. When the food is depleted they move *en masse* to a fresh plant. In September/October, at fourth instar, a well hidden white silken hibernaculum (nest) is constructed low down on the food plant. In favourable weather during the 'hibernation' period they emerge to bask. In spring, the colony subdivides and about April each larva becomes solitary in advance of pupation.

　　　　　　　　　　　　　　　　　　　　　　　　Marsh Fritillary

Pupa

The pupa is 12-15 mm long, cylindrical in shape, with round head and broad and curved abdomen. The ground colour is grey white and the head, wings, thorax and abdominal tubercules are marked with black and sometimes orange. The pupa is usually attached to a stick or stalk and kept in position by a cremaster but is occasionally found attached to the surface of a leaf. Completion of metamorphosis takes 15-26 days.

Additional information

There have been a number of reports of 'plagues' of larvae in the early 20th Century near Mullingar (Middleton 1902) and Co Fermanagh (Riley 1928; Donovan 1936) where the vegetation was blackened with many thousands of caterpillars. Its food plant Devil's-bit Scabious is very widespread in Ireland but there is not a full understanding of the butterfly's distribution and specific requirements. It is believed to have a particular need for nearby populations to avoid extinctions through fragmentation and isolation and experts refer to loosely associated 'metapopulations' being essential for its long term survival. Inbreeding may be a factor in losses of isolated populations. Sites vary from the exposed to the sheltered. In Victorian times, the Marsh Fritillary was commonly known as the "Greasy Fritillary" because, within a couple of days of emergence, the adult becomes darker or greasy in appearance due to loss of scales.

Larvae are reported to be parasitised by three generations of the braconid wasp *Cotesia bignelli* and also by *C. melitaearum*. *C. bignelli*, which is exclusive to the Marsh Fritillary, has recently been been reconfirmed at several sites in Donegal. The adult wasp lays many eggs in a Marsh Fritillary larva by injection. The eggs hatch and the grubs feed and when fully developed emerge from the dying larva. They immediately wrap themselves in a cocoon of silk and commence pupation. When the adult wasps emerge in autumn they parasitise further larvae and the process is twice repeated during the next nine months.

The butterfly is a *Priority Species* in Northern Ireland (UK) and is on the *Check List of Protected and Rare Species* in the Republic of Ireland. It was first "listed" in Appendix II of the Bern Convention of 1979 and subsequently in Annex II of the EU (EEC) Habitats Directive of 1992. It is the only Annex II butterfly species in Ireland and the State has long been required to protect it by the designation of SACs.

SATYRIDAE

Speckled Wood   *Pararge aegeria tircis*   Breachfhéileacán coille

First brood

General

The Speckled Wood is typically seen patrolling along hedgerows or partially shaded paths, 'dancing' singly or in pairs in the dappled sunlight, or basking in the sun with wings outstretched. This butterfly is unusual in that it may overwinter as either the larva or the pupa, thus resulting in several overlapping generations of adults from spring to early October. Heath and Emmet (1990) state that adults from overwintered pupae have larger and paler yellow patches, whereas those from overwintered larvae have greater wingspans and, together with second and third generation adults, smaller yellow patches.

Distribution

935 squares. It is widespread in woodland, copses, scrub, hedgerows, laneways, parks and larger gardens [Habitat: WN, WD, WL, WS]. Because of its overlapping generations, this butterfly is almost always on the wing and hence it is the most commonly reported species in Ireland, but not numerically the most plentiful. In Britain, it is expanding rapidly in the north and west of Scotland due to climate change, and has recently colonised the Isle of Man. It is prevalent in Europe as far as the Urals and is spreading northwards, and occurs in North Africa.

Adult

Wingspan is 46-56 mm. The ground colour of the uppersides is brown. The

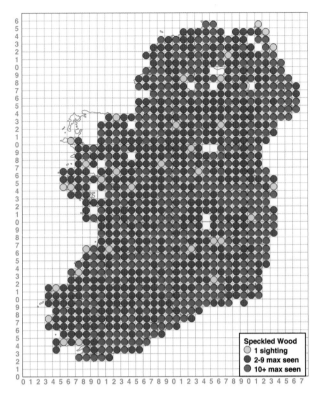

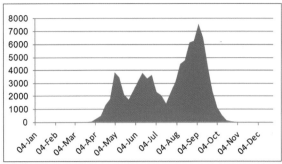

Speckled Wood
○ 1 sighting
● 2-9 max seen
● 10+ max seen

forewing is dappled with pale yellow patches. The sub-apical area has a black ocellus with a white pupil. The hindwing has six pale yellow patches, four of which are in the sub-marginal area. The first three patches have a white-pupilled black ocellus. The cilia is white, chequered with brown. The underside of the forewing is greyish-brown with a similar pattern to the upperside. The hindwing is darker distally with the post-discal area reddish brown with a series of 5-6 yellow-pupilled brown ocelli. The female wings are more rounded and the yellow patches are larger and more clearly defined.

Egg
The egg is spheroidal, flattened at the base, 0.7 mm wide x 0.8 mm high, finely reticulate. Initially shiny pale green yellow, it becomes grey before hatching in 4-10 days. Eggs are said to be laid singly on the leaves of broad-bladed grasses such as Cock's-foot, Yorkshire-fog, Common Couch (Scutch) and False Brome.

Larva
25-30 mm is length. The head, larger than the adjacent thorax segment, is green with two lobes and covered with white hairs. The bright green body is slim, tapers towards each end and has two short pale green anal points. A darker green dorsal line is edged with pale green, and there are other less well defined stripes. The ventral surface is a translucent green. Its whole body is

sparsely covered in tiny white setae with a sprinkling of black ones. Larvae rest on grass stems and feed during the day and at night. There are 4-5 instars and it is believed that only larvae that reach third instar by the end of the year can successfully overwinter in cold conditions. The summer brood spends a few weeks in the larval stage but the spring emerging brood may take seven months to mature.

Pupa

The pupa is 18 mm in length, stout with notched head and thorax and abdomen inflated. Initially, the pupa is a translucent bright green but becomes duller and is finely speckled. Wing cases are streaked with dark brown and there may be two rows of white spots on the abdomen. The pupa is attached by short cremaster to a silken pad attached low down to the food plant or litter. Pupation takes up to a month in summer and about six months for the overwintering cohort.

Wall Brown (Wall) *Lasiommata megera* Donnóg an bhalla

General

The Wall Brown is sun-loving and often found basking on bare ground or on walls with its wings incompletely open. It is very alert and difficult to approach. When disturbed the orange-brown of the upper wings is seen as it flies low for a few metres and then settles on a suitable surface. There are two full broods, centred in May and August, and sometimes a partial later one. Its Red List status is *endangered*.

Distribution

441 squares. The Wall Brown is widely distributed on open ground in rocky and heathy habitats along coasts, in brown field sites and on well drained hilly sites, banks and abandoned quarries inland. [Habitat: GS1, HH1, HH2, ER1, ER2, ED1, ED2, CD3, CD6]. Some observers are of the view that a significant country-wide fall off in populations has occurred in recent years. In Northern Ireland its last refuge is in Co Down, but numbers are healthy in Cos Donegal and Sligo.

Adult

Wingspan is 45-53 mm, the female being slightly the larger. The ground colour of the upper surfaces of the *male* forewing is orange-brown with the basal area speckled grey-brown. The veins and wing margins are greyish-brown. Three

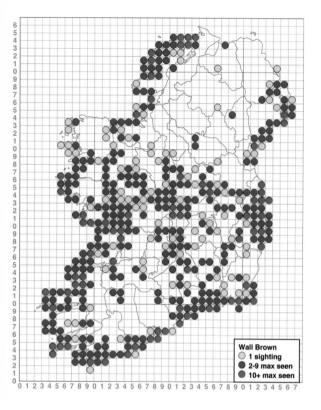

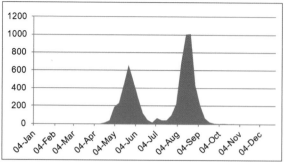

slanted narrow dark bands traverse the wing and a noticeable androconial bar extends from the cell to the middle of inner margin. There is one dark white-pupilled ocellus towards the apex. The ground colour and markings on the underside are lighter. The hindwing is grey and has six brown white-pupilled ocelli. Underneath, the wing patterns are similar with ground colour and markings much paler. The *female* has a significantly paler ground colour and a more rounded forewing.

Egg

The egg is spheroidal, widest near the base, finely reticulate, and 0.8 m wide x 0.9 mm high. It is initially translucent pale-green becoming white prior to hatching within 4-10 days. Several eggs may be deposited close together on food plants such as the Cock's-foot, Yorkshire-fog, Wavy Hair-grass, Fescues and Bent grass species, on the edges of tufts or on exposed roots.

Larva

23-27 mm in length. Its head is bluish-green, larger than the adjacent thorax segment and covered in short hairs. Its bright green body tapers at either end and has two short whitish anal points. It has a dark green dorsal stripe edged with white and three fine white to yellow sub-dorsal lines. The body is covered with white pinacula bearing short grey-white hairs and the spiracles are pale orange. Feeding is mainly nocturnal, and the larva goes through four instars

within a period of about a month. Normally the second summer generation larvae overwinter.

Pupa

The pupa is 16 mm in length, stoutish but more slender than other Satyrids. Its head is notched. The thorax is keeled, dorsally swollen and ventrally flattened. The abdomen is dorsally rounded and ventrally flattened. Overall colour is usually green, dusted with white but it can range to black. Wing veins and margins are white and the green stripe on the abdomen is delineated by two rows of white spots. The over-wintering pupa is attached by a short cremaster to a silken pad on the food plant and it spends seven months in this developmental stage.

Additional Information

Evidence from Britain shows clearly that the Wall Brown is a species undergoing a rapid decline in its population, especially at inland sites. Thomas and Lewington (2010) have stated that such fluctuations have previously occurred, but the reasons remain obscure. Peters (1962) assessed it as being abundant throughout Ulster in suitable habitat. Fifty years on it is on the brink of extinction in Northern Ireland. Elsewhere in Ireland there is evidence suggesting a possible inland decline. This butterfly is a *Priority Species* in Northern Ireland (UK) where it is now restricted to the south and east of Co Down.

Wall Brown

Grayling *Hipparchia semele hibernica* and *H. semele clarensis* Glasán

General

This cryptic (well camouflaged) butterfly rests with it wings closed, ocelli hidden, and its body angled towards the sun. It spends much of its time basking on dry sand, gravel or rock surfaces. When disturbed, it moves rapidly and merges into the background a few metres away. It may be found taking nectar from plants such as Wild Thyme and Heather (Ling). Two sub-species have been recognised for Ireland: *clarensis*, which is found on the limestone pavements of Cos Galway and Clare, is paler and greyer than the more widespread *hibernica* (De Lattin 1952). Its Red Data status is *not threatened*.

Distribution

237 squares. It is mainly a coastal species found on sand dunes and along coastal cliffs, in heathy places and rocky substrate, but is found inland in gravelly areas such as eskers and sand pits and on limestone pavement. Its headquarters is arguably the Burren and Co Galway and it is also found on offshore islands including Tory, Aran Islands and Inishturk. Inland sites include areas in Cos Fermanagh and Roscommon [Habitat: HH1, HH2, ER2, ER3, ED1, CD2/CD3, GS1]. Being very well camouflaged it is easily overlooked, but its non-coastal frequency appears to have declined considerably. In Britain it is predominantly coastal and in Europe it extends northwards into Scandinavia and is absent from part of the southeast. It is also present in western and northern Asia.

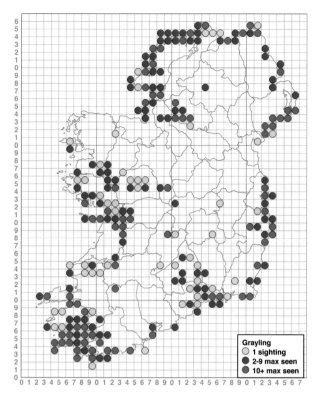

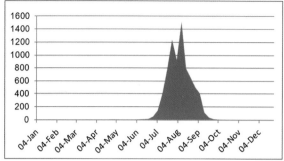

Grayling
○ 1 sighting
● 2-9 max seen
● 10+ max seen

Adult

Wingspan is 51-62 mm. The upperside of the male forewing has a warm brown ground colour. There are two dark brown ocelli in the post-discal area and androconial scales along the cubital vein. The hindwing margins are deep brown and the outer margin is scalloped. A single ocellus is present near the anal angle. Underneath, the forewing sub-marginal area is dark brown, mottled grey-white. The basal and discal area is fulvous-orange and ocelli are as above. The hindwing is dappled with light grey and brown, with the basal and discal areas chocolate-brown and streaked with a grey-white band. The female is very similar to the male with darker undersides.

Egg

The egg is a flattened sphere, 0.7 mm wide x 0.8 mm high, with about 30 longitudinal ribs which merge at the top. Initially it is white becoming dull yellow-green before hatching in 11-20 days. Eggs have been found singly on a number of grasses, depending on the habitat, including Fescues, Hair-grass and Marram, False-brome and Meadow-grass species.

Larva

26-32 mm in length. Its body narrows towards the head and tapers posteriorally to two anal points and is pale yellow, with a prominent black-brown mid-

dorsal line and red brown stripes in the sub-dorsal region. The head is light - brown with darker stripes continuous with those of the body.

Pupa
The pupa is 16 mm in length. The ground colour is reddish to dark brown without markings. Its head, thorax and abdomen are rounded with a waist between thorax and abdomen. The spiracles are prominent with a black projection on its thorax. Pupation takes place underground around June in a cocoon of soil particles tied with silk and is about four weeks in duration.

Additional information
Baynes (1964) commented that most of Irish Graylings are large and brightly coloured, but in "some mountainous districts such as Burren, Co. Clare and Connemara, Co. Galway, a smaller dull coloured form occurs, but it is not constant". There has been debate whether the adult's behaviour of adjusting its wing angle towards the sun is for concealment (minimisation of shadow), or for thermoregulation (control of body temperature). Findlay *et al.* (1983) have concluded that temperature control is the driving force for this behaviour. Rapid and large scale extraction of gravel from quarry sites is probably a significant factor in its decline. This butterfly is a Priority Species in Northern Ireland (UK).

Gatekeeper *Pyronia tithonus britanniae* Geatóir

General

The Gatekeeper's alternate name is the Hedge Brown and, where there are hedgerows interrupted by openings, it is seen patrolling back and forth. It may be found on the margins of scrubby grassland and woodland glades [Habitat: GS2, WL1, WS1, WD1]. Unlike the Meadow Brown, it is rarely found in open grassland and in the Raven, Co Wexford, it is to be seen in well lit areas throughout the conifer woodland on the dunes. It derives nectar from Brambles and other plants such as Ragwort.

Visitors to Ireland are not the only people who misidentify female Meadow Browns as Gatekeepers, especially specimens of the former which have twin white pupils in their eyespots. However, the Meadow Brown is normally significantly larger. The Gatekeeper spends a considerable amount of time basking with open wings. It is single brooded with the main flight period from mid-July into mid-September. Its Red List status is *near threatened*.

Distribution

78 squares. The current known distribution is along a mainly coastal strip from Wicklow to south Kerry. It is now largely absent from East Cork and continues

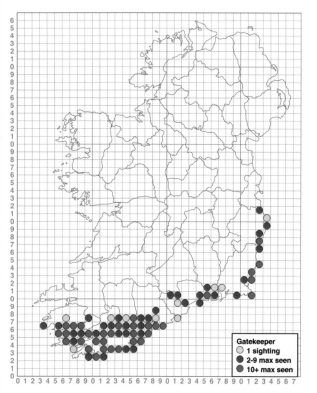

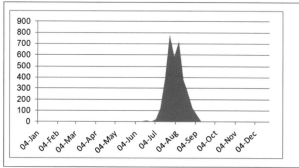

to be very scarce in Wicklow. Its frequency in Ireland is considered to have declined (SOBBI). Surprisingly, there is no evidence here of it spreading northwards as a result of climate change. In Britain, it has expanded in north Yorkshire and Durham. It is a Western Palaearctic species, known in southern Europe from Spain eastwards to Asia Minor and the Caucasus.

Adult

The wingspan is 37-48 mm. The ground colour of the upperside of the *male* is dark brown with a large bright fulvous central area and dark brown androconial scales. The sub-apical ocellus is dark brown with twin white pupils. The hindwing has a smaller fulvous patch and a white pupilled ocellus and a scalloped outer margin. The base and inner margin are clad in long, silky hair scales. The *underside* of the forewing is paler than above and the hindwing has a mixture of black, fulvous and orange with most ocelli minimised to white pupils. There is a yellow to fawn subcostal patch in the discal area and a fawn band traverses the hindwing. The upperside forewing of the *female* is paler and the hindwing has more extensive orange. Her appearance underneath is similar to the male.

Egg

The egg is a flattened sphere, 0.7 mm x 0.7 mm, with c.16 thin longitudinal

ribs. It is pale yellow when laid, becoming pale mottled brown and then grey before hatching in 3-4 weeks. Eggs are laid singly on the blades of finer grasses such as Bents or Fescues but sometimes are scattered close to the ground. 100-200 eggs are laid by each female.

Larva
23-26 mm in length. The body is stout, tapering towards either end with a two-lobed brown head. The final instar has two colour forms, light green or yellow-brown, with darker dorsal and paler lateral stripes. It is covered with short white setae. The freshly hatched larva is grey and feeds until late October and then hibernates until spring when it recommences nocturnal feeding. Pupation commences by early July.

Pupa
The pupa is short (12 mm long) and stout with two blunt points on its head and a distended thorax. The ground colour is cream with two rows of brown spots on the dorsal surface of the abdomen and dark streaks and patches on the wings and elsewhere. The pupa is attached to its larval exuviae low down in vegetation. Pupation occurs around late June and takes about three weeks.

Additional Information
Kane (1901) viewed this species as almost confined to the southern counties and considered it scarce in Co Wicklow with its headquarters in West Cork. Baynes (1964) refers to a report from Philip Graves of a single male at Killiney c.1901, but states that it was not resident in Co Dublin. The more recent Atlas (Ní Lamhna 1980) contains two records from the county but current work has not reconfirmed its presence. There are old reports from Co Monaghan and Glenarm, Co Antrim (BNFC 1874). Ken Bond (pers. com.) has suggested that the range of this species is limited by the cooler and wetter higher ground to the north and west of its current distribution. A variety of scientific and common names (*e.g.* Small Meadow Brown) were used and at one time the male and female forms were believed to be separate species.

Meadow Brown *Maniola jurtina iernes* Donnóg an fhéir

General

One of Ireland's commonest species, it is found in large numbers from mid-June to early September. It is single brooded. In flight, some dark males may be confused with the Ringlet. The presence of a second pupil in the ocellus sometimes leads to confusion with the Gatekeeper which is smaller and quite different in colouration and underwing pattern. When disturbed it typically drops low in the vegetation and initially one ocellus is visible before its wings completely overlap.

Distribution

969 squares. Its distribution is countrywide extending to western offshore islands. The habitat encompasses open situations in meadows, woodland clearings, coastal sand dunes, roadside verges, waste ground, urban parks and medium to large gardens. It is often seen flying with the Ringlet but prefers drier habitat. It is considered to have undergone some decline in numbers. In Britain it is widespread but is absent from the Shetlands. It is a western Palaearctic species found from North Africa to Scandinavia and eastwards to the Urals and Asia Minor.

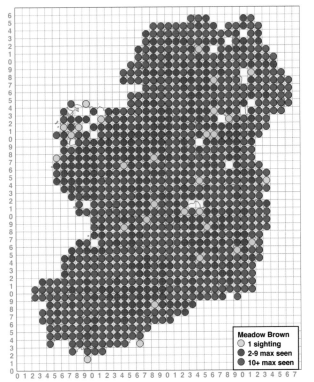

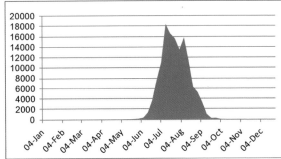

Meadow Brown
○ 1 sighting
● 2-9 max seen
● 10+ max seen

Adult

Wingspan is 33-37 mm. Appearance is quite variable but both sexes are similar. The upperside of the forewing of the *male* is fuscous brown, the basal area is speckled black and the sex brand extends from the discal cell to the inner border. The sub-apical black ocellus in space 6 often has two white pupils, and is set in a bright fulvous band. The similarly coloured hindwing is paler and lacks an ocellus. The underside forewing ground colour is limited to the costa and the outer and inner margins. The central region is bright-fulvous and divided into darker proximal and paler distal areas, by a broad fuscous band. The ocellus is as above. The scalloped hindwing is paler with minute or absent sub-terminal ocelli. The upperside of the forewing of the *female* has a fulvous post-discal area which is broader and paler than for the male. The underside forewing has a greater colour contrast than the male in the central area. The hindwing is bright-fulvous.

Egg

The egg is 0.5 mm x 0.5 mm, which is relatively small for a butterfly of this size. It is a ribbed sphere, flattened at top and bottom and is pale cream when freshly laid, becoming blotched and finally grey before hatching after up to a month. Eggs may be laid singly on blades of grass or jettisoned at the foot of vegetation. Hatching takes place after about three weeks.

Larva

25-28 mm in length. The bright green body is stouter in the middle, with a darker dorsal and a narrow white lateral stripe. The ventral surface and the head are dark green. The spiracles are red and the whole body is covered with short grey-white setae. The larva initially eats its eggshell and then feeds on grasses. In captivity, the food plants include Meadow-grass, Common Couch and Fescue species.

Pupa

The pupa is 16 mm long, its head has two short lobes and the abdomen is strongly curved. The pupa's markings are variable with the ground colour a translucent green. Appearance varies from pale forms with small black dots, to darker forms with extended black-brown markings. The colour variations may be related to environmental factors such as light, temperature and moisture. There is no cremaster but the pupa hangs from grass, attached to its larval exuvia. Pupation takes 2-3 weeks depending on ambient temperature and commences at the end of May.

Additional Information

Graves (1930) made a study of the Meadow Brown in Britain and Ireland while holidaying in Kerry. He concluded that the Irish form is larger and brighter and more varied underneath. He noted more frequent "bipupillation" of the apical ocellus which tended to be larger, and differences in wing shape. He proposed a new sub-species *iernes* for Ireland. The Dowdswell (1981) monograph *The life of the meadow brown* throws interesting light on variation in forms of this species.

Ringlet *Aphantopus hyperantus* Fáinneog

General

A dark brown butterfly, usually found in damp meadows, marshes, edges of woodlands and hedgerows. Unlike other butterflies it continues to fly in light rain in mild conditions. The Ringlet can be confused with a dark coloured Meadow Brown when in flight, but its white marginal scales helps to differentiate them. A key difference is the presence of prominent ocelli on the underwing which are visible at rest. It is univoltine with a flight season from the end of May to early September.

Distribution

912 squares. Widespread, its distribution often overlaps with the Meadow Brown but it has a preference for damper areas. Extensive drainage for agricultural purposes has reduced the available habitat. In Britain, it is scarce or absent in the Midlands and north of England and central and northern Scotland. In Europe it is absent from southern Iberia and Italy and northern Scandinavia, and extends eastwards through Asia to Japan.

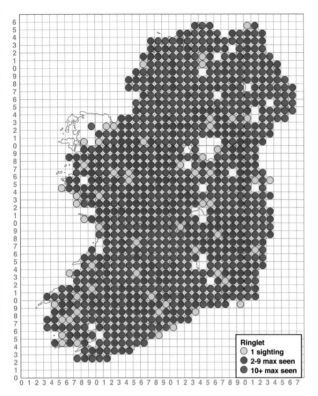

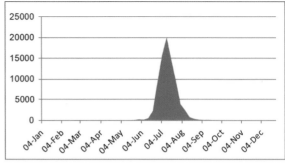

Adult

Wingspan is 42-52 mm. The ground colour of its forewings varies from dark brown to almost black with a whitish cilia and two obscure black ocelli on forewing. The hindwing is similar with 2-3 more obvious ocelli. The underside of the forewing has a paler ground colour with three white-pupilled black ocelli surrounded by a yellow disk and the hindwing has five ocelli. The female is very similar in appearance but has a paler ground colour.

Egg

The egg is dome-shaped with a concave base, 0.9 mm wide x 0.8 mm high, shiny, finely ribbed with a reticulate pattern. Initially, it is pale yellow becoming darker with age, and hatches in 11-20 days. In the wild, eggs are scattered singly near ground level among tussocky food plant grasses which include Cock's-foot and False Brome, the latter being very much a plant of shade.

Larva

21-24 mm in length, with a brown head covered with tubercules endowed with fine hairs. The ochreous body, is speckled dorsally with short reddish streaks and is densely covered with short pale brown hairs. The overall appearance is yellow with some brown. A brown sub-dorsal line fades away on the thoracic

segments and below the black spiracles is a pale lateral line with a red-brown line on either side. Its legs are pale brown. The larva enters partial hibernation in October, feeding at night only in mild weather and is fully grown by June. There are five instars.

Pupa
11-13 mm in length, it is stout and rounded, and inflated at middle of its body with the abdomen abruptly tapered. The female pupa is slightly longer than the male form. The body is yellow-brown to amber with darker spots and streaks and paler wings, becoming darker and almost black before completion of pupation after ten days. The pupa is formed in a primitive cocoon of silk and is unattached low down near ground level.

Additional Information
A number of variations have been reported mainly concerned with the ocelli. In aberration *lanceolata*, the ocelli are elongate and pear-shaped with pupils developed into streaks. Baynes (1964) reported specimens tending towards this form from Inver, Donegal and Huggins (1960) reported "a very small race" above 600 ft (180 m) on the Caha Mountains in Co Cork.

Small Heath   *Coenonympha pamphilus pamphilus*   Fraochán beag

♂

General

The Small Heath may be confused with the Large Heath, which is an insect of wet bogs, and both species may occur together on the margins. Neither size nor habitat is a totally reliable criterion for differentiation of the species. Generally, the Small Heath flies on bright days close to the ground and resettles after disturbance with its wings closed. Flight periods span mid-May to mid-September. The number of broods needs investigation but the position generally appears to be one main brood with a second partial brood in some coastal areas which may give rise to some overlap in the following year. Red List status is *near threatened*.

Distribution

527 squares. The Small Heath occurs in a wide variety of habitat with fine grasses, especially in semi-natural and rough grassland, heathland and coastal sand dunes [Habitat: GS1, GS2, HH1, HH2, CD3, PB4]. In the latter habitat it may be found in larger numbers. Its populations and distribution appear to

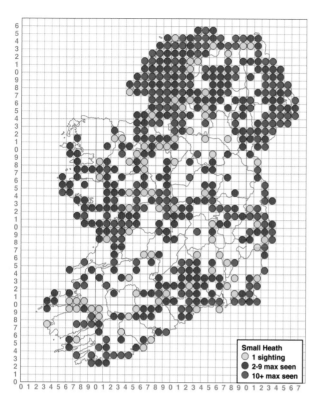

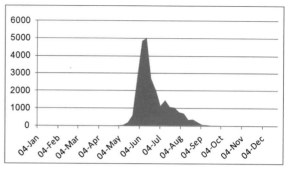

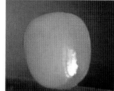

Small Heath
○ 1 sighting
● 2-9 max seen
● 10+ max seen

have declined especially in areas of intensive farming in the Midlands and East. However, systematic recording in Donegal suggests that the species may sometimes be overlooked. In Britain it is a widespread species and occurs throughout Europe and North Africa extending into Asia.

Adult
Wingspan is 33-37 mm. Appearance is quite variable but both sexes are almost identical. The insect invariably settles with its wings closed. The upperside of the forewing is tawny-yellow; the basal area is speckled-black and the outer margin is grey-black with one ocellus towards the apex which lacks a pupil. The hindwing is slightly darker without an ocellus. The underside of the forewing is darker than above with a white-pupilled ocellus. The underside hindwing basal half is black and speckled fulvous. This dark area has an irregular distal margin, beyond which the wing is pale buff and speckled except for a whitish post-discal patch. A post-discal series of 3-4 white dots occurs in spaces 2-5. The cilia is long, pale buff, extending from vein four to the costa.

Egg
The egg is almost spherical, 0.6 mm wide x 0.7 mm high, with a sunken micropyle and about 50 ribs. It is pale green when laid, becoming duller green

Small Heath

with purplish-grey blotches, before hatching in 11-20 days. Eggs are scattered on grass leaves or on dead plant matter where the larval food plants, Fescues, Bents and Meadow-grass species grow.

Larva
18-20 mm in length, with a green head that is larger than its adjacent thoracic segment. The body is overall green, darker ventrally, and covered with small white tubercules with short curved hairs. The mature larva has three dark longitudinal stripes bordered with white. The spiracular stripe is light brownish-green. A yellow-green sub-spiracula line runs the length of the body. The anal points are pinkish and the legs have a hint of lilac. The Small Heath overwinters as a larva.

Pupa
The pupa is short and stout with a rounded head and is 8-9 mm in length. The ground colour is pale green, peppered with darker green spots and the wings may be streaked with brown. The cremaster is yellow brown and the pupa is suspended from a silken pad from vegetation for 3-4 weeks before the first generation emerges in May.

Additional Information
The sub-species found in Ireland and almost all of Britain is *pamphilus*. Its main threat is the loss of rough grassland and upland areas due to scrub removal, reseeding, and afforestation. This butterfly is a Priority Species in Northern Ireland (UK).

Small Heath

Large Heath   *Coenonympha tullia polydama* and *C. tullia scotica*
Fraochán mór

scotica

polydama

General

This is a very variable butterfly and while two 'sub-species' or races have been recognised in Ireland and three in Britain, it is generally accepted that they are in fact different phenotypes rather than genotypes. On open raised bog, the Large Heath is often seen flying rapidly close to vegetation. On the margins, it may sometimes be found in the company of the Small Heath and size alone is not sufficient to discriminate between them. Normally, the Large Heath rests with its wings closed, but when taking nectar on heather species, part of their upperside may be seen. In dullish but warm weather, a small amount of sunshine is sufficient for it to become active. The species is univoltine but its flight period in different sites is quite variable ranging from early June to mid-July with rare August sightings. Its Red Data status is *vulnerable*.

Distribution

176 squares. Often overlooked because of its relatively isolated habitat of wet raised bog, blanket bog and moorland, it still can be found in midland raised bogs which have been spared the extensive damage caused by drainage and peat extraction, and sometimes on older traditional cutaway bog [Habitat: PB1-4]. In Co Donegal it is widely distributed west of Lough Swilly where habitat is suitable and it ranges from the south of the county eastwards through Cos Fermanagh and

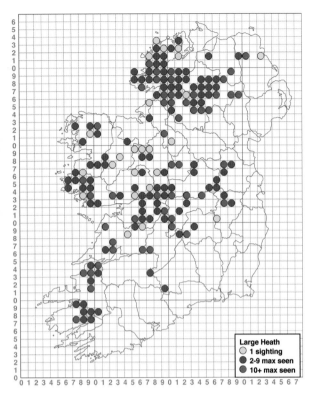

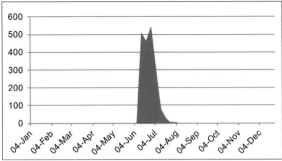

Large Heath
○ 1 sighting
● 2-9 max seen
● 10+ max seen

Tyrone into the Garron Plateau in Co Antrim. In Britain it is predominately a northerly species. It is found across Europe, Asia, Canada and western United States. The Large Heath is considered under threat in Europe as a whole (van Swaay and Warren 1999; van Swaay *et al.* 2010), but not within the EU(27).

Adult

Wingspan c.40 mm. The sexes are similar in appearance, with the female of a lighter hue. The descriptions below relate to the males of the two sub-species found in Ireland.

scotica: The ground colour of the upperside of forewing is pale ochre and the sub-apical ocellus is much reduced or absent. The hindwing is darker and sometimes without an ocellus. The underside of the forewing is similar with the apex and the terminal area grey and an ocellus may be present. The hindwing has a grey ground colour, a broad transverse white band, a darker basal area and 1-2(-6) ocelli are present along outer margins. Extreme forms may be difficult to differentiate from the Small Heath.

polydama: The upperside of the forewing is darker, usually with two dark-centred ocelli and the hindwing has up to four ocelli. Underneath there is a sub-apical ocellus and 1-3 lower down. The hindwing has 0-6 white-pupilled ocelli. In general, northern forms are much less spotted and closer to *scotica* but a considerable range may be found on some sites.

Egg

The egg is spherical shaped but truncated at the top, 0.6 mm wide x 0.8 mm high, with a swollen micropyle, and many lateral and irregular longitudinal ribs giving a reticulated appearance. Initially pale coloured, it develops brown blotches

Large Heath

and becomes grey prior to hatching. Eggs are laid singly on Hare's-tail Cotton-grass and possibly on Narrow-leaved Cotton-grass.

Larva
22-26 mm in length, with a green head, small brown ocelli and a brown mouth. The body is green, broadest one-third of length from head, with a very dark green dorsal line bordered by a thin off-white stripe. Additional white or pink stripes are found in both the sub-dorsal and spiracular regions. The larvae of the sub-species are indistinguishable. The third instar enters hibernation in September, recommences feeding in spring and the fifth instar pupates at the end of May. In captivity, the larva will feed on grasses such as Fescues.

Pupa
11 mm in length. Bright green in the early stages but later it becomes deeper in colour with a dark line along the inner margin of the wings and 0-4 black streaks on the wing cases. The cremaster has dense amber coloured hooks. Pupation takes place on a plant stem and takes about 23 days.

Additional information
Computer modelling (*e.g.* Settele *et al.* 2008) would suggest that climate change in Britain and Ireland may well result in the extinction of the species by the end of the 21st century. In captivity, the larvae will also feed on a variety of fine grasses, Jointed Rush and White-beaked Sedge. The latter is no longer considered to be the preferred foodplant in the wild. Melling (1987) has reported that the Large Heath can be reared on a two year cycle with larvae pupating in their second year, but it is not known whether this phenomenon occurs in Ireland. The different forms of the adult may be the result of environmental factors such as temperature, sunshine and rainfall. This butterfly is a Priority Species in Northern Ireland (UK).

VAGRANTS and RARE MIGRANTS

Monarch *Danaus plexxipus* Bleachtfhéileacán

This large butterfly's prominent black and orange markings are classic warning signs to potential predators of its toxicity. The first known Irish report was from Castletownshend, Co Cork, in October 1916 and the next report was 16 years later from Corbally, Co Limerick. Baynes (1964) was aware of ten sightings and there have been occasional subsequent reports. 1999 was the most prolific year when at least four individuals were seen (Cromien & O'Connor 2001). Reports are typically from bird watchers along the southern coast but the Monarch was seen in Belfast, Co Antrim and at St John's Point, Co Down in 1995.

The Monarch (Milkweed) is resident in America from south Peru to Canada and its migration patterns and hibernation sites are well documented. It is also found in India, Australia, New Zealand, the Canaries (from 1880) and the south of Spain (1980). There is evidence that Irish vagrants originate in North America, as they have been accompanied by birds from the same region driven off course by residual hurricanes. Their survival time in Ireland is very limited and the Milkweed larval food plants do not occur in the wild in Ireland.

Monarch
○ 1916-2010

Monarch

Camberwell Beauty *Nymphalis antiopa* Bé na fallainge

First reported from Caragh Lake, Kerry, in 1865 (Baynes 1964), this large butterfly is an infrequent vagrant/migrant to Ireland and is indigenous in Northern and Eastern Europe and North America. There have been some 30 observations in Ireland. 1995 was an exceptional year with four sightings in Northern Ireland and one from Co Donegal. The origin of the 1995 vagrants are likely to have been North America where it is known as the Mourning Cloak. Its larval food plants, Willow and Poplar are plentiful in Ireland but it is reckoned that our damp and mild climate inhibits successful breeding and hibernation.

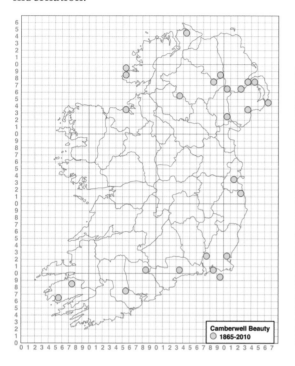

Camberwell Beauty
○ 1865-2010

Camberwell Beauty

Pale Clouded Yellow *Colias hyale*
Buíóg liath

Kane first reported this butterfly in 1868 from Howth, Dublin, and in the south of Ireland flying with Clouded Yellows. There were three reports in 1973 and two from the south/south-east coast in 1974 (Hickin 1992), from Cos Wexford, Waterford and Cork. There have been other unconfirmed sightings which are difficult to evaluate in the absence of either specimen or photograph. It is easily confused with the pale *helice* form of the Clouded Yellow which may comprise up to 15% of females. The very similar Berger's Clouded Yellow has never been reported from Ireland. The Pale Clouded Yellow is found eastwards from the Pyrenees and northwards to Denmark.

Pale Clouded Yellow

Bath White *Pontia daplidice* Bánóg bhath

There are only three confirmed reports from Ireland, comprising one from Wexford (1893) and two from Kerry consisting of four individuals in 1945 and one in the following year. This species could be confused with the female Orange Tip, due to the blotchy green marbling under the hindwing, although the normal flight season for the Bath White is usually late summer.

Bath White

Queen of Spain Fritillary

Queen of Spain Fritillary *Issoria lathonia* Fritileán niamhrach

There have only been three confirmed records of this butterfly in Ireland, from Kerry in 1864 and from Co Waterford nearly a hundred years later in 1960 and again in 2011 (Tony Bryant). A 1975 report from West Cork was later withdrawn. There was also a recent report from a ferry near Tuskar Rock off the Wexford coast. It is widespread in Europe from Spain and Romania to the Baltic and is a well-known migrant. There is some evidence of successful breeding in Suffolk in England during the 1990s (*Millennium Atlas*). It is distinguished from other fritillaries by the prominent elongated metallic silver blotches under the hindwing.

Vagrants and Rare Migrants

American Painted Lady *Vanessa virginiensis* Áilleán Meiriceánach

This is a very rare trans-Atlantic vagrant, only confirmed in Ireland on three occasions between 1901 and 1930 in Cos Cork and Kerry. The American Painted Lady resembles our familiar North African migrant, and may perhaps not be recognised. The forewing of *V. virginiensis* is more indented, the ground colour is a dark brown and the black bars in the median area are narrower. Its hindwing is a deeper grey with a white band from the costa to the inner margin, it has two prominent dark blue eyespots and two large spots rather than a row with a dark blue centre. There are three old records from Cos Cork and Kerry. This species is resident in the Canaries.

American Painted Lady

Small Mountain Ringlet *Erebia epiphron* (sub-species *mnemon*)
Fáinneog shléibhe

The earliest report of this little brown butterfly was in 1854 on the slopes of Croagh Patrick, Mayo (Birchall 1866) and the last record is for 1897. So, in the absence of any further records this species is technically considered to be extinct. There are six specimens in the National Museum in Dublin, three of them labelled: "Croagh Ptk? Fetherston H. 64-97"; "Sligo McClean 17.1895"; one with three labels ["Mr Birchall", "Male Co Mayo", "Given by Mr. E. Birchall"] and the remaining two each labelled "Coll. Kane 74.1903" with no indication of origin (Chalmers-Hunt 1982). There is a seventh in the Ulster Museum in Belfast labelled "Irish 30/6/18" whose provenance is obscure. Canon R McClean's location which has been stated as "being on the hilly slopes near the eastern shore of Lough Gill" (= Leitrim, not Sligo) is considered improbable. It should be remembered that Kane travelled widely and may well have collected specimens when he was working on his *European Butterflies*. In Britain, the butterfly occurs on higher ground in Cumbria and south-west

Small Mountain Ringlet

Scotland and is a species of the Alps and Dolomites on mainland Europe. Kane (1901), in his *Supplementary List*, refers to having been fortunate to meet with a few specimens on Nephin and in the Clare Island Report of 1912 he belatedly confirms his Nephin report giving the date as "9th June, 1897" stating that it only flies in bright sunshine (Paul 1985). No related labelled specimen from Kane is known. Donovan (1936) also refers to a specimen held by Dudley Westropp labelled "Mr. Birchall" but its origin and whereabouts are also a mystery. Was the species on the verge of extinction when it was found in Ireland? Its preferred larval food plant is understood to be Mat-grass which is not uncommon on grassy higher ground. Being a difficult butterfly to find, the possibility of it still existing in Ireland should not be entirely dismissed.

Heath Fritillary   *Melitaea athalia*   Fritileán fraoigh

The first and only report from Ireland was by Birchall about 1865. He described the Heath Fritillary as being plentiful in Killarney where its food plant Common Cow-wheat is still to be found. It has a certain resemblance to the Marsh Fritillary but without its mosaic of colours. Is this report an error by Birchall or did he find another species on the brink of extinction? In Britain, it is confined to small areas in the far south and on the European Continent it is found from Spain to Greece and northwards to Scandinavia.

Large Copper   *Lycaena dispar*   Copróg mhór

The male resembles a large Small Copper, while the female is a plain coppery colour all over. It has never been known to be native to Ireland. The Large Copper (sub-species *rutilus* from Germany) was introduced, together with its

Water Dock food plant in 1913/14 to a fen at Greenfield, Co Tipperary by Captain E.B. Purefoy. There it persisted until c.1930. In 1926 further stock (this time sub-species *batavus* from Holland) was released, survived until 1937/38 and was then reintroduced in 1943. The Large Copper finally died out in 1954 when the site ceased to be managed. Henry Heal undertook another introduction near Downpatrick, Co Down in 1970, but although larvae were found the following year, the area was subsequently drained resulting in destruction of the habitat. In Europe, the species ranges from France to Bulgaria and north to southern Finland. Purefoy also tried unsuccessfully to introduce the Cleopatra to Tipperary.

Swallowtail *Papilio machaon* and Long-tailed Blue *Lambides boeticus*

Both these species have been reported in Ireland, but they are not dealt with here because they are certainly not native, and there is no evidence that they have ever been part of the Irish fauna or genuine migrants to the island. The Long-tailed Blue has, on a number of times, emerged from consignments of legumes imported from Kenya. There has also been a sighting of the Tiger Swallowtail *Papilio glaucus*, presumed to be an escape or release from captivity.

Small Skipper *Thymelicus sylvestris* Léimneoir beag

As previously mentioned, there has been an unvalidated report of this species in Ireland. A sighting by Niamh Lennon from Timahoe, Co Kildare in 2011 awaits reconfirmation. In the field, it is quite difficult to distinguish it from the Essex Skipper. The absence of black scales on the underside of the tip of its antennae is a useful differentiation character. But the authors have noted that the Essex Skipper does readily lose scales in this area, as it ages. The Small Skipper's food plants are reported as being a selection of grasses especially Yorkshire-fog which is widespread and common in Ireland. However, the butterfly overwinters as a caterpillar making it more unlikely, compared with the Essex Skipper, that it could have been accidentally transported with dried animal fodder. The Small Skipper is widespread in both England and Wales.

8 Site Descriptions

Introduction

These site descriptions are provided as a rough guide to some places worthwhile visiting in order to see butterflies. The list, which is presented by province and county, is not intended to be comprehensive and the quality and size of the areas will vary. The fact that they are listed here does not imply any right of access, as some of these sites are, in part or in whole, in private ownership, or with restricted entry. In addition, they may not have an obvious or recognised public entrance, so permission to visit should be sought from the current land owners, where appropriate. Entry will be entirely at your own risk. In general, landowners have become less welcoming because of concerns related to the 'site designation' process and anticipated regulation. A variety of terminology is used here to describe site status, for example designated or candidate Special Area of Conservation (SAC), National Park, Natural Heritage Area (NHA), Area of Special Scientific Interest (ASSI) etc. Because of changing site designations, enquiries should be addressed to the appropriate National Authority or to an up-to-date website of the NIEA or NPWS. Unfortunately, the condition of sites can change very rapidly with changes in management regime. In some accounts here mention is made of interesting or scarce plants, not because they are 'butterfly plants', but rather to give the reader an indication of the richness of a site. Butterflies are excellent botanists who are highly skilled in plant identification. Grid references, which are generally given in four digit format (e.g. V9786 for Killarney National Park) are intended to guide visitors to the area and allow them to do their own exploration.

CONNAUGHT

Coole – Garryland Complex SAC/SPA (M4304 & M4103)**, Co Galway** H15

Coole Park, with an area of 363 ha, is located just north of Gort currently just off the N18. The Coole-Garryland reserve contains a variety of floral habitats including well developed woodland with oak and holly on deeper soils, scrubby woodland on karstic limestone and a turlough-lake complex. A large portion of this reserve was formerly owned by Lady Gregory, co-founder with W.B. Yeats of the Abbey Theatre. The turloughs are fringed by a range of habitats on limestone pavement and Buckthorn and Blackthorn are major scrub components. A variety of violet species are present. As might be anticipated, Brimstone, Holly Blue, Purple Hairstreak and Brown Hairstreak butterflies frequent the area. Garryland is the most easterly location from which the Pearl-bordered Fritillary has been confirmed. Entry to this Special Protection Area is via Coole Park or Garryland to the west.

Western side of Lough Corrib: Moycullen to Oughterard (M1939), Co Galway H16

Lough Corrib is situated to the north of Galway city and is the second largest lake in Ireland with an area of approximately 18,000 hectares. The lower Corrib (to the south) is a shallow basin underlain by Carboniferous Limestone. The area being briefly described here is west and south of the lake and is bounded by the N59 on the west, from just south of Moycullen to Oughterard. The karst countryside is a mosaic of limestone pavement and rock outcrop, with lakes, fen, bog and heathland, a mixture of scrub woodland (some now coniferous) and calcareous grassland. Butterflies are plentiful inland from the shores of Lough Corrib. Further exploration is required, but Marsh Fritillary has been found near Oakfield and Garrynagry with Brown Hairstreak, Small Blue and Brimstone at Corranellistrum. The Silver-washed Fritillary and Wall Brown are abundant near Kylemore, the Large Heath south-west of Ballyquirke Lake and the Dingy Skipper at Larragan and Hurney Point. The Pearl-bordered Fritillary was seen once near Carrowmoreknock in the mid-1980s, but not more recently. This locale is under pressure from 'development', agricultural 'improvement' and peat extraction.

Lough Carra

Lough Carra SPA (M1872), Co Mayo H26

East of the N84 from Ballinrobe to Castlebar, Lough Carra is a mostly shallow, hard water lake with a surface area of around 1,560 hectares. The lake, which extends for over 9 km along its long axis, lies to the north-east of Lough Mask, within the Corrib lake and river catchment area. It was one of the best examples in Ireland of a hard water marl lake but is now mesotrophic. The highly indented lake is bordered by limestone and wetland habitats, deciduous woodland and mixed woodland, scrub, grassland, fen, peat bog and heath. Twenty three butterfly species have been recorded. The presence of significant populations of Marsh Fritillary, Silver-washed Fritillary, Holly Blue, Common Blue and Brimstone, together with Dingy Skipper, Grayling and Green Hairstreak, confirm that the lakeshore habitats form a nationally important butterfly area. Wall Brown has also been recorded in the past and there is also the possibility that both species of Wood White occur in the vicinity. There is access to the public at Castleburke, Brownstown and Moore Hall.

Castlesampson Esker

Castlesampson Esker SAC (M9440), Co Roscommon H25

Eskers are ridges of stratified sand and gravel deposited through glaciation and are spread across the middle of Ireland. Many of them have been damaged by agriculture and others have gradually, or rapidly, disappeared as gravel has been extracted for the construction industry. Castlesampson is the most westerly of a cluster of eskers centred on Ardnacloon Hill in south-east County Roscommon. It is approximately 9 km west of Athlone and to the east of Taghmaconnell which is on the R357 from Ballinasloe to Roscommon. The site is dominated by a steep-sided, crescent-shaped esker situated on the south side of a road. Despite extensive gravel extraction parts of the esker and associated pits still survive. The vegetation is a mix of species-rich calcareous and improved grassland species. Plant species found include Wild Thyme, Common Bird's-foot-trefoil, Carline Thistle, Kidney Vetch and a variety of Orchids. Common Blue, Dingy Skipper, Grayling, Small Blue and Cryptic Wood White may be observed here. The neighbouring Breeole Hills are worthy of further exploration.

St John's Wood Nature Reserve (M9956), **Lough Ree, Co Roscommon** H25

St John's Wood is on the western shores of Lough Ree, the fourth largest lake in Ireland, on the River Shannon system. The woodland, in a limestone depression, is recognised as the largest and least altered woodland in the Midlands. The periphery of St. John's Wood has bog woodland containing Birch and Alder Buckthorn on cutaway peat. The main wood contains Hazel, Pedunculate Oak, Holly, Yew, Wild Cherry, Bird Cherry and Irish Whitebeam. Notable butterflies are the Brimstone and Purple Hairstreak with Holly Blue to be anticipated. As part of experimental management this old woodland has been subject to recent coppicing but this has not resulted in any significant enhancement of open areas with nectar sources. Access is via very narrow roads from Lecarrow on the N61 from Athlone to Roscommon, or possibly by boat from the lough.

Bunduff and Mullaghmore

Bunduff Lough, Machair and **Trawalua/ Mullaghmore SAC** (G7155 etc.), **Co Sligo** H28

This district is situated on the south side of Donegal Bay, 5 km south-west of Bundoran off the N15 from Sligo to Ballyshannon, near Cliffoney. Sandunes and machair are present and further inland fen vegetation extends to the south-west of the Bunduff Lough. Grass-of-Parnassus, Common Spotted Orchid and Marsh Helleborine are prominent members of the plant community. This area is rich in invertebrates especially butterflies, moths and hoverflies, and the Hairy Dragonfly has been recorded here. Marsh Fritillary is plentiful in the grazed wet fields and areas beside the lake. Orange Tip, Meadow Brown and Ringlet are widespread in season as are Cryptic Wood White, Grayling and Small Copper. Large Heath and Small Blue have been recorded in the general area.

LEINSTER

Portrane Burrow (O2552) and Corballis (O2448), Co Dublin H21

This area in the north of the county was formerly extremely rich in habitat and still boasts of the tallest sand dunes in Ireland. The peninsula is bounded on the west by the Dublin to Belfast railway line and is accessible from Donabate station and the nearby M1 motorway. Much has changed over the years with the spread of temporary and permanent holiday homes, the virtual disappearance

Portrane towards Rush

of livestock grazing and a proliferation of golf courses. Green-winged Orchid and some of Ireland's rarer poppies still survive in well-drained sandy habitat. One of the private golf links has been sensitively managed permitting Small Blue, Grayling and Wall Brown to continue to exist in viable numbers. On the seaside towards the north end of the Portrane Burrow, Kidney Vetch is locally plentiful with significant pockets of Small Blue and occasional Dark Green Fritillary and Cryptic Wood White sightings have been made.

Lullymore West Bog (N6926), Co Kildare H19

This 4.5 ha site is part of the Bog of Allen and is located on the north western edge of the mineral soil island of Lullymore, approximately 7 km from Allenwood off the R414 to Rathangan. The site is mainly cutaway bog sheltered by a conifer plantation, birch/willow woodland and scrub. Marsh Fritillary is found in a damp grassland area dominated by Purple Moor-grass. The site is undergoing experimental management to encourage selected indigenous Lepidoptera namely the Marsh Fritillary and Dingy Skipper – the only site in the RoI being specifically managed for butterflies. More than twenty species of butterfly have been recorded here including the Brimstone, Cryptic Wood White, Dark Green Fritillary, Silver-washed Fritillary, Wall Brown and Holly Blue. The

Lullymore

food plants for the Brimstone – Buckthorn and Alder Buckthorn – both grow in the immediate area. The site is owned by the Irish Peatland Conservation Council which has its headquarters, the Bog of Allen Nature Centre, nearby.

Thomastown Quarry SAC (S54), Co Kilkenny H11

Thomastown Quarry is situated along the R700 north of the town. This site is in private ownership. It comprises a disused limestone quarry in which an excellent range of calcareous habitat has developed. On deeper calcareous soils species such as Quaking Grass, Lady's Bedstraw, Carline Thistle, Common Rest-harrow and Pyramidal Orchid flourish. In the presence of an abundance of Meadow Vetchling and Common Bird's-foot-trefoil it is not surprising to find both Cryptic Wood White and the Dingy Skipper which is rare in the south-east of Ireland. These two species may also be seen at the Ahenny Quarries near Windy Gap.

Raheenmore Bog (N4432), Clara Bog (N2530) and Mongans Bog (N0330) SACs, Co Offaly H18

These three raised bogs are considered to be the best of the few remaining relatively intact raised bogs in the Midlands. The inexperienced visitor should take extreme care in the treacherous boggy terrain. Raheenmore, in a small basin in the catchment of the Brosna and the Boyne, is situated about 5 km west of Daingean. It is a classical example of a Midland Raised Bog and has been the subject of a major international study (Schouten 2002). The peat is now the deepest in Ireland, being up to 15 m in places. The bog has a well-developed hummock and hollow system. Peat extraction has ceased and the water levels are being monitored/ controlled. Merlin, grouse and snipe have been known to breed in the area. Large Heath, with a considerable range of colour and markings, has been seen as late as 23rd July and other species are found on the fringes.

Raheenmore Bog

Clara Bog is about 2 km south of Clara and is dissected by a road. The alternative 'official entrance' is from the esker on the N80 to Tullamore. Much of it is state-owned and designated a Statutory Nature Reserve. To the east there a transition into calcareous woodland, and to the north into an esker ridge. Large Heath is numerous on the raised bog and Dingy Skipper, Cryptic Wood White and Brimstone occur on the ridges.

Mongans Bog is 12 km north of Shannonbridge and on the R444 immediately east of the monastic site of Clonmacnoise. It is in a basin surrounded on part of its perimeter by high ground with mineral soil. The bog has well-developed hummocks, pools and 'lawns' and has been an important area for wetland birds. Typical plant species are Cross-leaved Heath, Cotton-grasses and White Beak-sedge. There is a good variety of bog mosses (*Sphagnum* species) and other bryophytes. The adjacent Pilgrim's Way road runs along the esker line. The bog itself is an excellent site for Large Heath and the nearby eskers and Clorhane NHA have a wide range of butterfly species.

Ballyteigue Burrow SAC (S9306), Co Wexford H12

The Burrow stretches westwards, for a distance of 8 km, along the south coast of Wexford from Kilmore Quay to the estuary of the Duncormick River. Ballyteigue has a full range of dunes from embryonic to fixed with a wide range of plants, notably Sea-holly, Wild Pansy, Burnet Rose and the Wild Asparagus. The dune heath element is typified by Bracken and Gorse. Neighbouring estuarine areas have been reclaimed as polders and are intensively managed

Ballyteigue Burrow

for agriculture, but a section of the sand dunes is subject to a more conservative regime. Dark Green Fritillary is extremely plentiful in summer and Meadow Brown and Gatekeeper are on the wing later in the season. Common Blue, Small Copper, Wall Brown, Whites (with the exception of Cryptic Wood White and Brimstone) and Vanessids are numerous.

The Raven Point Nature Reserve (SAC and Ramsar site) (T1124), Co Wexford H12

The Raven SPA is situated on the north side of Wexford Harbour, and incorporates the sand dune system of the Raven Point. The coastal system extends

The Raven

northwards to Blackwater Head. It is accessible from Curracloe on the R742 north of Wexford. Much of the dunes were planted with conifers in the 1930s and 1950s as a coastal defence measure designed to stabilise them and to protect the slobs (polders) behind. The area, amongst and under the mature conifers, is quite open and is criss-crossed by paths providing habitat for the Meadow Brown, Gatekeeper and Silver-washed Fritillary. The Comma has been seen in small numbers in recent years and appears to be resident.

The sand dune system supports a good variety of butterflies including Grayling, Small Blue, the occasional Wall Brown, Common Blue and Small Heath. The migrant Clouded Yellow appeared to be establishing itself here until the cold winter of 2009/10. Dark Green Fritillary is present in small numbers only and the colonising Essex Skipper has recently arrived. Overall, this site should be ranked as one of the most diverse butterfly areas in Ireland. A number of rare and protected plants have also been recorded from the dune system including Round-leaved Wintergreen, Lesser Centaury and Wild Asparagus.

Buckroney and Brittas Dunes (T2979 & T3183), Co Wicklow H20

These sites are a complex of coastal habitats located about 10 km south of Wicklow town on the R750. They comprise two main sand dune systems, Brittas Bay and Buckroney Dunes, separated by the rocky headland of Mizen. This area is very popular with visitors and has suffered considerably from the development of caravan sites and golf courses with resultant degradation and loss of habitat. Nevertheless, it continues to support some rare plant species. Wild Asparagus sub-species *prostratus* in its most northerly Irish station, Meadow Saxifrage, Green-flowered Helleborine, Bird's-foot and Spring Vetch are the most notable plants. Sufficient habitat survives to allow the continued presence of Grayling, Small Blue, a substantial colony of Dark Green Fritillary, Wall Brown, Small Copper and other more common species.

Glen of the Downs

Glen of the Downs SAC (O2611), Co Wicklow H20

This site is a semi-natural Oak wood situated within the largest glacial overflow channel in Ireland. It is bisected by the Dublin to Wexford N11 about 7 km south of Bray and, despite recent road widening, has largely survived. Much of the woodland cover is Sessile Oak. The shrub layer is sparse but Holly is locally common. This is Purple Hairstreak country and on warm days females can be seen ovipositing at eye level on steep slopes wherever oak branches sweep the ground. Holly Blue, Speckled Wood, Silver-washed Fritillary, Small Copper, Wall Brown are all reported from here but there have been no recent sightings of the Cryptic Wood White.

The rather similar Deputy's Pass woodland is near Glenealy and is part of an internationally important series of Oak woods in Co Wicklow (Glendalough, Clara Vale and Ballinacor amongst others), which retain a significant part of their original characteristics.

MUNSTER

The Burren (R3194), Co Clare H9

The Burren region of Co Clare is well known for its karst landscape and flora. It is generally considered to be the area bounded by Ballyvaughan, Kinvara, Tubber, Corofin, Kilfenora and Lisdoonvarna, extending 40 km east to west and 30 km from north to south. Arctic-alpine plants live side-by-side with Lusitanian, calcicole (lime loving) and calcifuge (acid loving) plants. Much of the Burren is designated as a SAC and contains limestone pavement with hazel scrub and a range of deciduous woodland, calcareous grassland, fen, turlough and permanent lake habitat. The National Park, which has its origins in the purchase of a site at Mullaghmore by An Taisce, occupies just 15 km^2 and is

The Burren

situated on the south-eastern side of the Burren (R3396). To access the park, from Corofin, take the R476 to Kilnaboy and then turn east and travel about 5 kilometres to Mullaghmore.

The great diversity of nectar sources and larval food plants makes this ideal butterfly territory. All of Ireland's native butterflies with two exceptions may be found here. The Gatekeeper is absent being a more southerly species in Ireland and the Cryptic Wood White has not been recorded in limestone pavement country. The Wood White (*Leptidea sinapis*) is plentiful and in most years a small second brood is seen in late summer. The Pearl-bordered Fritillary in Ireland is restricted to the Burren and parts of neighbouring parts of Cos Clare and Galway. It is has recently been discovered in the Aran Islands which are biogeographically considered to be part of Co Clare. The original Pearl-bordered Fritillary report in 1922 was from near Clooncoose and it may still be seen here along the 'green road'. It is generally found in relatively open areas where there is Hazel and Bracken scrub and its foodplant Dog-violet is plentiful.

The Brown Hairstreak, another species with a very restricted range in Ireland, is closely associated with Blackthorn scrub and roadside hedges. Marsh Fritillary is found in areas where Devil's-bit Scabious is plentiful. The Common Blue (sub-species *mariscolore*) is very blue and sometimes misidentified by visitors as the Adonis Blue. The very grey form of the Dingy Skipper seen here has been elevated to the sub-species *baynesi*. There are many butterfly areas to be explored away from the very popular Mullaghmore and its nearby lakes. Suggested sites include Ballyeighter Lakes and Woods, Slieve Carran, Cooloorta, Termon and Lough Bunny (outside the Burren), but follow your instincts.

Dromore Wood and Loughs (R3586), Co Clare H9

This SAC, an area of about 400 hectares, is situated in central Clare, 9 km north-north-west of Ennis, off the Ennis-Galway road (currently the N18) on the southern edge of the Clare limestones. The topography is a continuation of the Burren type landscape with thin soils at a lower elevation (15-35 metres above sea level). Habitat is very varied in an area including river, lake, turlough, callow, limestone pavement and species-rich woodland. The SAC and the adjacent area are noted for its wide variety of plants, water fowl, birds of prey, rarer invertebrates and aquatic plants. Butterflies that are seen in the immediate area include Silver-washed Fritillary, Brimstone, Brown Hairstreak, Dingy Skipper, Pearl-bordered Fritillary and possibly Dark Green Fritillary.

Dursey Island (V4840), Co Cork H3

Dursey Island, which has approximate dimensions of 6.5 by 2.5 km is well worth a visit. This beautiful rocky island has been amputated from the end of the Beara Peninsula by the erosive power of the Atlantic Ocean. It is reached by taking the R572 from Castletown Bearhaven to Ballaghboy. Since 1969, Ireland's only cable-car links Dursey with the mainland. It is licensed to carry three people and a cow. Off the headland, there are three little islands: The

Bull, The Cow, and The Calf. The Bull has the largest gannet colony in Ireland. The island's strategic position in the Atlantic results in the arrival in substantial numbers of migrant Lepidoptera and other insects. The island acts as a fuelling station for hungry northbound insects which then spread out as they move inland. Dursey's resident and visiting lepidopterists often provide the first reports of the arrival of the migrant Red Admiral, Clouded Yellow and Painted Lady. Migrants also include species such as Large White and Small Tortoiseshell which augment our native populations. Information from Dursey shows that there are often small almost undetected migrations at various times of the year. The Wall Brown is quite widespread. Grayling, Dark Green Fritillary and the Green Hairstreak are seen in substantial numbers and the Speckled Wood has recently spread from the mainland perhaps availing of improved shelter afforded by domestic gardens.

Sherkin Island (W0225), Cape Clear Island (V9621), Roaring Water Bay (W03), Cork H3

Roaring Water Bay, Cork, is a wide shallow bay located on the southwest coast served by Baltimore harbour. The Bay and its islands is a SAC. The bedrock is composed of Devonian Old Red Sandstone reefs and troughs which culminate in a summit of 160 metres on Cape Clear. The bay is of particular interest because of the variety of marine life including seabirds. The islands' terrestrial habitat hosts a number of rare southern plants such as Hairy Bird's-foot-trefoil, Spotted Rock-rose and Yellow Bartsia. More than twenty different species of butterfly have been seen on Sherkin Island and it is a good location to see migrants such as Painted Lady and Clouded Yellow. Small numbers of Marsh Fritillary, Dark Green Fritillary and Holly Blue and substantial numbers of the Gatekeeper have been reported.

Sherkin Island

Cape Clear Island (Oileán Chléire) has had a bird observatory since 1959 and keeps a log of both birds and Lepidoptera. Marsh Fritillary was seen in 1967 but there have been no subsequent sightings. However, it may be present on some of the other islands of Roaring Water Bay. Reports of both the Pale Clouded Yellow and the Queen of Spain Fritillary have been logged but conclusive evidence, either in the form of specimens or photographs, is lacking. As might be expected for such a strategic location for migrants and vagrants, the Monarch has been seen on a number of occasions in autumn.

Killarney National Park (V9786), Co Kerry H1 and H2

South and west of the town of Killarney in Co Kerry are the McGillycuddy Reeks, the highest mountain range in Ireland, rising to 1000 metres. At the foot of these mountains nestle the well-known lakes of Killarney. Here, where the mountains sweep down to the wooded lake shores, is the 10,000 hectare Killarney National Park. The combination of mountains, lakes, woods and waterfalls under ever-changing skies has long been acknowledged as a beauty spot. The Park contains many features of national and international importance such as the native oak and yew woods together with an abundance of evergreen trees and shrubs and a profusion of bryophytes and lichens which thrive in its mild moist climate. Killarney National Park was designated as a Biosphere Reserve by UNESCO in 1981.

Up to twenty species of butterfly have been reported at one time or another from the Park but the Gatekeeper and the Marsh Fritillary have not recently been seen. The Purple Hairstreak is present in large numbers, for example, in Derrycunnihy Wood which has been described as the most natural remaining Sessile Oak wood in Ireland. The understorey contains much Holly, so not surprisingly the Holly Blue is frequent in the Killarney area. Perhaps the best places to view butterflies are in the areas of Ross and Dinis Islands and the Muckross Peninsula. Silver-washed Fritillary and Cryptic Wood White are found in the open areas and margins of the woods, Green Hairstreak flourishes in the more open boggy areas and in sheltered corners where its food plants Bilberry and Gorse abound. The wet mountain slopes are Large Heath territory.

Barrigone (R2849), Aughinish Island (R2852) and Creeves (R2946), Co Limerick H8

These sites are all in the Askeaton area of Limerick immediately south of the Shannon Estuary. Active quarrying is in progress at Barrigone and Creeves. Aughinish Island is in the shadow of and owned by an aluminium processing company which has declared a portion of the island a butterfly reserve. Barrigone is situated approximately 5 km west of Askeaton and the site comprises an area of dry, species-rich, calcareous grassland and patches of scrub on a gentle north-east-facing slope. There is limestone pavement and open calcareous grassland which supports a good variety of plant species, such as Cowslip, Mountain Everlasting, Wild Thyme, Orchid species and Hairy

Creeves

Violet. An old Pearl-bordered Fritillary sighting has never been confirmed and Lavery (1993) reported a large population of Marsh Fritillary in the area. Dingy Skipper, Small Blue, Cryptic Wood White, Wall Brown and the occasional Dark Green Fritillary are notable species.

Carney Commons (R8792), Co Tipperary H10

The site is located in North Tipperary, 7 km west of Borrisokane on the road to Newchapel (Kilbarron). It has a variety of flora representing its scrub woodland and fen habitat. This is a fen-turlough site supporting a mosaic of wetland habitats with a small amount of Scots Pine on the margins. Characteristic plants are Buckthorn, Juniper, Blue Moor-grass, Irish Whitebeam, Fly Orchid and Grass-of-Parnassus. Dingy Skipper, Marsh Fritillary and Brimstone flourish here and this is one of a very small number of presently known sites for the Brown Hairstreak east of the Shannon.

Tramore Burrow (S6100), Co Waterford H6

The Burrow lies at the head of Tramore Bay, east of Tramore town. The Burrow is the result of growth of a spit of shingle and sand across a shallow bay which has expanded eastwards. The dunes here range from old fixed type to new fore dunes, consequently there should be a broad range of plants and habitat suitable for butterflies which has, however, become somewhat limited by the absence of grazing which has permitted scrub to develop. Bee Orchid and the rare prostrate Wild Asparagus persist here. The sand dunes have been considerably degraded but Dark Green Fritillary, Small Heath, the migrant Clouded Yellow, Painted Lady and Red Admiral and Common Blue, Grayling and Dark

Green Fritillary may still be found. Holly Blue and Gatekeeper are restricted to the 'back strand'.

ULSTER
Montiaghs Moss (J0965), Co Antrim H39

Part of this mosaic of habitats contains a SAC of 151 ha in area which was designated in 1997. Pronounced "Munchies", it is only a short distance from the village of Aghagallon off the A26 near the south-east corner of Lough Neagh. The area consists of cutaway bog with pools and drains interspersed with small hay fields, alder and willow carr and tall mature hedgerows. The numerous resident invertebrates, especially the dragonflies, beetles and butterflies, are considered to be of significance. The Moss contains one of the largest

Montiaghs Moss

and well established populations of Marsh Fritillary in Northern Ireland. This butterfly is scattered through the site demonstrating the presence of suitable habitat supporting its larval foodplant Devil's-bit Scabious. Other butterflies of note on the site are the Green Hairstreak, Cryptic Wood White and Small Heath. Irish Lady's-tresses, Frogbit and Cowbane are a few of the rarer plants which have been reported from here. Part of Montiaghs Moss is being grazed by small highland cattle and goats, as part of a scrub management experiment.

Oxford Island National Nature Reserve (J0461), Co Armagh H37

This very popular area for visitors is a peninsula on the south-east coast of Lough Neagh and is well served with an education centre and nearby water recreation facilities. It is easily reached from Junction 10 of the M1 or by public transport from Lurgan. There are approximately five miles of pathways traversing the site. The Reserve contains a wide variety of habitat from reed beds to woodland, scrub and meadow. Of particular interest to the butterfly enthusiasts are the Kinnego Meadows, which are primarily damp grassland with a good range of plant species. Meadow Brown, Ringlet, Green-veined White, Common Blue, Small Copper, Speckled Wood and Small Heath are plentiful. Holly Blue and Cryptic Wood White are seen along the paths and field perimeters with Vanessids (as adults or larvae) on or near sunny stands of their nettle foodplant. The environs of the nearby Craigavon Lakes have a large population of the Cryptic Wood White.

Peatlands Park (H9060), Co Armagh H37

Part of the Park of 207 ha is a SAC, readily accessible from the M1 (Junction 13) east of Dungannon. The site is close to Lough Neagh and the designation as an area of scientific interest was because of the drumlin woodland and the peatland-wetland flora and fauna. The raised bog has been mostly degraded by the removal of peat but there is still an intact area at Mullenakill. Widespread vascular plants present include Cross-leaved Heath, Cotton-grass species, Bog Rosemary, Bilberry, Cranberry and Gorse. The bog woodland is dominated by Downy Birch, Grey Willow and old Sessile Oak woodland containing Holly. Butterflies species include Large Heath, Green Hairstreak and the Holly Blue first reported in October 2008. The rare Bordered Grey, Forester, Light Knot-

Peatlands Park

grass and Dark Tussock moths have been confirmed recently. The Marsh Fritillary was still present when the site was first designated in 1985.

Cruit Island (B7320), Co Donegal H35

Cruit (pronounced "Critch") is in the Rosses area of north-west Donegal, west of the R259 and south of Kincaslough (Cionn Caslach). The island is now joined to the mainland by a causeway and its name Cruit is derived from the Irish word which indicates a hump or a hillock. Of dimensions 5 km long and 1.5 km wide at its widest, Cruit has a mixture of low rocky cliffs and small beaches along its perimeter. Marsh Fritillary is present on the island in large numbers in good years. In autumn, on top of the low south facing cliffs, larval webs may be readily seen on a wide variety of exposed substrates including Heather, Crowberry, Black Bog-rush and Marram and elsewhere on lower ground near sea level in typical Donegal machair habitat. The Small Blue is quite abundant on sandy hillocks where Kidney Vetch grows. Wall Brown is scattered over the island and there have been more occasional sightings of Dark Green Fritillary and Grayling.

Cruit Island

St John's Point SAC (G7069), Co Donegal H35

St. John's Point, off the N56 from Donegal to Killybegs, is a 10 km long narrow low peninsula running south-west from Dunkineely into Donegal Bay. It is the most southerly part of south-west Donegal and, because of its topography, weather fronts often pass over instead of lingering. The underlying geology is carboniferous limestone. Part of the peninsula is a Special Area of Conservation because of its orchid-rich grassland with limestone pavement and fen. Bloody Crane's-bill, Northern Bedstraw, Stone Bramble, Blue Moor-grass are some of its more typical lime-loving plants.

The poorly drained v-shaped valleys are sheltered from the colder winds, extending the range of vegetation. Light grazing by cattle has helped to maintain the diversity of the vegetation and invertebrates. Up to twenty butterfly species are found here with strong colonies of Marsh Fritillary, Small Blue and Wall Brown. Marsh Fritillary webs are to be found on Devil's-bit Scabious on sunny limestone slopes. The Green Hairstreak is seen in small numbers in the absence of either of its regular food plants – Bilberry and Gorse– probably feeding on Common Bird's-foot-trefoil. As some of the valleys contain scrubby Blackthorn and Bramble, there is shelter enough for the Speckled Wood and the recently discovered Cryptic Wood White.

Sheskinmore (G6895), Co Donegal H35

The Sheskinmore area is one of the more important coastal SPAs in Ireland and the jewel in the crown of the north-west of Ireland. Access is from the road opposite Kiltoorish Lake. Coming from Glenties, Ardara and Portnoo (R261) the visitor must initially head in the Rosbeg direction. The area contains an intricate complex of coastal habitats. The grassland and marsh habitats merge with machair forming a system which includes Marram, fixed and decalcified dunes. Salt marsh, freshwater marsh and fen, lake and heathy upland habitats add to the habitat diversity. The flora includes the relatively rare Dense-flowered Orchid and the aquatic Slender Naiad. The locality is highly regarded by lepidopterists and has a good variety of butterflies. Of special interest is the large population of Marsh Fritillary which flourishes in the flat and windswept area between the sand dunes and the lake. Small Blue,

Sheskinmore

Dingy Skipper and Grayling are widespread, but local, on the drier terrain and scores of Dark Green Fritillary and other commoner butterflies inhabit the sand dune system.

Killard Point National Nature Reserve (J6143) and Sheepland Coast ASSI (J5839), Co Down H38

First designated in 1967, Killard is part of the Lecale Area of Outstanding Natural Beauty with excellent views of the Mourne Mountains and the Isle of Man. Situated eight miles east of Downpatrick and south of Strangford Lough between Killard and Ballyhornan, it looks down on Benderg Bay. It is adjudged to be the most pristine and intact coastal site in Northern Ireland with maritime grassland, low dunes and acidic/heathy grassland habitat. Of note are Spring Squill, Bluebell, Bulbous Buttercup, Kidney Vetch, Violet species, Wild Thyme, Field Scabious, Bee Orchid and the Green-winged Orchid at its only known Northern Ireland site. With nectar sources and larval food plants aplenty, Common Blue and Meadow Brown occur in abundance with lesser numbers of Small Heath, Dark Green Fritillary and Grayling. The Wall Brown possibly lingers on, on the verge of extinction. Killard is an excellent location for observing the arrival of migrant Lepodoptera.

Killard Point

The Sheepland Coast ASSI's status was confirmed in 2008, with the primary criteria for designation being geological. The exposed rocks are mainly fine-grained sandstones and siltstones of Palaeozoic origins and are part of the Scottish Southern Uplands/Irish Down-Longford Terrane formed on the closure of the Iapetus Orogeny (395 million years BP). This site is 2.5 km north-east of Ardglass off the A2 and has a range of habitats and species similar to Killard with the best remaining population of the Wall Brown in Northern Ireland, a species which has suffered a disquieting decline in the north-east over recent decades.

Lagan Meadows (J3369), Belfast H39

Managed by the Ulster Wildlife Trust and within the Lagan Valley Regional Park, the Meadows are about 2 miles south from the city centre occupying an area formerly used for the city water supply. The main access routes are from Bladon Drive (Malone Road) and Knightsbridge Park (Stranmillis Road). It is a managed mosaic of semi-natural meadows, scrubland, ponds, hedgerows and wetlands where livestock grazing is an integral part of the site regime. The nectar producing plants Bird's-foot-trefoil species, Bramble, Knapweed, Holly and Common Ivy are plentiful. Butterflies to look out for include Holly Blue (1st and 2nd brood), Common Blue, Cryptic Wood White, Meadow Brown, Ringlet and the Vanessids.

Murlough National Nature Reserve (J3933), Co Down H38

Part of the Murlough is designated as SAC and ASSI and has an area of 282 ha. Situated between Dundrum and Newcastle, it may be reached from the A2 coast road. This is Northern Ireland's first National Nature Reserve dating from 1967 and managed by the National Trust. It contains a 6000 year old system with grey and white sand dunes, woodland, scrub and heath. The fixed dunes have a rich variety of herb species including Moonwort, the rare Shepherd's Cress, Common Rest-harrow, Wild Thyme, and Common Bird's-foot-trefoil. The presence of an array of Priority Annex I habitats and of the Annex II species Marsh Fritillary were the primary reasons for its designation as a SAC. Over twenty other species of butterfly have been reported from here including Grayling, Dark Green Fritillary, Cryptic Wood White, Common Blue and Small Heath. In excess of 200 night-flying moths have been recorded here.

Murlough

Magilligan Umbra-Downhill Sand Dune Complex (C6837), Co Londonderry H40

Initially, it was designated as an Area of Special Scientific Interest in 1994 and at a later date as a Special Area of Conservation, with a total area greater than 1000 hectares. It is a major component of the Binevenagh Area of Outstanding Natural Beauty and is accessed from the A2 coast road. This is a locale of estuaries, mud flats, sand flats, lagoons, sand dunes and machair extending along the north coast from Magilligan Point at the mouth of the Foyle eastwards to Downhill Strand. Part of the area is under the control of the

Umbra

Ministry of Defence. Within the SAC is the Umbra, owned by the Ulster Wildlife Trust [entry is normally restricted to members], a 45 ha undisturbed sand dune complex, with well developed dune grasslands, damp dune slacks and a smaller area of scrub and Hazel. Plants include the Frog Orchid, Grass-of-Parnassus and Marsh Helleborine. Twenty two butterfly species have been seen at the Umbra, including the Dark Green Fritillary, Silver-washed Fritillary, Grayling, Small Heath, Cryptic Wood White and migrant species. The Marsh Fritillary has not been recently seen at the Umbra but it is home to the rare Scarce Crimson and Gold and Small Eggar moths.

Monawilkin, Co Fermanagh (H0953) H33

It is a designated Special Area of Conservation and ASSI with a total area 175 ha, close to the village of Derrygonnelly, and may be approached from the B81. The area is considered to be the best example of unimproved calcareous grassland on Upper Carboniferous limestone in Northern Ireland. There are two main limestone masses, Monawilkin and Callow, with limestone cliffs and

Monawilkin area

steep valleys. Calciole plants include Kidney Vetch, Crested Hair-grass, Wild Thyme and, more locally, Irish Eyebright, Blue Moor-grass and perhaps the best array of orchids in NI flourish here. This is the last known site for the Small Blue in Northern Ireland but it has not been confirmed here since 2001 despite the continued presence of Kidney Vetch. Seventeen resident and breeding butterflies including Dingy Skipper, Silver-washed Fritillary, Green Hairstreak, Cryptic Wood White and Grayling may be seen here.

Site Locations

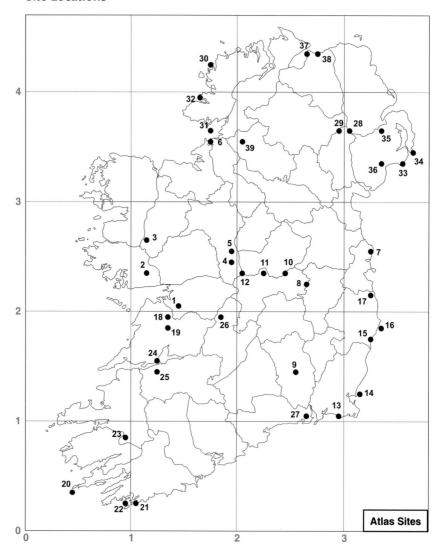

Atlas Sites

1. Coole-Garryland	15. Buckroney	28. Montiaghs Moss & Oxford Island
2. Moycullen	16. Brittas	
3. Lough Carra	17. Glen of the Downs	29. Peatlands Park
4. Castlesampson	18. The Burren	30. Cruit Island
5. St John's Wood	19. Dromore	31. St John's Point
6. Bunduff	20. Dursey Island	32. Sheskinmore
7. Portrane Burrow	21. Sherkin Island	33. Killard Point
8. Lullymore	22. Cape Clear Island	34. Sheepland
9. Thomastown	23. Killarney National Park	35. Lagan Meadows
10. Raheenmore	24. Barrigone & Aughnish Island	36. Murlough
11. Clara	25. Creeves	37. Magilligan
12. Mongans Bog	26. Carney Commons	38. Umbra
13. Ballyteigue Burrow	27. Tramore Burrow	39. Monawilkin
14. The Raven		

Marsh Fritillary

Common Blue

Appendices

Appendix 1: **TOPOGRAPHICAL INDEX**

Alphabetical list of sites with county and approximate grid reference.

Aghagallon	Antrim	J1063	Buckroney Dunes	Wicklow	T2979
Ahenny	Kilkenny	S4130	Bundoran	Donegal	G8258
Allenwood	Kildare	N6926	Bunduff Lough	Sligo	G7155
Aran Islands	Galway	L90	Burren NP	Clare	R3396
Ardara	Donegal	G7390	Cahore Point	Wexford	T2247
Ardnacloon Hill	Roscommon	M9541	Cape Clear Isl.	Cork	V9621
Ards Forest Park	Donegal	C0634	Carney Commons	Tipperary	R8792
Ards Peninsula	Down	J5950	Carnsore Point	Wexford	T1103
Arklow Head	Wicklow	T2570	Carrowmoreknock	Galway	M2140
Askeaton	Limerick	R3350	Castlebar	Mayo	M1490
Athenry	Galway	M5028	Castleburke	Mayo	M1677
Athlone	Westmeath	N0241	Castlesampson	Roscommon	M9440
Aughinish Island	Limerick	R2852	Castletown Bearhaven	Cork	V6746
Ballaghboy	Cork	V5041	Castletownshend	Cork	W1831
Ballinacor	Wicklow	T1186	Clara	Offaly	N2532
Ballinrobe	Mayo	M1964	Clara Bog	Offaly	N2530
Ballintra	Donegal	G9169	Clara Vale	Wicklow	T1792
Ballyhornan	Down	J5941	Cleengort	Donegal	G8099
Ballyquirke Lake	Galway	M2331	Clew Bay	Mayo	M98
Ballyteigue	Wexford	S9306	Cliffoney	Sligo	G7053
Ballyvaughan	Clare	M2307	Clonmacnoise	Offaly	N0030
Barrigone	Limerick	R2849	Clonmel	Tipperary	S1922
Beara Peninsula	Cork	V64	Clooncoose	Clare	R2894
Belfast	Antrim	J3474	Clorhane	Offaly	M9927
Benderg Bay	Down	J6043	Cobh	Cork	W7966
Benone	Londonderry	C7136	Connemara NP	Galway	L7456
Birr	Offaly	N0505	Coole Park	Galway	M4304
Blackstairs Mtns	Carlow, Wexford	S64	Corballis	Dublin	O2448
Blackwater Head	Wexford	T1432	Corbally	Limerick	R5858
Bog of Allen	Offaly	N62	Cork	Cork	W6771
Borrisokane	Tipperary	R9193	Corofin	Clare	R2888
Boston	Clare	R3798	Corranellistrum	Galway	M1940
Bray	Wicklow	O2618	Craigavon Lakes	Armagh	J0456
Breeole Hills	Roscommon	M8642	Cratloe	Clare	R4861
Brittas Bay	Wicklow	T5082	Creeves	Limerick	R2946
Brittas Dunes	Wicklow	T3183	Croagh Patrick	Mayo	L9080
Brownstown	Mayo	M1971	Cruit Island	Donegal	B7320

Curracloe	Wexford	T0928	Kenmare	Kerry	V9070
Daingean	Offaly	N4727	Kilbarron	Tipperary	R8492
Deputy's Pass	Wicklow	T2390	Kilfenora	Clare	R1893
Derry City	Londonderry	C4317	Kilkenny	Kilkenny	S5055
Derrycunnihy Wood	Kerry	V9080	Killard	Down	J6143
Derrygonnelly	Fermanagh	H1152	Killarney	Kerry	V9690
Dingle	Kerry	Q4401	Killarney NP	Kerry	V9786
Dingle Bay	Kerry	V49	Killiney	Dublin	O2525
Doagh Isle	Donegal	C4151	Killybegs	Donegal	G7176
Donabate	Dublin	O2249	Kilmore Quay	Wexford	S9603
Donegal Bay	Donegal	G87	Kilnaboy	Clare	R2791
Downhill	Londonderry	C7536	Kiltoorish Lake	Donegal	G6797
Downpatrick	Down	J4844	Kincaslough	Donegal	B7419
Dromore Wood	Clare	R3586	Kinvara	Galway	M3710
Dublin	Dublin	N1534	Kylemore (Oughterard)	Galway	M1939
Duncormick	Wexford	S9109	Lagan Meadows	Down	J3369
Dundrum	Down	J4036	Larragan	Galway	M2238
Dungannon	Tyrone	H7962	Lecarrow	Roscommon	M9655
Dungarvan	Waterford	X2693	Lisdoonvarna	Clare	R1398
Dunkineely	Donegal	G7675	Longford	Longford	N1375
Dursey Island	Cork	V4840	Lough Carra	Mayo	M1872
Edenderry	Offaly	N6332	Lough Corrib	Galway	G14
Ennis	Clare	R3377	Lough Derg	several	R89
Galway	Galway	M2925	Lough Erne, Upper	Fermanagh	H2930
Garryland	Galway	M4103	Lough Eske	Donegal	G9682
Garrynagry	Galway	M1939	Lough Gill	Sligo	G73
Glen of the Downs	Wicklow	O2611	Lough Mask	Mayo	G16
Glenageary	Dublin	O2427	Lough Neagh	several	J07
Glenarm	Antrim	D3115	Lough Ree	several	N05
Glendalough	Wicklow	T1296	Lullymore West	Kildare	N6926
Glenealy	Wicklow	T2492	Lurgan	Armagh	J0758
Glenties	Donegal	G8194	Magilligan Dunes	Londonderry	C6638
Gort	Galway	M4502	Malahide	Dublin	O2246
Great Saltee	Wexford	X9496	McGillicuddy Rks	Kerry	V8084
Greenfield	Tipperary	R8945	Mizen Head	Wicklow	T3080
Greystones	Wicklow	O2912	Monawilkin	Fermanagh	H0953
Holywood	Down	J4079	Mongans Bog	Offaly	N0330
Howth	Dublin	O2839	Montiaghs Moss	Antrim	J0965
Hurney Point	Galway	M2531	Moore Hall	Mayo	M1974
Inis Meáin	Galway	L9305	Mourne Mountains	Down	J22
Inis Mór	Galway	L8409	Moycullen	Galway	M2132
Inishtrahull	Donegal	C4865	Mullaghmore	Clare	R3295
Inishturk	Mayo	L6174	Mullaghmore	Sligo	G7057
Ireland's Eye	Dublin	O2841	Mullingar	Westmeath	N4352

Murlough	Down	J3933	Sheskinmore	Donegal	G6895	
Nephin Beg	Mayo	F9310	Slieve Bloom Mtns	Laois	N3106	
Newcastle	Down	J3731	Slieve Gullion	Armagh	J0220	
Newchapel	Tipperary	R8492	St John's Point	Donegal	G7069	
Oakfield	Galway	M1740	St John's Point	Down	J5233	
Oileán Chléire	Cork	V9621	St John's Wood	Roscommon	M9956	
Oughterard	Galway	M1242	Strangford	Down	J5849	
Oxford Island	Armagh	H9060	Taghmaconnell	Roscommon	M8838	
Peatlands Park	Armagh	H9060	Termon	Clare	M2900	
Pollardstown	Kildare	N7615	Thomastown Quarry	Kilkenny	S54	
Portballintrae	Antrim	C9242	Timahoe	Kildare	N7632	
Portnoo	Donegal	G7099	Timoleague	Cork	W4643	
Portrane Burrow	Dublin	O2552	Tory Island	Donegal	T8546	
Powerscourt	Wicklow	O2116	Tralee	Kerry	Q8314	
Raheenmore Bog	Offaly	N4332	Tralee Bay	Kerry	Q61	
Rathlin Island	Antrim	D1451	Tramore	Waterford	S5701	
Raven	Wexford	T1124	Tramore Burrow	Waterford	S6100	
Roaring Water Bay	Cork	W03	Trawalua Strand	Sligo	G6954	
Rosbeg	Donegal	G6697	Tubber	Galway	R4094	
Roscommon	Roscommon	M8764	Tulla	Clare	R4979	
Rosses	Donegal	B71	Tullamore	Offaly	N3324	
Shannon	Clare	R4062	Umbra, The	Londonderry	C7235	
Shannonbridge	Offaly	M9625	Wexford	Wexford	T042	
Sheephaven Bay	Donegal	C03	Wicklow	Wicklow	T3193	
Sheepland Coast	Down	J5838	Wicklow Mtns	Wicklow	T09	
Sherkin Island	Cork	W0225	Windy Gap	Kilkenny	S4034	

Appendix 2: **PLANT SYNONYMS**

Ageratum *Ageratum houstonianum*
Agrimony, Hemp *Eupatorium cannabinum*
Alyssum, Sweet *Lobularia maritima*
    Yellow *Alyssum saxatile*
Arabis, White *Arabis albida*
Ash *Fraxinus excelsior*
Asparagus *Asparagus officinalis*
Aubretia *Aubretia deltoides*

Bartsia, Yellow *Parentucellia viscosa*
Bedstraw, Northern *Galium boreale*
    Lady's *G. verum*
Bent-grass *Agrostis* species
Bilberry *Vaccinium myrtillus*
Birch, Hairy *Betula pubescens*
Bird's-foot *Ornithopus perpusillus*
Bird's-foot-trefoil, Common *Lotus corniculatus*
    Greater *L. pedunculatus*
    Hairy *L. subbiflorus*
Bitter-cress, Hairy *Cardamine hirsuta*
    Wavy *C. flexuosa*
Bitter-vetch *Lathyrus linifolius*
Blackthorn (Sloe) *Prunus spinosa*
Bluebell *Hyacinthoides non-scripta*
Bog Rosemary *Andromeda polifolia*
Bog-rush, Black *Schoenus nigricans*
Bracken *Pteridium aquilinum*
Bramble *Rubus fruticosus*
    Stone *R. saxatile*
Brome, False *Brachypodium sylvaticum*
Broom *Cytisus scoparius*
Buckthorn *Rhamnus cathartica*
    Alder *Frangula alnus*
Bugle *Ajuga reptans*
Burdock *Arctium minus*
Buttercup, Bulbous *Ranunculus bulbosus*
Butterly-bush *Buddleja davidii*
    Yellow *B. x weyeriana*

Cabbage *Brassica oleracea*
Campion, Red *Silene dioica*
Candytuft *Iberis umbellata*
Celandine, Lesser *Ficaria verna* (*Ranunculus ficaria*)
Centaury, Lesser *Centaurium pulchellum*
Charlock *Sinapis arvensis*
Cherry, Wild *Prunus avium*
    Bird *P. padus*
Chrysanthemum *Chrysanthemum* species
Clover, Red *Trifolium pratense*
    White *T. repens*
Cock's-foot *Dactylis glomerata*
Cotton-grass, Narrow-leaved *Eriophorum angustifolium*
    Hare's-tail *E. vaginatum*
Couch, Common (Scutch) *Elytrigia repens*

Cowbane *Cicuta virosa*
Cow-wheat, Common *Melampyrum pratense*
Cowslip *Primula veris*
Cranberry *Vaccinium oxycoccus*
Crane's-bill, Bloody *Geranium sanguineum*
Cress, Shepherd's *Teesdalia nudicaulis*
Crowberry *Empetrum nigrum*
Currant *Ribes* species
Cuckooflower (Lady's Smock) *Cardamine pratensis*

Dahlia *Dahlia* species
Daisy, Michaelmas *Aster novi-belgii*
    Ox-eye *Leucanthemum vulgare*
Dame's-violet *Hesperis matronalis*
Dandelion *Taraxacum officinale*
Dock, Broad-leaved *R. obtusifolius*
    Water *R. hydrolapathum*

Egg-plant, Poached *Limnanthes douglasii*
Elephant-ears *Bergenia cordifolia*
Elm *Ulmus* species
Escallonia *Escallonia* species
Everlasting, Mountain *Antennaria dioica*
Eyebright, Irish *Euphrasia salisburgensis*

Fescue *Festuca* species
Firethorn *Pyracantha* species
Fleabane, Common *Pulicaria dysenterica*
Foxtail, Meadow *Alopecurus pratensis*
    Marsh *A. geniculatus*
Frogbit *Hydrocharis morsus-ranae*

Goldenrod *Astilbe x arendsii*
    Canadian *Solidago canadensis*
Gorse *Ulex europaeus*
Grass, Quaking *Briza media*
Grass-of-Parnassus *Parnassia palustris*

Hair-grass *Aira praecox*
    Crested *Koeleria cristata*
    Tufted *Deschampsia cespitosa*
    Wavy *D. flexuosa*
Hawthorn *Crataegus monogyna*
Hazel *Corylus avellana*
Heartease *Viola tricolor*
Heath, Cross-leaved *Erica tetralix*
Helleborine, Marsh *Epipactis palustris*
    Green-flowered *Epipactis phyllanthes*
Holly *Ilex aquifolium*
Honesty *Lunaria biennis*
Honeysuckle *Lonicera pericylmenum*
Hyacinth *Hyacinthus orientalis*

Ivy Common *Hedera helix*

Juniper *Juniperus communis*

Knapweed *Centaurea nigra*

Lady's-tresses, Irish *Spiranthes romanzoffiana*
Lavender *Lavendula* species
Leopard's-bane *Doronicum pardalianches*
Lilac *Syringa vulgaris*
    Californian *Ceanothus* species
Ling (Heather) *Calluna vulgaris*
Loosestrife, Purple *Lythrum salicaria*

Mallow *Malva* species
Marigold *Calendula officinalis*
    French *Tagetes patula*
Marjoram, Wild *Origanum vulgare*
Marram *Ammophila arenaria*
Mat-grass *Nardus stricta*
Mayweed *Tripleurospermum maritimum*
Meadow-foam *Limnanthes douglasii*
Meadow-grasses *Poa* species
Medick, Black *Medicago lupulina*
Milkweed *Asclepia* species
Moonwort *Botrychium lunaria*
Moor-grass, Blue *Sesleria caerulea*
    Purple *Molinia caerulea*
Mustard, Garlic *Alliaria petiolata*
    Hedge *Sisymbrium officinale*

Naiad, Slender *Najas flexilis*
Nasturtium *Tropaeolum majus*
Nettle, Common *Urtica dioica*

Oak, Sessile *Quercus petraea*
    Pedunculate *Q. robur*
Orchid, Bee *Ophrys apifera*
    Early-purple *Orchis mascula*
    Fragrant *Gymnadenia conopsea*
    Fly *O. insectifera*
    Frog *Coeloglossum viride*
    Green-winged *Anacamptis morio*
    Pyramidal, *A. pyramidalis*

Pansy, Field *Viola arvensis*
    Wild *Viola tricolor*
Parsley, Cow *Anthriscus sylvestris*
Phlox *Phlox paniculata*
Pine, Scots *Pinus sylvestris*
Pink, Sea (Thrift) *Armeria maritima*
Plantain *Plantago* species
Polyanthus *Primula veris x vulgaris*
Potentilla (Cinquefoil) *Potentilla* species
Primrose *Primula vulgaris*
Privet *Ligustrum* species

Radish *Raphanus raphanistrum*
Ragwort *Senecio jacobaea*

Rest-harrow *Ononis repens*
Rock-rose, Spotted *Tuberaria guttata*
Rose, Burnet *Rosa spinosissima*
Rosemary *Rosmarinus officinalis*
    Bog *Andromeda polifolia*
Rush, Jointed *Juncus articulatus*
    White-beaked *Rhynchospora alba*
Rye-grass *Lolium* species

Saxifrage, Meadow *Saxifraga granulata*
Scabious, Caucasian *Scabiosa caucasica*
    Devil's-bit *Succisa pratensis*
    Field *Knautia arvensis*
Sea-holly *Eryngium martimum*
Sedge, White-beaked Sedge *Rhynchospora alba*
Self-heal *Prunella vulgaris*
Senecio *Senecio (greyii) laxifolius*
Soldiers & Sailors (Lungwort) *Pulmonaria saccharata*
Sorrel, Common *Rumex acetosa*
    Sheep's *R. acetosella*
Spotted-orchid, Common *Dactylorhiza fuchsii*
    Heath *D. maculata*
Squill, Spring *Scilla verna*
Stock, Hoary *Matthiola incana*
Stonecrop, Butterfly *Sedum spectabile*
    English *Sedum anglicum*
    Yellow (Biting) *Sedum acre*

Teasel *Dispacus fullonum*
Thistle, Creeping *Cirsium arvense*
    Carline *Carlina vulgaris*
    Globe *Echinops ritro*
    Marsh *C. palustre*
    Spear *C. vulgare*
Thrift see Pink
Thyme, Wild *Thymus polytrichus*
Timothy *Phleum pratense*
Toadflax, Yellow *Linaria vulgaris*
    Mallow, Tree *Lavatera arborea*
Tree, Strawberry *Arbutus unedo*
Trefoil, Lesser *T. dubium*
Turnip, Wild *Brassica rapa*

Valerian, Red *Centranthus ruber*
Verbena (Vervain) *Verbena bonariensis*
Vetch, Kidney *Anthyllis vulneraria*
    Spring *Vicia lathyroides*
    Tufted *V. cracca*
Vetchling, Meadow *Lathyrus pratensis*
Viburnum *Viburnum* species
Violet, Dog *Viola riviniana/ reichenbachiana*
    Hairy *Viola hirta*
    Heath Dog *Viola canina*
    Field Pansy *Viola arvensis*

Water-cress *Rorippa nasturtium-aquaticum*

Appendix 3: RED LIST OF IRISH BUTTERFLIES

Species	Criteria	All-Ireland Assessment	Northern Ireland Assessment
Mountain Ringlet *Erebia epiphron* (Knoch 1783)		RE	
Dark Green Fritillary *Argynnis aglaja* (L. 1758)	A4ac	EN	
Pearl-bordered Fritillary *Boloria euphryosyne* (L. 1758)	B2ab(ii, iii, iv)	EN	
Small Blue *Cupido minimus* (Fuessly 1775)	A4c, B2ab(ii, iii, iv)	EN	RE
Wall Brown *Lasiommata megera* (L. 1767)	A2ac	EN	CR (B2ab(i,ii,iii), A2ac)
Large Heath *Coenonympha tullia* (Müller 1764)	A4ac	VU	
Marsh Fritillary *Euphydryas aurinia* (Rottemburg 1775)	A2c	VU	
Dingy Skipper *Erynnis tages* (L. 1758)	A3c	NT	
Gatekeeper *Pyronia tithonus* (L. 1767)	A2ac	NT	
Grayling *Hipparchia semele* (L. 1758)	A4c	NT	
Small Heath *Coenonympha pamphilus* (L. 1758)	A2c	NT	
Wood White *Leptidea sinapis* (L. 1758).	A2c	NT	
Brimstone *Gonepteryx rhamni* (L. 1758)		lc	
Brown Hairstreak *Thecla betulae* (L. 1758)		lc	
Common Blue *Polyommatus icarus* (Rottemburg 1775)		lc	
Clouded Yellow *Colias croceus* (Fourcroy 1785)		lc	
Green Hairstreak *Callophrys rubi* (L. 1758)		lc	
Green-veined White *Pieris napi* (L. 1758)		lc	
Holly Blue *Celastrina argiolus* (L. 1758)		lc	
Large White *Pieris brassicae* (L. 1758)		lc	
Meadow Brown *Maniola jurtina* (L. 1758)		lc	
Orange Tip *Anthocharis cardamines* (L. 1758)		lc	
Painted Lady *Vanessa cardui* (L. 1758)		lc	
Peacock *Inachis io* (L. 1758)		lc	
Purple Hairstreak *Favonius quercus* (L. 1758)		lc	
*Cryptic Wood White *Leptidea juvernica nov. aut.*		lc	
Red Admiral *Vanessa atalanta* (L. 1758)		lc	
Ringlet *Aphantopus hyperantus* (L. 1758)		lc	
Small Copper *Lycaena phlaeas* (L. 1758)		lc	
Small Tortoiseshell *Aglais urticae* (L. 1758)		lc	
Small White *Pieris rapae* (L. 1758)		lc	
Silver-washed Fritillary *Argynnis paphia* (L. 1758)		lc	
Speckled Wood *Pararge aegeria* (L. 1758)		lc	

RE = regionally extinct, CR = critically endangered, EN = endangered, VU = vulnerable, NT = near threatened, dd = data deficient, lc = least concern, na = not applicable (a taxon is not applicable when evaluation against the criteria is not possible as the species has been introduced, is a vagrant, or is a recent migrant that has been in the country for less than 10 years).

*Formerly *Leptidea reali*

Summary of the five criteria (A-E) used to evaluate if a taxon belongs in a threatened category (Critically Endangered, Endangered or Vulnerable)

Use any of the criteria A-E	Critically Endangered	Endangered	Vulnerable
A. Population reduction	Declines measured over the longer of 10 years or 3 generations		
A1	> 90%	> 70%	> 50%
A2, A3 & A4	> 80%	> 50%	> 30%

A1. Population reduction observed, estimated, inferred, or suspected in the past where the causes of the reduction are clearly reversible AND understood AND, ceased based on and specifying any of the following:
- (a) direct observation
- (b) an index of abundance appropriate to the taxon
- (c) a decline in area of occupancy (AOO), extent of occurrence (EOO) and/or habitat quality
- (d) actual or potential levels of exploitation
- (e) effects of introduced taxa, hybridisation, pathogens, pollutants, competitors or parasites.

A2. Population reduction observed, estimated, inferred, or suspected in the past where the causes of reduction may not have ceased OR may not be understood OR may not be reversible, based on any of (a) to (e) under A1

A3. Population reduction projected or suspected to be met in the future (up to a maximum of 100 years) based on any of (b) to (e) under A1.

A4. An observed, estimated, inferred, projected or suspected population reduction (up to a maximum of 100 years) where the time period must include both the past and the future, and where the causes of reduction may not have ceased OR may not be understood OR may not be reversible, based on any of (a) to (e) under A1.

	Critically Endangered	Endangered	Vulnerable
B. Geographic range in the form of either B1 (extent of occurrence) OR B2 (area of occupancy)			
B1. Either extent of occurrence	< 100 km²	< 5,000 km²	< 20,000 km²
B2. or area of occupancy	< 10 km²	< 500 km²	< 2,000 km²

and 2 of the following 3:
- (a) severely fragmented or # locations = $1 \leq 5 \leq 10$
- (b) continuing decline in (i) extent of occurrence (ii) area of occupancy, (iii) area, extent and/or quality of habitat, (iv) number of locations or subpopulations and (v) number of mature individuals.
- (c) extreme fluctuations in any of (i) extent of occurrence, (ii) area of occupancy, (iii) number of locations or subpopulations and (iv) number of mature individuals.

	Critically Endangered	Endangered	Vulnerable
C. Small population size and decline			
Number of mature individuals	< 250	< 2,500	< 10,000

and either **C1** or **C2**:

C1. An estimated continuing decline of at least 25% in 3 years, 20% in 5 years 10% in 10 years, up to a maximum of 100 years or 1 generation or 2 generations or 3 generations

C2. A continuing decline and (a) and/or (b)

	Critically Endangered	Endangered	Vulnerable
(a) (i) # mature individuals in largest subpopulation	< 50	< 250	< 1,000
(a) (ii) or % mature individuals in one subpopulation =	90-100%	95-100%	100%
(b) extreme fluctuations in the number of mature individuals			
D. Very small or restricted population			
Either (1) number of mature individuals	< 50	< 250	< 1,000
or (2) restricted area of occupancy	na	na	typically: AOO < 20km² or # locations ≤5

	Critically Endangered	Endangered	Vulnerable
E Quantitative Analysis			
Indicating the probability of extinction in the wild to be at least	50% in 10 yrs or 3 generations (100 years max)	20% in 20 yrs or 5 generations (100 years max)	10% 100 yrs

Appendix 4: USEFUL ADDRESSES

The Dublin Naturalists' Field Club
35 Nutley Park, Dublin 4
dnfc@butterflyireland.com
www.butterflyireland.com
www.dnfc.net

The Belfast Naturalists' Field Club
www.bnfc.org.uk

Butterfly Conservation (NI)
www.bcni.org.uk

Butterfly Conservation (UK)
www.butterfly-conservation.org

UK Butterflies
www.ukbutterflies.co.uk

Eggs, Larvae, Pupae and Adult Butterflies and Moths
www.ukleps.org

Moths of Ireland
www.mothsireland.com

Butterfly Conservation Ireland
www.butterflyconservation.ie

Steven Cheshire's British Butterflies
www.britishbutterflies.co.uk

Straffan Butterfly Farm
www.straffanbutterflyfarm.com

Waterford Wildlife
www.waterfordwildlife.com

Wexford Wildlife
www.wildside.ie

Lough Carra
www.loughcarra.org

Irish Grid Reference
www.gridreference.ie

The Heritage Council
www.heritagecouncil.ie

Northern Ireland Environment Agency
www.doeni.gov.uk/niea

National Museums Northern Ireland
www.nmni.com

CEDaR
www.nmni.com/cedar

National Parks and Wildlife Service
www.npws.ie

The National Museum of Ireland
www.museum.ie

National Biodiversity Data Centre
www.biodiversityireland.ie

Appendix 5: THE IRISH VICE-COUNTY SYSTEM

The Irish Vice-County System was first proposed by Robert Lloyd Praeger in the early 20th Century and has since been used by biological recorders for comparative purposes. The larger counties have been subdivided because of their size. With some exceptions, the system follows the 'original' county boundaries and has the advantage of being immune from the civil and administrative changes that have since been made to several county boundaries due to increased urbanisation.

H1 South Kerry	H9 Clare	H17 NE Galway	H25 Roscommon	H33 Fermanagh
H2 North Kerry	H10 North Tipperary	H18 Offaly	H26 East Mayo	H34 E Donegal
H3 West Cork	H11 Kilkenny	H19 Kildare	H27 West Mayo	H35 W Donegal
H4 Mid Cork	H12 Wexford	H20 Wicklow	H28 Sligo	H36 Tyrone
H5 East Cork	H13 Carlow	H21 Dublin	H29 Leitrim	H37 Armagh
H6 Waterford	H14 Laois	H22 Meath	H30 Cavan	H38 Down
H7 South Tipperary	H15 SE Galway	H23 Westmeath	H31 Louth	H39 Antrim
H8 Limerick	H16 West Galway	H24 Longford	H32 Monaghan	H40 Londonderry

Appendix 6: IRISH NATIONAL GRID SYSTEM

Each relevant omit 100 km square on the Irish National Grid is identified using an alphabetical character in the range B to X. The hundred km square is further subdivided into 100 10 km squares and so on. So the grid reference O2639 for Howth Harbour is a statement of its location to a 1 km resolution. The first (two) digits are the 'eastings' and the final digits the 'northings'. Grid references may be obtained from the Discovery/Discovery Series Maps, by using a GPS or going to a website such as *www.gridreference.ie*.

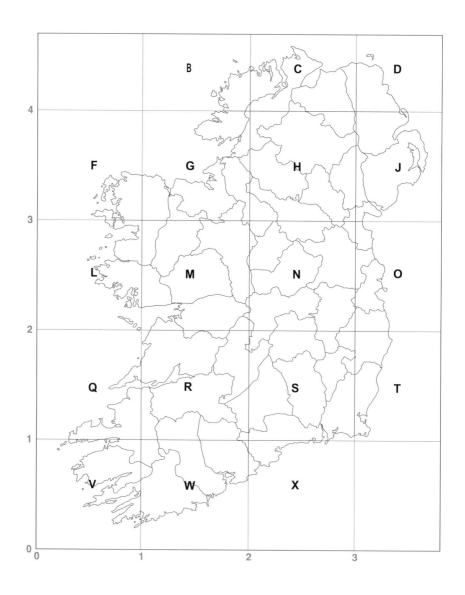

Ireland, showing Ordnance Survey 100 km Grid Squares

Appendix 7: REFERENCES and BIBLIOGRAPHY

Aldwell, B. (2005-2010). *Donegal local butterfly surveys.* Unpublished.

Aldwell, B. & Nash, D. (2005). Recent abundance of the Holly Blue butterfly *Celastrinus argiolus* (L.) in Co Dublin. *Irish Naturalists' Journal* **28**:120-122.

Andrews, W. (1860). The occurrence of *Gonepteryx rhamni* and *Thecla betulae* in Kerry. *Proceedings of the Dublin Natural History Society* **1**:28-29.

Anonymous (1990). *Handbook for phase 1 habitat survey – a technique for environmental audit.* Revised reprint 2003. Joint Nature Conservancy Council, Peterborough.

Anonymous (2008a). *The Status of EU protected habitats and species in Ireland.* National Parks and Wildlife Service, Department of the Environment, Heritage and Local Government, Dublin.

Anonymous (2008b). *State of the environment report.* Environmental Protection Agency, Johnstown Castle.

Asher, J., Warren, M., Fox, R., Harding, P., Jeffcoate, G. & Jeffcoate, S. (2001). *The millennium atlas of butterflies in Britain and Ireland.* Oxford University Press, Oxford.

Barkham, P. (2010). *The butterflies isles: A summer in search of Emperors and Admirals.* Granta Books, London.

Barrett, C.G. (1893–1907). *The Lepidoptera of the British Isles.* Reeve & Co. London.

Baynes, E.S.A. (1961). Report on migrant insects in Ireland for 1960. *Irish Naturalists' Journal* **13**:200-204.

Baynes, E.S.A. (1963). *Thecla betulae* L (Lep. Lycaenidae) in Ireland. *Entomologist's Gazette* **14**:124.

Baynes, E.S.A. (1964). *A revised catalogue of Irish Macrolepidoptera (butterflies and moths).* Classey, Hampton.

Baynes, E.S.A. (1970). *Supplement to revised catalogue of Irish Macrolepidoptera.* Classey, Hampton.

Beirne, B.P. (1947). The development of Irish entomology. *Irish Naturalists' Journal* **9**:81-84.

Beirne, B.P. (1955). Natural fluctuations in abundance of British Lepidoptera. *Entomologist's Gazette* **6**:21-52.

Beirne, B.P. (1985). *Irish entomology: the first hundred years.* Special entomological supplement to the *Irish Naturalists' Journal.*

Belfast Naturalists' Field Club (1874). *Guide to Belfast and the adjacent counties.* The Belfast Naturalists' Field Club.

Birchall, E. (1866). Catalogue of the Lepidoptera of Ireland. *Proceedings of the Dublin Natural History Soc.* **5**:57-85.

Birchall, E. (1873). The Lepidoptera of Ireland. *The Entomologist's Monthly Magazine* **10**:153-56.

Boyd, T. & More, A.G. (1858). On the geographical distribution of butterflies in Great Britain. *The Zoologist* **16**:18-27

Boyd, T.D. (1947). Silver-washed fritillary and clouded yellow in Co Down. *Irish Naturalists' Journal* **9**:99.

Boyd, T.D. (1948). Irish immigrant Lepidoptera. *Irish Naturalists' Journal* **9**:180.

Briscoe, A.D. & White, R.H. (2005). Adult stemmata of the butterfly, *Vanessa cardui* express UV and green opsin mRNAs. *Cell Tissue Research* **319**:175-9.

Chalmers-Hunt, J.M. (1982). On some interesting Irish Lepidoptera in the National Museum of Ireland. *Irish Naturalists' Journal* **20**:531-537.

Corke, D. (2002). The affair of the 'Long-willied (Réal's) Wood White'. *British Wildlife.* April:240-43.

Crichton, M. & Ní Lamhna, É. (1975). *Provisional atlas of butterflies in Ireland* (Part of European Invertebrate Survey). Irish Biological Records Centre, An Foras Forbartha, Dublin.

Cromien, S. & O'Connor, J.P. (2001). A record of the Monarch butterfly *Danaus plexxipus* L. (Insecta: Lepidoptera) from County Wexford, Ireland, with a review of other Irish occurrences. *Bulletin of the Irish Biogeographical Society* No. **25**:3-6.

De Lattin, G. (1952). Two new sub-species of *Hipparchia semele*. *Entomologist's Records and Journal of Variation* **64**:335-336.

Dennis, R.L.H. (ed.) (1992). *The ecology of butterflies in Britain*. Oxford University Press, Oxford.

Dennis, R.L.H. (1993). *Butterflies and climate change*. Manchester University Press, Manchester.

Dennis, R.L.H., Porter, K. & Williams, W.R. (1986). Ocellation in *Coenonympha tullia*. Population differentiation and clinal variation in the context of climatically induced antipredator defence strategies. *Entomologist's Gazette* **37**:133-172.

Dennis, R.L.H. & Shreeve, T.G. (1996). *Butterflies on British and Irish offshore islands. Ecology and biogeography*. Gem Publishing Company, Wallingford.

Department of the the Environment and Northern Ireland Environmental Agency Website (2011). http://www.doeni.gov.uk/niea/protected_areas_home

Dincă, V., Lukthanov, V.A., Talavera, G. & Vila, R. (2011). Unexpected layers of cryptic diversity in wood white *Leptidea* butterflies. doi: 10.1038/ncomms1329.

Donovan, C. (1936). *A catalogue of the Macrolepidoptera of Ireland* (with supplement). Printed by Ed. Burrow, Cheltenham.

Dowdswell, W.H. (1981). *The life of the meadow brown*. Heinemann, Portsmouth.

Emmet, A.M. & Heath, J. (1990). *The moths and butterflies of Great Britain and Ireland*. **7**(1):Hesperiidae to Nymphalidae. Harley Books, Colchester.

Farris, S.M. & Schulmeister, S. (2011). Parasitoidism, not sociality, is associated with the evolution of elaborate mushroom bodies in the brains of hymenopteran insects. *Proceedings Royal Society* **B278**:94-951. doi:10.1098/rspb.2010.2161.

Findlay, R., Young, M.A. & Findlay, J.A. (1983). Orientation behaviour in the Grayling butterfly: thermoregulation or crypsis. *Ecological Entomology* **8**:145-153.

Ford, E.B. (1990 edn). *The New Naturalists' butterflies*. Bloomsbury Books, London.

Forester, T. (2000). [Translation of] *Giraldus Cambriensis, The Topography of Ireland*. Mediaeval Latin Series, Cambridge, Ontario.

Fossitt, J.A. (2000). *A guide to habitats in Ireland*. The Heritage Council, Kilkenny.

Foster, G. (1932). Lepidoptera of County Down. *Proceedings Belfast Naturalists' Field Club* **9**:Appendix 5.

Fox, R. & Asher, J. (2010). *2010 Atlas of butterflies in Britain and Ireland*. Butterfly Conservation, Wareham. (*Butterfly Conservation Report No. S10-20*).

Fox, R., Asher, J., Brereton, T., Roy, D. & Warren, M. (2006). *The state of butterflies in Britain and Ireland*. Pisces Publications, Newbury.

Friberg, M. & Wiklund, C. (2007). Generation-dependent female choice: behavioural polyphenism in a bivoltine butterfly. *Behavioral Ecology* doi:10.1093/behco/arm037 pp 758-763.

Frohawk, F.W. (1924). *The natural history of British butterflies* (2 vols). Hutchinson, London.

Frohawk, F.W. (1934). *The complete book of British butterflies*. Ward Lock & Co., London.

Good, J.A. & Linnie, M. (1990). The history of the early nineteenth Coleoptera collection of James Tardy. *Irish Naturalists' Journal* **23**:298-305.

Goodson A.L. (1948). New varieties of *Argynnis adippe* L. and *Lycaena phlaeas* L. *The Entomologist* **81**:177-178.

Graves, P.P. (1924). *Brenthis euphrosyne* in Ireland. *The Entomologist* **57**:198-199.

Graves, P.P. (1930). The British and Irish *Maniola jurtina*. *The Entomologist* **63**:75-81.

Greene, J. (1854). A list of Lepidoptera hitherto taken in Ireland as far as the end of the Geometrae. *Natural History Review* **1**:165-168, 238-244

Greene, J. (1870). *The insect hunter's companion*. 2nd edn, Van Voorst, London.

Greer, T. (1922). Gyandromporphs of *Euchloe cardamines* in east Tyrone. *Irish Naturalist* **31**:139.

Greer, T. (1923). The Lepidoptera of the North of Ireland. *Proceedings Belfast Naturalists' Field Club* **8**: Appendix 4.

Greer, T. (1923). Aberrations of Rhopalocera in east Tyrone, 1922. *Entomologists' Record and Journal of Variation* **35**:36-37.

Greer, T. (1925). Yellow forms of *Pieris napi* in Ireland. *Entomologist's Record and Journal of Variation* **37**:46.

Harding, J.M. (2008). *Discovering Irish butterflies and their habitats*. Published privately, Maynooth.

Hackney, P. (ed.) (1992). *Stewart & Corry's flora of the north-east of Ireland, edn 3*. The Queen's University, Belfast.

Haynes, R.F. (1963). Notes on the Lepidoptera in the West of Ireland, 1962. *Irish Naturalists' Journal* **14**:174-77.

Heal, H.G. (1965). The Wood White *Leptidea sinapis* L. and the railways. *Irish Naturalists' Journal* **15**:8-13.

Heath, J. (1970). *Provisional atlas of the insects of the British Isles*. Part 1: Lepidoptera Rhopalocera butterflies. Biological Records Centre, Abbots Ripton.

Heath, J., Pollard, E. & Thomas, J.A. (1984). *Atlas of butterflies in Britain and Ireland*. Viking, Harmondsworth.

Hickin, N. (1992). *The butterflies of Ireland: a field guide*. (ed. T.A. Lavery) Roberts Rinehart, Schull.

Higgins, L.G. & & Riley, N.D. (1970). *A field guide to the butterflies of Britain and Europe*. Collins, London.

Hillis, P. (1975). New locations for the purple hairstreak *Quercusia quercus* (L.) and Small Blue *Cupido minimus* Fuessly, butterflies. *Irish Naturalists' Journal* **18**:193.

Howarth T.G. (1971). The status of Irish *Hipparchia semele* (L.) (Lep., Satyridae) with descriptions of a new sub-species and aberrations. *Entomologist's Gazette* **22**:123-129.

Huggins, H.C. (1948). Variation in Irish insects. *The Entomologist* **81**:35-36.

Huggins, H.C. (1956). The Irish race of *Gonepteryx rhamni* (Lep. Pieridae). *The Entomologist* **89**:65-66.

Huggins, H.C. (1956). The Burren sub-species *Erynnis tages* Linn. *The Entomologist* **89**:241-242.

Huggins, H.C. 1960. A naturalist in the kingdom of Kerry 1959. *Proceedings and Transactions of the South London Entomological and Natural History Society* 1959:176-83.

Johnson, W.F. (1901). *Vanessa c-album* in Ireland. *Entomologist* **34**:18-9.

Johnson, W.F. (1902). Lepidoptera, in The Belfast Naturalists' Field Club's *A Guide to Belfast and the Counties of Down and Antrim* pp 198-204. M'Caw, Stevenson & Orr, Belfast.

Kane, W.F. de V. (1885). *European butterflies*. MacMillan and Co., London.

Kane, W.F. de V. (1894). Catalogue of Irish Lepidoptera. *The Entomologist* **27**:16-17.

Kane, W.F de V. (1901). *A catalogue of the Lepidoptera of Ireland (with supplement)*. West Newman & Co., Hatton Garden, London. [Also published in parts in *The Entomologist* 1893-1901, vols **26-33**].

Kida, Y., Numata, H., Hideharu & Fujii, H. (1997). Summer diapause in females of *Minois dryas* (Lepidoptera: Satyridae). *Environmental Entomology* **26**:201-206.

Kristensen, N.P. (ed.) (2003). *Lepidoptera, moths and butterflies* (2 vols). W de Bruyter, Berlin.

Kristensen, N.P. & Chauvin, G. (2003). In N.P. Kristensen (ed.) *Lepidoptera, moths and butterflies* 2:2 Morphology, Physiology and Development. W de Gruyter, Berlin.

Kudrna, O. (2002). The *distribution atlas of European butterflies*. Oedippus, Schweinfurt.

Lafranchis, T. (2004). *Butterflies of Europe*. Diatheo, Paris.

Lavery, T.A. (1993). A review of the distribution, ecology and status of the Marsh Fritillary (*Euphydryas aurinia* Rottemburg), 1775 (Lepidoptera: Nymphalidae) in Ireland. *Irish Naturalists' Journal* **24**:192-99.

Layberry, R.A., Hell, P.W. & Lafontaine, J.D. (1998). *The butterflies of Canada*. Toronto University Press.

Lees, E. & Archer, D.M. (1974). Ecology of *Pieris napi* (L.) (Lep., Pieridae) in Britain. *Entomologist's Gazette* **25**: 231-237.

Lorković, Z. (1993). *Leptidea reali* Reissinger 1989 (= *lorkovicii* Reál 1988), a new European species (Lepid., Pieridae) *Natura Croatica* 2:1-23.

Lucas, G.E. (1940). Second brood of holly blue in Ireland. *Irish Naturalists' Journal* 7:304.

May, P.R. (2003). *Larval foodplants of the butterflies of Great Britain and Ireland*. The Amateur Entomologists' Society, Orpington.

McGrath, R. & Lynch, P. (eds) (2008). *Ireland in a warmer climate*. Community Climate Change Consortium of Ireland, Dublin.

McElwain, L., Sweeney, J. (2006). *Key meteorological indicators of climate change in Ireland*. Environmental Protection Agency, Johnstown Castle.

MacNeill, N. (1973). A revised and tabulated list of the Irish Hemiptera-Heteroptera. Part I Georcorisae. *Proceedings of the Royal Irish Academy* (B)73:57-60.

Melling, T. (1987). *The ecology and population structure of a butterfly cline*. Ph.D. Thesis, University of Newcastle.

Meteorological Service (1974). *Climatological atlas of Ireland*. Dublin.

Middleton, B.L. (1902). Abundance of *Melitaea aurinia* in Co Westmeath. *The Entomologist* 35:27.

Morris, F.O. (1895). *A history of British butterflies*. John C. Nimmo, London.

Müller L. & Kautz H. (1939). *Pieris bryoniae* O. und *Pieris napi* L. Abhandlungen des Österreichischen Entomologen-Vereines 1:76.

Nash, D.W., Boyd, T. & Walsh, P.M. (2010). Lepidoptera Review, 2008. *Irish Naturalists' Journal* 31:71-72.

Nash, O. (1983). *I wouldn't have missed it. Selected poems of Ogden Nash*. André Deutsch, London.

Nash, R. (1975). The butterflies of Ireland. *Proceedings of the British Entomological and Natural History Society* 7:69-73.

Nash, R. (1997). The variation of the Green-veined White *Pieris napi* in Ireland. *BCNI Annual Report* pp.23-28.

Nash, R. (1983). A brief summary of the development of entomology in Ireland during the years 1790-1870. *Irish Naturalists' Journal* 21:145 -150.

Nash, R. & Samson, C. (1990). A fourth Irish specimen of the Small Mountain Ringlet *Erebia epiphron* Knoch. (Lepidoptera) *Irish Naturalists' Journal* 23:339.

National Parks and Wildlife Service, Dublin (2011). Website: http://www.npws.ie/protectedsites/.

Nelson, B., Hughes, M., Nash, R., Warren, M. (2001). *Leptidea reali* Reissinger (Lep.: Pieridae) 1989: a butterfly new to Britain and Ireland. *Entomologist's Record* 113:97-101.

Newman E. (1871). *The natural history of British butterflies and moths*. W.H. Allen & Co. London.

Ní Lamhna, É. (1980). *Distribution atlas of butterflies in Ireland* (European Invertebrate Survey). Irish Biological Records Centre, An Foras Forbartha, Dublin.

O'Donnell, M. & Wilson, C. (2009). *The Lepidoptera of County Wexford*. The Wexford Naturalists' Field Club, Wexford.

O'Meara, M. (2001). *The Lepidoptera of Waterford City & County*. Waterford Wildlife, Waterford.

O'Sullivan, D.C. (2009). *The natural history of Ireland: included in book one of zoilomastix*. Cork University Press, Cork.

O'Sullivan, M.J. (2001). The Brown Hairstreak butterfly (*Thecla betulae* L.) in Ireland: an examination of its historical and current status. *Proceedings & Transactions of the British Entomological and Natural History Society* 14:85-90.

Paul, J. (1985). Confirmation of *Erebia epiphron* Knoch: Mountain Ringlet as Irish. *Entomologist's Record* 97:63.

Peters, J.V. (1962). The butterflies of Northern Ireland. *Irish Naturalists' Journal* 14: 21-32.

Phillips, R.A. (1923). The Pearl-bordered Fritillary in Ireland. *The Irish Naturalist* 32:91-2.

Porter, J. (1997). *Caterpillars of the British Isles*. Penguin Group, London.

Pollard, E. (1985). Larvae of *Celastrina argiolus* (L) on male holly bushes. *Entomologist's Gazette* 36:3.

Porter, K. (1992). Eggs and egg-laying. In Dennis, R.L.H. (ed.) *The ecology of butterflies in Britain*: pp.46-72. Oxford University Press, Oxford.

Praeger, R.L. (1949). *Some Irish naturalists. A biographical note-book*. Dundalgan Press, Dundalk.

Purefoy, E.B. (1902). *Gonepteryx rhamni* and *cleopatra* in Ireland. *Entomologist* 35:301-04.

Pyle, R.M. (1981). *The National Audubon Society field guide to North American butterflies*. Alfred A. Knopf, New York.

Réal, P. (1988). Lépidoptères nouveaux principalement Jurassiens. *Mémoires du Comité de Liaison pour les Recherches Ecofaunistiques dans le Jura* 4:17.

Redway, R.B. (1981). Some comments of the reported occurrence of *Erebia epiphron* (Knoch) (Lepidoptera: Satyridae) in Irleand during the Nineteenth Century. *Entomologist's Gazette* 32:157-159.

Regan, E.C., Nelson, B., Aldwell, B., Bertrand, C., Bond, K., Harding, J., Nash, D., Nixon, D., Wilson, C.J. (2010) *Ireland red list No. 4: Butterflies*. National Parks and Wildlife Service, Department of Environment, Heritage and Local Government, Dublin, Ireland.

Riley, A.M. (2007). *British and Irish butterflies*. Brambleby Books, Luton.

Riley, N.D. (1928). A swarm of *Melitaea aurinia* larvae. *The Entomologist* 61:210.

Rippey, I. (1986). The butterflies of Northern Ireland. *Irish Naturalists' Journal* 22: 133-40.

Rippey, I. (1989). Butterflies (Lepidoptera) in Northern Ireland 1986-87: Addendum. *Irish Naturalists' Journal* 23:27-30.

Rippey, I. (2010). Obituary: Trevor Dempster Boyd MBE, FRMetS 1931-2010. *Irish Naturalists' Journal* 31:83-84.

Rohan, P.K. (1986). *The climate of Ireland*. The Stationery Office, Dublin.

Salmon, M.A. (2000). *The Aurelian legacy British butterflies and their collectors*. Harley Books, Colchester.

Schouten, M.G.C. (ed.) (2002). *Conservation and restoration of raised bogs*. Department of the Environment and Local Government / Staatsbosbeheer.

Settele, J., Kudrna, O., Harpke, A. *et al.* (2008). *Climatic risk atlas of European butterflies*. Pensoft, Sofia-Moscow.

Settele, J., Shreeve, T., Konvicka, M. & Van Dyck, H. (eds) (2009). *Ecology of butterflies in Europe*. Cambridge University Press, Cambridge.

Seugé, J. and Veith, K. (1976). Diapause de *Pieris brassicae*: rôle des photorécepteurs céphaliques, étude des caroténoides cérébraux. *Journal of Insect Physiology*: 22:1229-1235.

Shintani, Y., Shiga, S. & Numata, H. (2009). Different photoreceptor organs are used for photoperiodism in the larval and adult stages of the carabid beetle, *Leptocarabus kumagaii*. *Journal of Experimental Biology* 212:3651-3655.

Sláma, K. (2005). The brain-independent autonomic neuroendocrine system of insects (Coelopulse). Abstract for Entomological Society of America, Annual Meeting, Fort Lauderdale, Florida.

Smyth, F. & Nash, D.W. (2008). Overwintering of the Red Admiral butterfly (*Vanessa atalanta* (L.)) on the Howth Peninsula, Co Dublin. *Irish Naturalists' Journal* 29:81-86.

Snodgrass, R.E. (1935). *Principles of insect morphology*. McGraw-Hill Inc., US.

Socha, J.J., Wah-Keat, L., Harrison, J.F., Waters, J.S., Fezzaa, K. & Westneat, M.W. (2008). Correlated patterns of tracheal compression and convective gas exchange in a carabid beetle. *Journal of Experimental Biology* 211:3409-20.

Srivastava, K.P. (1975). On the respiratory system of the Lemon-butterfly, *Papilio demoleus* L. (Lepidopera: Papilionidae). *Australian Journal of Entomology* 14:363-370. DOI: 10.1111/j.1440-6055.1975.tb02052.x

Storey, K.B. & Storey, J.M. (2011). Heat shock proteins and hypometabolism: adaptive strategy for proteome preservation. *Research and Reports in Biology* 2:57-58. DOI 10.22147/RRB.S13351.

Strausfeld, N.J., Hansen, L., Yongshen, L., Gomez, R.S. & Kei, I. (1998). Evolution, discovery and interpretations of Arthropod mushroom bodies. *Learning Memory* 5:11-37. DOI: 10.1101/lm.5.1.11

Tauber, M.J., Tauber, C.A. & Masaki, S. (1986). Seasonal adaptations of insects. Oxford University Press, USA.

Thomas, J. A. (1986). *Butterflies of the British Isles*. Country Life Books, Middlesex.

Thomas, J. & Lewington, R. (2010). *The butterflies of Britain & Ireland*. British Wildlife Publishing, Gillingham.

Thompson, R. & Nelson, B. (2006). *The butterflies and moths of Northern Ireland*. National Museums Northern Ireland, Belfast.

Tolman, T. (1997). *Butterflies of Britain & Europe* (Collins field guide, illustrated by R. Lewington). HarperCollins, London.

van Swaay, C. & Warren, M. (1999). *Red data book of European butterflies* (*Rhopalocera*). Nature and the Environment, No. 99. Council of Europe, Strasbourg.

van Swaay, C., Cuttelod, A., Collins, S., Maes, D., Lopez Munguira, N., Šaši , M., Settele, J., Verovnik, R., Verstrael, T., Warren, M., Wiemers, M. & Wynhof, I. (2010). *European red list of butterflies*. European Union, Luxembourg.

Vickery, M. (1998). *Gardening for butterflies*. Butterfly Conservation, Wareham.

Walsh, P. (2007). Lepidoptera review, 2006. *Irish Naturalists' Journal* 28: 473-475.

Walsh, P. (2008). Lepidoptera review, 2007. *Irish Naturalists' Journal* 29:145-147.

Walsh, P.M., Boyd, T., Nash, D.W., Rolston, E. & Tyner, A. (2009). Report on migrant and notable Lepidoptera in Ireland, 2006. *Irish Naturalists' Journal* 30:40-50.

Walsh, P.M., Boyd, T., Nash, D.W., Rolston, E. & Tyner, A. (2010). Report on the migrant and notable Lepidoptera in Ireland, 2007. *Irish Naturalists' Journal* 31:23-32.

Walsh, P.M., Boyd, T., Nash, D.W., Rolston, E. & Tyner, A. (2010). Report on migrant and notable Lepidoptera in Ireland, 2008. *Irish Naturalists' Journal* 31: 100-07.

Warren, M.S. (1984). The biology and status of the Wood White butterfly in the British Isles. *Entomologist's Gazette* 35:207-223.

Wigglesworth, V.B. (1964). *The life of insects*. Weidenfeld and Nicolson, London.

Wiklund, C. (1977). Courtship behaviour in relation to female monogamy in *Leptidea sinapis* (Lepidoptera). *Oikes* 29:275-283.

Wasserthal, L.T. (2003). *Respiratory System* in N.P. Kristensen (ed.) Lepidoptera, moths and butterflies 2:189-204.

Williams, H.B. (1916). Notes on the life history and variation of *Euchloe cardamines* L. *Transaction of City of London Natural History Society* [1915]:62-84

Williams H.B. (1946). The Irish form of *Leptidea sinapis* L. *The Entomologist* 79:1-3.

Williams, R.P. (1858). On the occurrence of *Colias edusa* in the County of Waterfrod. *Proceedings of the Dublin Natural History Society* 2:17-18.

Wilson, C.J., Goodwin, J. and Bond, K. (2007). New Irish record for the Small Skipper butterfly *Thymelicus sylvestris* (Poda) (Lepidoptera: Hesperiidae). *Irish Naturalists' Journal* 28:385-86.

Wilson, C.J., Goodwin, J. and Bond, K. (2009). Addition of Essex Skipper butterfly (*Thymelicus lineola* (Ochsenheimer, 1808)) (Lepiodptera: Hesperiidae), to the Irish list and deletion of previously reported occurrence of Small Skipper (*Thymelicus sylvestris* (Poda, 1761)) in Ireland. *Irish Naturalists' Journal* 29:133-134.

Wilson, R.J., Gutiérrez, D., Gutiérrez, Martinez D., Agudo, R. & Monserrat, V.J. (2005). Changes to the elevation limits and extent of species ranges associated with climate change. *Ecology Letters* 8:1138-1146.

Appendix 8: **GLOSSARY OF TERMS**

The glossary contains some of the technical terms used in the text.
For more detailed definitions the reader should consult a specialised biology dictionary.

abdomen – third division of body
adipokinetic – relating to an agent that mobilises stored lipids
anal claspers – last pair of prolegs
androconia – scent scales
antenna – sensory appendage to head
anterior – towards front cf posterior
apex – tip (of wing)
apodeme – any cuticular ingrowth of the body wall.
apolysis – separation
aposematic – warning
asynchronous – not in phase
axon – nerve fibre

basal – see base, or minimum
base – near the body
bivoltine – produces two generations in a season

carr – wetland with Willow
cell, the – a space within a wing
cephalic – of the head
chemoreceptor – chemical sensor
chiasma – a crossing of nerve tracts within the nervous system.
chitin – a horny substance, forming hard parts of body
chordotonal organ – an internal mechanoreceptor that may serve as a proprioceptor.
chrysalis – pupa
cilia – fringe of wing
countrywide – wide distribution
cocoon – pupal case
coelopulse – part of the autonomic nervous system
connective – a tract of nerve fibres connecting successive ganglia.
convection – movement of fluids
costa – anterior margin of wing
cremaster – hook for attachment
crenulate – with small rounded teeth
cryoprectant – anti-freeze
cuticle – outer skin layer without cells

dendrite – extension of a nerve cell
diapause – a period of enforced dormancy

dilatation – enlargement
discal [cell] – disc-shaped
distal – away from the point of attachment to the body
dormancy – rest period
dorsal – of the upper surface or back

eclosion – emergence or hatching
ecdysis – moulting
ecdysone – moulting hormone
ectotherm – relies on environment for heat control
embryogenesis – foetus formation
endemic – found only in a particular area or region
endocrine – **[system]** of glands, each of which secretes a hormone directly into the bloodstream (see exocrine)
endocrine – hormonal
epi – prefix for *upper* or *outer*
epidermis – the inner layer of the exoskeleton that forms the overlying cuticle
exocrine – [glands] whose secretions pass into a system of ducts that lead to the exterior of the body (see endocrine)
exoskeleton – external skeleton
extrinsic – pertaining to anything external or originating outside
exuvia – the parts of the cuticle discarded at the moult

fluid – gas or liquid
frass – debris or excrement
frenulum – a spine that couples a pair of wings
fulvous – brownish-yellow

ganglion – a central mass of nerves.
genotype – genetic type
gley – a waterlogged soil with little oxygen
glycogen – a form of glucose
gynandromorph – part male and female

habitat specialist – [has] specific habitat requirements
haemocoele – the open space in the insect's body (body cavity) that is filled with haemolymph
haemocytes – blood cells present mainly in the haemolymph.
haemolymph – insect blood

hibernaculum – a protective covering in which certain insects pass the winter

Holarctic – zone comprising Europe, Asia and N America

holometabolous – undergoes complete metamorphosis

homeostasis – maintaining internal stability of biological systems by continuously interacting with and adjusting to changes

hyperparasite – a parasite of a parasite

imaginal – relating to or resembling an imago

imago – the adult form of an insect

innervate – supply nerves to

instar – stages of larval change, brought about by successive moults during the metamorphosis of the insect

integument – exoskeleton

interneural – between the veins

intrinsic – within

invertebrate – animal with no backbone

IUCN – International Union for Conservation of Nature

jugum – growth at wing base

lamina – plate or lamella

larva – caterpillar

lek – assembly of males

lipid – type of fat

lumen – central space in vessel

lunula – crescent-shaped mark

mandible – lower jaw

mechanoreceptor – sensor that responds to mechanical stimuli such as movement, tension or pressure.

medial – towards middle

meso – middle

metabolism – the physical and chemical changes occurring within a living cell or organism that are necessary for maintaining life

metabolite – a substance necessary for or taking part in a particular metabolic process.

metamorphosis – change in the animal's form and structure from immature to adult, during which time there is a series of distinct stages.

micropyle – small opening in egg

migrant – [butterfly] which migrates

Millennium Atlas – see Asher *et al.* (2001)

mitosis – cell division

morphogenesis – the developmental changes of growth and differentiation occurring in the structure and form of the various organs and parts of an organism

mycelium – branching vegetative part of fungus

neuro – nerve related

neuron(e) – nerve cell

neuropil(e) – mass of fibrous tissue, such as axons and dendrites, within a ganglion

Newcomer's gland – gland which secretes a honey-like fluid which is highly attractive to ants

ocellus – a simple eye or light receptor (sensillum) or false eye

ochreous – yellow with some brown

oenocytes – large specialised cells found in the body cavity of most insects and associated with fat cells

ommatidium – element of a compound eye

oocyte – female germ cell

ostia – valves in 'heart'

Palaearctic – zone comprising Europe, North Africa and northern Asia

palp – elongated sensor near mouth

parasite – an insect that lives off a host

parasitoid – a parasite that ultimately kills its host

perianth – calyx and corolla of a flower

peri-visceral – around internal organs

pinaculum (pl. pinacula) – swelling containing a seta

pharate – between stages of development where the new exoskeleton is still covered by the old one

phenotype – the physical form, *cf* genotype

pheromone – chemical attractant

photoperiod – length of daylight

phragma – plate-like lobes or apodemes in the region of the wing bearing tergal plates

podzol – a leached soil in moist climate

post – beyond

posterior – back cf anterior

proboscis – a slender, tubular feeding and sucking organ of certain invertebrates

process – projection or appendage

procuticle – combined endocuticle and exocuticle

prolegs – false legs

proprioceptor – sensor of orientation

prothorax – 1st segment of thorax

proximal – near the point of attachment to the body

pulsatile – beating rhythmically

pupa – chrysalis

quiescent – inactive

recurrent – turning back so as to run in the opposite direction

reticulate – resembling or forming a network

rhopalocera – Lepidoptera with club-shaped antennae

sclerite – any sclerotised area of the body wall

sclerotisation – hardening of the body wall by the deposition of sclerotising substances in the exocuticle

secrete – to generate or release by secretion.

secretion – a functionally specialized substance released from a gland or cell

sensillum – an insect's sensory organ consisting of one or a few cells at the peripheral end of a sensory nerve fibre

seta – hair or bristle

SOBBI – see Fox *et al.* (2006)

spiracle – one of a series of small openings located along each side of the thorax and abdomen through which air enters and leaves the tracheal system

steroid – an organic compound belonging to the general class of bio-chemicals called lipids

sub – below

sub-apical – below the apex

sub-dorsal – below the back

stomodaeal – relates to the gut

sympatric – occurring together

synchronous – in phase

taenidia – spiral thickenings of the cuticle inside the trachea

tawny – light brown to brownish-orange

termen – outer margin of wing

terminal – at the tip

tetrad – 2 km x 2 km square

thermoregulation – temperature control

token – indirect [stimulus]

tornus – anal angle of wing

trehalose – a crystalline sugar that occurs in yeast and certain fungi

tubercule – swelling

univoltine – produces one generation per season

vagrant – [butterfly] outside its normal range

ventral – of the lower surface.

Appendix 9: **HABITAT CLASSIFICATION**

The table below gives a summary of the habitat classification (Fossitt 2000) together with what is considered to be a near equivalent from Phase 1 of the Joint Nature Conservation Council (Anon. 1990).

Habitat Type (Fossitt 2000)	JNCC Equivalence (Anon. 1990)
FW4 Drainage ditches	G1 Standing water
GA1 Improved agricultural grassland	B4 Improved Grassland
GS1 Dry calcareous and neutral grassland	B2 Neutral grassland,
GS2 Dry meadows and grassy verges	B3 Calcareous grassland
GS3 Dry-humid acid grassland	B1 Acid grassland
GS4 Wet grassland	B5 Marsh/marshy grassland
GM1 Marsh	
HH1 Dry siliceous heath	D1.1 Dry heath – acid
HH2 Dry calcareous heath	D1.2 Dry heath – basic
HH3 Wet heath	D6/E1 Wet heath/acid grassland/bog
PB1 Raised bog	E1.6.2 Raised sphagnum bog
PB2 Upland blanket bog	E1.6.1 Blanket sphagnum bog
PB3 Lowland blanket bog	
PB4 Cutover bog	E1.7 and E1.8 modified bog
PF1 Rich fen and flush	E2.2 Flush and spring – basic flush
PF2 Poor fen and flush	E2.1 Flush and spring – acid/neutral
WN1 Oak-birch-holly woodland	A1.1 Broadleaved woodland – semi-natural
WN2 Oak-ash-hazel woodland	
WD2 Mixed broadleaved/conifer woodland	A1.3 Mixed woodland
WD5 Scattered trees and parkland	A3 Parkland/scattered wood
WS1 Scrub	A2 Scrub
WL1 Hedgerow	J2 Hedges, boundaries
ER1 Exposed siliceous rock	I1.4.1 Acid/neutral rock exposure
ER2 Exposed calcareous rock	I1.3 Limestone pavement
ER3/4 Scree	I1.2 Scree
ED1 Exposed sand, gravel and till	I2.1 Quarry
ED2 Spoil and bare ground	J4 Bare ground
BC4 Flower beds and borders	J1.5 Flowers and gardens
CS1 Rocky sea cliffs	H8 Maritime cliff and slope
CD2 Marram dunes	H6.8 Open dune
CD3 Fixed dunes	H6.5 Dune grassland
CD4 Dune scrub and woodland	H6.7 Dune scrub
CD5 Dune slacks	H6.4 Dune slack
CD6 Machair	H6.5 Machair

Appendix 10: **INDEX**

This is an index for species and to the sites which are mentioned in the *Site Descriptions*.
Additional place names together with their county locations and grid references are included in the
separate *Topographical Index*.
Common names of butterflies that are resident or in the species accounts are both shown in **bold type**.
Scientific names are given in *italics*. Where there have been recent changes, an older name may also
be given.
A list of larval food plants is to be found in the section *Gardening for Butterflies*.
Scientific/horticultural plant names are given in the *Plant Synonyms* Appendix.

A
Aghagallon 234
Aglais urticae 168-170, 250
Ahenny 215
Áilleán 165-167
    Meiriceánach 217
Aimiréal dearg 162-164
Anthocharis cardamines 138-140, 250
Aphantopus hyperantus 205-207, 250
Argynnis aglaja 180-182, 250
    paphia 183-185, 250
Aughinish Island 232

B
Ballinacor 229
Ballyeighter 230
Ballyquirke Lake 221
Ballyteigue 180, 226
Bánóg bhath 216
    bheag 132-134
    choille 121-123
    choille dhuaithne 118-120
    mhór 129-131
    uaine 135-137
Barr buí 138-140
Barrigone 232
Bé na fallainge 214
Blackwater Head 228
Bleachtfhéileacán 214
Boloria euphrosyne 177-179
Blue, Chalkhill 11
    Common 12, 30, 83, 108, 153, **156-158**, 159, 222, 227, 228, 230, 233, 235-239, 244, 250
    Holly 30, 102, 103, 108, **159-161**, 221-24, 229, 231-235, 239, 250
    Large 155
    Long-tailed 219
    Silver-studded 11

Small 26, 30, 34, 39, 42, 62, 82, 108, **153-155**, 158, 221-224, 228, 233, 236, 237, 241, 250
Breachfhéileacán coille 190-192
Breeole Hills 222
Brimstone 30, 46, 51, 107, 123, **126-128**, 129, 221-227, 230, 233, 250
Brittas 228
Brown Argus 12
Brownstown 222
Buckroney 228
Buíóg liath 215
    chróch 123-125
    ruibheach 126-128
Bunduff Lough 223
Burren 10, 14, 19, 114, 118, 121, 122, 126, 144, 147, 149, 153, 177, 179, 180, 196, 198, 229, 230

C
Cacyreus marshalli 32
Callophrys rubi 141-143
Callow 240
Camberwell Beauty 42, 110, 214
Camóg 174-176
Cape Clear Island 135-231
Carney Commons 233
Carrowmoreknock 221
Castleburke 222
Castlesampson 222
Celastrina argiolus 159-161, 250
Clara Bog 225
Clara Vale 229
Cleopatra 128, 219
Clooncoose 14, 177, 179, 230
Clouded Yellow 14, 30, 32, 41, 107, **123-125**, 228, 231-233, 250
    Pale 215
Coenonympha pamphilus 208-210,

250
    tullia 211-213, 250
Clorhane 226
Cooloorta 230
Comma 30, 32, 52, 108, **174-176**, 228
Corballis 224
Colias croceus 123-125
    hyale 215
Coole 220, 221
Copper, Large 218
    Small 30, 104, 108, **150-152**, 218, 223, 227, 227-229, 235, 250
Copróg bheag 150-152
    mhor 218
Corofin 229, 230
Corranellistrum 221
Cotesia bignelli 47, 189
    glomerata 48, 131
    inducata 161
    melitaearum 189
    rubecula 134
Craigavon Lakes 235
Creeves 232
Cruit Island 236
Cupido minimus 153-155
Curracloe 228

D
Danaus plexxipus 214
Deputy's Pass 229
Derrycunnihy 232
Derrygonnelly 240
Dinis Island 232
Donnán 114-116
Donnóg an bhalla 191-195
    an fhéir 202-204
Downhill 240
Dromore 144, 230
Duke of Burgundy 10, 11

Appendix 11: RECORDERS (1995–2010)

Abbeyleix South NS, M Abernethy, G Acheson, F Adair, P Adams, F Agnew, E Aiken, S Alcorn, B Aldwell, M Alexander, All Saints NS, D Allen, B Allen, M Allen, R Allen, A Allen, P Almond, Y Anders, D Anderson, M Anderson, P Anderson, R Anderson, CJ Andrews, D Andrews, J Andrews, P Andrews, A Archdale, M Archdale, P Archdale, E Archer, M Archer, J Ard, Ardough NS, M Armstrong, T Aughney, A Austin, C Ayres, T Babiarz, V Babington, R Bain, A Baine, S Baine, A Baird, MA Baker, E Balcombe, R Ballentine, KM Bannon, FL Barr, RL Barr, C Barrett, F Barrett, T Barrett, I Barthorpe, A Bartol, A Barton, C Barton, R Barton, K Beattie, S Beesley, The Belfast Naturalists' Field Club, M Ball, C Bell, J Bell, L Bell, M Bell, T Bell, W Belshaw, G Bennett, C Bentley, D Berridge, C Bertrand, N Bingham, RW Bingham, E Birch, BirdWatch Ireland, H Black, S Black, D Blakely, RJ Bleakley, J Bloomer, J Board, KGM Bond, A Borawska, H Bothwell, L Bourke, S Bourke, Bowe family, T Boyd, H Boyd, M Boyd, S Boyd, VJE Boyd, E Boyle, H Boyle, M Boyle, W Bradley, R Brakespear, C Breen, D Breen, K Breen, S Breen, A Brennan, M Brennan, P Brennan, PD Brennan, L Brewer, C Brewster, CA Brewster, D Brick, C Briody, P Brittain, S Brook, I Brophy, D Broughton, A Brown, B Brown, D Brown, N Brown, P Brown, R Brown, RA Brown, S Brown, A Browne, D Browne, N Browne, V Browne, J Bruck, R Brush, W Brush, M Bryan, T Bryant, B Bryce, R Bryers, Botanical Society of the British Isles, T Buckley, J Bullock, L Burke, H Lucy Burke, M Burke, D Burrows, R Butcher, E Butler, J Butler, T Butter, Butterfly Conservation, A Byrne, B Byrne, B Cahalane, JJ Cahill, L Cahill, E Cahoon, J Calladine, S Callagy, M Calvey, C Campbell, G Campbell, M Campbell, O Campbell, Camross NS, Cape Clear Bird Observatory, T Carey, M Carmody, B Carolan, F Carroll, P Carruthers, L Carson, M Carson, V Carter, E Carty, H Carty, P Casement, M Cashman, L Cassells, Castlesampson NS, C Cavendish, S Cawley, M Cawley, W Chambers, R Chambers, T Chambers, EA Chapman, HKP Chavasse, T Chavasse, P Chester-Williams, J Christie, J Clancy, P Clancy, G Clarke, K Clarke, C Clenaghan, P Clerkin, S Clifford, D Clifford, D Cloney, H Cloney, Cloonbonniffe NS, Clooncagh NS, E Close, W Cochrane, Cogaula NS, M Coghlan, H Cole-Baker, S Cole-Baker, K Collins, R Collins, J Combes, D Comerford, DM Comerford, J Conaghan, D Coney, S Connolly, T Connolly, D Conroy, M Conway, AM Coogan, D Cooke, S Cooke, T Cooney, Copeland Bird Observatory, A Copeland, P Corbett, P Cormacain, C Cornelissen, J Corrigan, K Corrigan, N Corry, W Corry, J Costello, A Cotter, A Cotton, D Cotton, M Cotton, R Cotton, P Courtney, J Coveney, E Cowen, M Cowming, A Cox, R Cox, M Craig, B Crawford, R Cremin, J Cromie, M Cronin, A Cronin, M Cronin, K Cronin, A Crooks, A Crory, J Crosher, R Crothers, B Crowe, P Crushell, T Cuffe, W Culbert, D Cullen, J Cullen, R Cunningham, D Curtis, J Curtis, P Cutler, A Dainty, A Dakin, L Daley, G Daly, D Daly, M Dalton, B Danaher, G D'Arcy, S D'Arcy-Burt, Darley NS, R Daunt, W Davis, C Dawson, P Dawson, GV Day, I de Mange, B Deegan, K Deering, L Deery, EV Delaney, H Delaney, P Delaney, E Dempsey, D Dennis, M Densley, M Deverell, F Devery, R Devine, J Devlin, Z Devlin, L Diamond, JM Dick, G Dickey, D Dillon, T Dines, E Diver, D Doherty, H Doherty, N Doherty, E Donaghy, W Donaldson, T Donnelly, G Donnelly, NJ Donnithorn, I Doogan, D Doogue, E Douglas, K Douglas, J Dowdall, DN Dowling, M Dowling, N Dowling, P Dowling, R Dowling, P Doyle, D Drewett, H Dring, D Duane, I Duane, J Duane, The Dublin Naturalists' Field Club, K Duff, A Duffin, G Duffy, MA Duggan, D Duggan, R Duggan, T Dunbar, L Duncan, B Dunleavy, J Dunleavy, S Dunlop, C Dunne, G Dunneice, E Dunwoody, R Dwyer, J Earley, T Earley, G Early, J Early, T Early, R Eddleston, D Edgar, R Edge, D Edmonds, J Edwards, J Eiffe, S Elliott, M Ellis, I Enlander, R Ennis, D Enright, M Enright, D Eyre, K Fahy, F Farrell, M Farrell, D Farrer, J Faulkner, L Feeney, D Feeney, A Fennell, R Fennelly, A Fenner, I Fennessy, U Fenton, R Field, B Finch, K Finch, AR Finegan, A Finigan, M Finlay, J Finn, T Finnen, Firoda NS, J Fisher, R Fitzgerald, RD Fitzgerald, D Fitzpatrick, U Fitzpatrick, A Flanagan, S Fleischer, N Fleming, C Flynn, E Flynn, J Fogarty, M Foley, O Foley, R Forbes, A Forde, B Forristal, P Foss, N Foster, S Foster, S Foucar, B Fox, M Fox, MS Fox, E Foyle, E Franklin, B Fraser, G Freeburn, K Freeman, B French, I Frost, P Frost, D Fuller, P Fulton, R Fulton, R Fussell, Gaggle, B Gallagher, O Gallagher, J Gamble, P Gardener, G Garner, M Garner, P Garvey, C Gates, L Gates, S Gavin, M Gawlikowska, J George, J Geraty, N Geraty, S Geraty, D Gibson, K Giles, D Gillespie, W Gillespie, N Gillespie, E Gilligan, C Gilmore, R Gilmore, J Gingell, T Gittings, K Glasgow, G Glass, S Glass, B Gomes, R Gomes, B Good, J Good, R Goode, A Goodhand, R Goodwillie, J Goodwin, L Goodyear, G Gordon, J Gordon, K Gordon, P Gordon, T Gordon, A Gore, V Gotto, K Grace, JL Graham, I Graham, M Graham, P Grant, L Grant, D Gray, L Gray, M Gray, N Gray, R Gray, D Greaves, R Greaves, G Green, P Green, PR Green, S Greene, H Greenlee, L Greer, E Greeves, R Greeves, M Greenlee, S Greenleese, E Grennan, M Grey, L Grieves, B Guest, M Guthrie, SH Guthrie, P Hackney, R Hadden, D Hadrick, P Hadrick, C Haire, P Haire, T Haire, P Hale, R Hale, L Hall, B Hamill, R Hamill, E Hamilton, R Hanna, K Hanna, D Hannan, K Hannan, S Hannan, J Harahan, K Harahan, D Hardiman, L Hardiman, J Harding, A Harding, J Harding, A Harrington-Rees, D Harrison, W Harron, Y Harte, S Harvey, T Harvey, W Hatrick, K Hauschild, RR Havercroft, D Hawthorne, M Healy, C Heardman, E Heath, S Heery, ML Heffernan, J Helly, P Hemmens, G Henderson, I Henderson, G Heneghan, C Henry, J Henry, S Henry, I Herbert, R Heslip, J Higgins, A Hill, E Hill, JP Hillis, M Hirst, R Hodd, T Hodd, D Hodgers, D Hodges, B Hodkinson, R Holme, Holy Family NS, D Honnyman, E Hort, L Houston, R Houston, M Hughes, D Hughes, J Hughes, M Hughes, P Hughes, S Hughes, J Hull, G Hunt, T Hunter, M Hunter, J Hurley, R Hurley, H Hussey, C Huxley, M Hyndman, S Hynds, A Hynes, I Hynes, Irish Field Club Union, Irish Peatlands Conservation Council, I Irvine, R Irvine, K Irvine, E Irvine, P Irwin, A Jackson, G Jackson, I Jackson, M Jacob, A James, G Jeffcoate, S Jeffcoate, S Jennings, A Johnson, S Johnson, B Johnson, AM Johnston, D Johnston, E Johnston, G Jones, S Jones, T Jones, GW Jordan, R Jordan, N Joyce, M Kane, J Kazimierczak, J Keane, H Kee, D Keegan, T Keely, M Keesham, J Kehoe, E Kehoe, A Kelly, AG Kelly, D Kelly, G Kelly, J Kelly, K Kelly, M Kelly, P Kelly, T Kelly, R Kemp, J Kendall, D Kennedy, J Kennedy, L Kennedy, W Kennedy, L Kenny, E Keogh, N Keogh, N Keogh, NT Keogh, R Keogh, A Kernohan, F Kerr, SH Kettle, K Keys, T Kilbane, Kilcolman NNR, C Killeen, Killyan NS, A Kilmer, B King, G King-Slater, M Kingston, M Kinley, G Kinney, L Kirk, J Kirk, G Knight, J Knipe, Knocksink Nature Reserve, I Knox, P Lambert, JD Lamont, T Lancaster, PH Langton, C Lauder, A Lavin, E Lawlor, J Lawlor, P Lawlor, S Ledwith, J Lee, M Lee, TA Lee, M Leech, P Lenihan, N Lennon, S Lenoir, B Leonard, K Leonard, J Leslie, R Leslie, B Leyden, R Liggett, B Lodge, S Lombard, D Looney, J Lorimer, C Loughran, J Lovatt, J Lucey, F Lucy, J Lucy, F Lunny, J Lynch, N Lynch, P Lynch, R Lynch, N Lynn, F Lyons, J Lyons, JW Lyons, M Lyons, D Lysaght, L Lysaght, S I MacArthur, N MacCoitir, P MacCrossan, C MacCrosain, M MacDougall, A MacFadyen, C MacLochlainn, E MacLochlainn, G MacLochlainn, C MacMathuna, M MacPolin, D McAllister, K McAllister, K McAney, B McAnuff, J McBean, H McBride, M McCafferty, R McCafferty, I McCambridge, L McCann, P McCann, B McCarne, P McCausland, J

McClean, J McCleery, P McClelland, S McClure, A McCombe, C McConnell, D McConnell, S McCormack, D McCormick, J McCormick,V McCormick, D McCready, T McCreery, V McDonagh, D McDonnell, IC McDonald, R McDonnell, I McDougall, M McDougall, W McDowell, A McElwaine, G McElwaine, S McElwaine, P McEvoy, L McFaul, A McFerran, D McFerran, E McFerran, K McFerran, L McFerran, E McGlinchey, E McGonagle, L McGrath, D McGrath, E McGreal, J McGregor, E McGuigan, A McGuire, A McGurdy, P McHaffie, H McHale, W McIlmoyle, B McIlwrath, A McIntosh, N McIntyre, C McIvor, J McKee, P McKee, B McKee, N McKee, ND McKee, PW McKee, S McKee, A McKeown, JB McKeown, I McLaine, C McLarnon, D McLaughlin, V McLoughlin, B McMahon, T McLucas, J McMahon, RM McMullen, J McMurray, A McMurtry, D McNamara, W McNamara, C McNaughton, D McNeill, G McNeill, I McNeill, P McNulty, T McNulty, S McRobert, G McRoberts, T McRoberts, A McWilliam, P McVeigh, T McVeigh, S MacAmhalaghaidh, C Mackey, A Mackie, P Mackie, B Madden, E Magee, J Medhurst, H Meehan, E Meharg, M Meharg, C Mellon, O Merne, E Merriman, J Magee, C Maguire, A Malcolm, M Malcolm, J Malins, M Malley, S Malone, J Manley, D Mann, J Mann, JO Mann, M Mann, R Masefield, N Marchant, G Marshall, M Marshall, D Martin, B Martin, M Martin, A Martyn-Seale, V Mathers, J Matthews, M Maunsell, P May, C Mhic Daeid, J Milburne, A Miller, I Miller, J Miller, L Miller, N Milligan, R Milligan, R Milliken, G Mills, J Millsopp, D Mitchel, I Mitchell, R Moffit, G Monteith, R Monteith, B Montgomery, J Montgomery, J Montgomery-Watson, F Moore, J Moore, P Moore, T Moore, E Moorkens, D Moran, J Moran, T Moran, D Morgan, K Morgan, L Morgan, M Morgan, D Morris, M Morris, A Morrison, C Morrison, E Morrison, O Morrison, W Morrogh, D Morrow, R Moss, Mount Talbot NS, N Mugan, E Mullally, A Mullan, C Mullan, S Mullan, A Mullen, M Mullett, E Mullholland, R Mullholland, R Mundy, A Murphy, C Murphy, F Murphy, J Murphy, K Murphy, M Murphy, N Murphy, P Murphy, R Murphy, S Murphy, P Murray, T Murray, Muscott, JS Myles, T Nagle, C Nash, D Nash, R Nash, The National Trust, B Nelson, S Nelson, S Nesbitt, G Neuen, M Newell, M Newing, Newcastle NS, C Ni Dheaghaidh, A Nic an tSithigh, A Nicholson, HD Nicholson, D Nixon, L Nixon, D Noe, A Nolan, H Nolan, J Nolan, L Nolan, G Noonan, J Noonan, North Hertfordshire Bio Soc. , H Northridge, RH Northridge, M Norton, L Nunan, J Nunn, J O'Boyle, N O'Brien, WB O'Brien, D O Broin, C O'Connell, B O'Connor, J O'Connor, A O'Doherty, C O'Donnell, E O'Donnell, J O'Donnell, O'Driscoll, S O'Donoghue, P O'Dwyer, C O'Flaherty, D O'Flynn, S O'Gaoithin, J O'Kane, J O'Keefe, C O'Mahony, B Omars, M O'Meara, J O'Neill, E O'Rane, B O'Regan, E O'Riordan, J Orr, J O'Shea, S O'Shea, D O'Sullivan, M O'Sullivan, M O'Sullivan, C Osthoff, A Palmer, S Paolucci, N Parker, F Parkinson, M Parr, S Parr, N Parry, J Parsons, I Patience, M Paul, Mrs. Patton, G Pearson, E Peel, D Peelo, E Pellon, C Peppiatt, E Perry, A Peters, B Phalan, A Phelan, G Phillips, P Phillips, J Phillips, G Phipps, J Piper, R Piper, L Playle, I Pobjoy-Littwins, R Pollen, R Poole, Poole family, B Porter, S Porter, W Potts, McPowell, B Power, U Power, JA Power, M Power, T Power, D Price, I Quaile, P Quigley, U Quigley, T Quinn, M Quirke, M Rafferty, M Ramsey, E Randall, S Redican, R Reeners, A Reeves-Smith, S Reeves-Smith, E Regan, P Reilly, J Reynolds, S Reynolds, T Rich, P Richard, B Richardson, M Richardson, A Riley, D Riley, I Rippey, S Rippey, T Rippey, D Roberts, E Roberts, G Roberts, B Robson, N Roche, C Roden, T Roderick, G Rodgers, M Rolston, T Rolston, D Romer, C Ronayne, A Rosler, SJ Roy, B Russell, J Rutherford, T Ryall, F Ryan, J Ryan, M Ryan, R Ryan, S Ryan, A Sage, S Sage, G Salter, M Salter, J Samuel, G Saunders, V Santorum, G Saunders, A Scales, P Scally, Scoil Muire, Scoil Naomh Brid, D Scott, J Scott, L Scott, R Scott, J Scott-Bolton, M Scottham, P Scovell, E Seale, C Seale, R Sellar, J Semple, N Semple, W Semple, J Shackleton, D Sharkey, G Sharkey, C Sharpe, C Shaw, E Shaw, P Sheahan, L Sheppard, R Sheppard, B Sheridan, P Sheridan, T Sheridan, V Sheridan, Sherkin Marine Station, C Sherwood, T Shevlin, C Shiel, S Shiels, T Shine, A Silke, S Shortell, A Simms, M Simms, S Simms, R Simpson, D Skehan, B Skinner, M Slater, T Slattery, D Smallwood, J Smallwood, R Smart, B Smith, J Smith, U Smith, M Smith, C Smyth, F Smyth, J Smyth, L Solosy, G Solosy, C Somerville, F Somerville, G Somerville, D Soper, V Soper, S Spain, A Spearman, A Stallworthy, C Stamp, K Stanfield, DA Stanley, D Stanley, S Stapleton, T Stapleton, R Stedman, D Steele, J Steele, R Steele, L Steer, S Stefanescu, R Stephenson, DG Stevenson, G Stewart, J Stewart, P Stewart, T Stinson, B Stirling, K Stohr, B Strickland, P Strickland, L Stronge, C Sullivan, M Sullivan, P Summers, B Swingler, C Swingler, J Symington, M Taggart, K Tambling, T Tarpey, M Taylor, T Tedstone, R Teesdale, F Tennant, P Thomlinson, E Thompson, G Thompson, H Thompson, K Thompson, R Thompson, GM Thurgate, H Thurgate, M Tickner, MT Tiller, J Tinman, A Toland, K Tomkins, E Tom, M Toomey, D Toomey, J Torney, A Towers, P Townsend, J Tregale, B Tucker, K Turner, F Turtle, RS Twist, E Twomey, A Tyner, J Tyner, Z Tyner, F Ui Chinneide, The Ulster Wild Life Trust, Unknown, A Upton, Valley NS, B Vaughan, W Veale, M Viney, J Vinycomb, W Voles, A Vrieling, J Waddell, M Waldron, M Walker, B Walker, M Walls, A Walsh, F Walsh, M Walsh, PM Walsh, G Walshe, J Wann, M Ward, M Warden, W Warham, J Warnock, F Warren, M Warren, M Waterman, Waterford Botany Group, Waterford Wildlife, F Watson, J Watson, S Watson, G Watson, B Watson-Russell, CE Watts, I Watts, W Watts, R Weatherup, J Weiger, D Weir, D Welsby, R Weyl, Wexford Naturalists' Field Club, R Weyl, RS Weyl, J Whatmough, L Wheatland, R Wheeldon, B Wheeler, J Whelahan, P Whelan, F White, S White, J Whitehouse, L Whiteside, H Wiggins, J Wilde, M Wilkes, G Wilkinson, B Williams, M Willis, AM Wilson, CJ Wilson, F Wilson, J Wilson, R Wilson, T Wilson, F Winder, S Wing, I Winters, SA Wolfe-Murphy, R Wood, B Woodall, R Woods, H Woolsey, G Woulahan, M Wright.

Message to All Butterfly Enthusiasts

The distribution maps presented in this publication are based on the most recent available information.

There are many gaps in our detailed knowledge of the distribution of butterflies in Ireland and the data here has generally been presented on a 10 km resolution. So a single dot may indicate only one known colony, or perhaps very many, in an area of 100 square kilometres.

Much has been happening in our landscape that is affecting the habitat available to butterflies. A continuous supply of data is needed by the Dublin Naturalists' Field Club National Butterfly Database to keep our information up to date.

You can help by recording details (site, grid reference, date, number ...) of casual sightings in your garden or elsewhere and/or by doing more systematic searching for butterflies in your locality or region. The best sites are generally areas with 'low maintenance' where the land is subject to relatively benign management or neglect.

Please submit your records for the Republic of Ireland online, by email or post to The Dublin Naturalists' Field Club, 35 Nutley Park, Dublin 4, *www.butterflyireland.com, dnfc@butterflyireland.com.*

Records for Northern Ireland should be sent to Butterfly Conservation Northern Ireland *www.bcni.org.uk.*

ACKNOWLEDGEMENTS

The Boyd family, especially Heather and Peter, for their encouragement, interest and support during the completion of the publication;

The many Recorders throughout Ireland and the members of The Dublin Naturalists' Field Club (DNFC) without whose efforts in the field this book would have been impossible;

Bob Aldwell for many discussions and insights into butterfly behaviour, productive days spent in the field especially in Donegal, access to many photogenic specimens of adults, eggs, larvae and pupae and for his comments on the draft text;

Frank Smyth for his many field observations and reports especially with regard to the Marsh Fritillary;

Martin Warren, Richard Fox, Maurice Hughes, Jim Asher and others from Butterfly Conservation for their encouragement and for the stimuli provided by the *Butterflies for the New Millennium* project;

Dave Allen, Con Breen, Declan Doogue and Franchea Rooney for their reading of the text and for their many constructive and insightful comments and challenges;

Jim O'Connor for facilitating access to the National Museum of Ireland and its facilities;

The Ulster Wildlife Trust for permission to visit the Umbra reserve;

Ken Bond, Maurice Hughes, Brian Nelson and Jim Whitehouse for information on the Wood White species in Ireland;

Mark Shaw for the identification of parasitoids;

Pádraig Connaughton of the Geological Survey of Ireland for the simplified geology map;

Eddie McDonald of Teagasc for the soil map;

Met Éireann, the University of Ulster and the Environmental Protection Agency for the weather maps and charts;

The Royal Entomological Society for the photograph of Rev. J. Greene;

Peter Eeles (UK Butterflies), Paul Kipling, Reg Fry (UK Leps), Ben Smart, Derek Ramsay, Margaret and Freddie Walsh for permission to use their photographs;

The Carlton Publishing Group for permission to reproduce *The Caterpillar* by Ogden Nash;

The Heritage Council for a grant award under its Heritage Education, Community and Outreach Scheme;

The Environmental Recorders' Group (ERG) for a grant facilitated by National Museums Northern Ireland and the Northern Ireland Environmental Agency;

The Belfast Naturalists' Field Club (BNFC) for its support.

Gatekeeper